Anorexics and Bulimics Anonymous

Anorexics and Bulimics Anonymous

The Fellowship Details its Program of Recovery for Anorexia and Bulimia

Anorexics and Bulimics Anonymous™
Edmonton, Alberta
Canada
2002

Anorexics and Bulimics Anonymous™
Main P.O. Box 125
Edmonton, Alberta T5J 2G9
Canada
www.anorexicsandbulimicsanonymousaba.com

The brief excerpts from *Alcoholics Anonymous* are reprinted, and the Twelve Steps and Twelve Traditions are reprinted and adapted, with permission of Alcoholics Anonymous World Services, Inc. (A.A.W.S.). Permission to reprint and adapt the Twelve Steps and Twelve Traditions does not mean that A.A.W.S. has reviewed or approved the contents of this publication, or that A.A.W.S. necessarily agrees with the views expressed herein. A.A. is a program of recovery from alcoholism only—use of the Twelve Steps and Twelve Traditions in connection with programs and activities which are patterned after A.A., but which address other problems, or in any other non-A.A. context, does not imply otherwise.

The Al-Anon Family Groups are a fellowship of relatives and friends of alcoholics only, whose sole purpose is to help families and friends of alcoholics. It has no affiliation with any other organization, nor does it endorse the use of the Twelve-Step Program for any purpose other than recovery from the disease of alcoholism and from its effects on families. Al-Anon Family Group Headquarters, Inc. has not reviewed or approved the contents of this publication, and reference herein to the literature of the Al-Anon Family Groups does not imply otherwise.

The biblical quotation in Chapter 2 is from the *Good News Bible* © 1966 by American Bible Society, New York: American Bible Society, 4th edition 1976. All other biblical quotations are from *The New Jerusalem Bible* © 1985 by Darton, Longman & Todd Ltd. and Doubleday, New York: Bantam Doubleday Dell Publishing Group, Inc., 1990.

National Library of Canada Cataloguing in Publication

Anorexics and Bulimics Anonymous
Anorexics and Bulimics Anonymous: the fellowship details its program of recovery for anorexia and bulimia.

Includes bibliographical references and index.
ISBN 978-0-9731372-0-0 (bound).—ISBN 978-0-9731372-1-7 (pbk.)

1. Anorexics and Bulimics Anonymous. 2. Anorexia nervosa–Patients–Rehabilitation. 3. Bulimia–Patients–Rehabilitation. I. Title.

RC552.A5A6 2002 616.85'2606 C2002-903581-3

Editor: Faith Farthing, *FinalEyes Communications*

Logo and book design by Wendy Smith, *Print Doctor*
Originally published in hardcover in December 2002
First softcover printing: January 2004
Third printing: January 2005
Fourth printing: November 2005
Fifth printing: March 2007
Sixth printing: March 2008
Seventh printing: October 2009

Printed and bound in Canada by Friesens Book Division
First Edition

Acknowledgments

A WORK of this magnitude is of necessity a collaborative effort by many individuals. We are inexpressibly grateful to all of them.

We thank our authors, those women working tirelessly together over the past two years to birth the content of this book. They must, of course, remain unnamed. They and the Creator know who they are, and that is sufficient.

We are grateful to our editorial committee. They had a great deal to accomplish, and they did it with cheerfulness and a spirit of loving cooperation that is an inspiration to us all.

There are so many people outside Anorexics and Bulimics Anonymous who contributed to the project that it is difficult to know where to begin in naming them. We are indebted to those women and men in the Ab-Anon Fellowship who gave so generously of themselves, both in writing and orally, thereby enabling us to compose Chapter 15. They, like us, remain anonymous, that all credit may be attributed to the Power behind their reflections.

We are grateful to all who reviewed and criticized (constructively, we might add) the manuscript or parts of it. The comments of Pat Truman, Joan Coambs, and Kerri Kumasaka were particularly helpful.

Many physicians gave liberally of their time and knowledge in appraising this work, without expectation of personal gain. Vancouver psychiatrist Deborah Schwartz evaluated an early draft of the manuscript in its entirety and provided support and encouragement. Three Edmonton psychiatrists and two other physicians reviewed Chapter 1 and offered important suggestions. The willingness of these good women and men to work with us in the preparation of this text helps to solidify one of our most important aims: to cooperate always with medical practitioners while pursuing our common interest in serving individuals afflicted with eating disorders.

Our gifted editor, Faith Farthing of FinalEyes Communications, merits special mention. She helped keep us on track and used her considerable skill to guide us in polishing the final draft.

Local author Sharon Guenette encouraged us to move forward with the business of self-publishing and provided many helpful suggestions as we did so. Rob McDonald and Don Tompkins of Miller Thomson LLP rendered invaluable advice on matters legal, and Rolinda Mack pointed us in their direction. Stewart Shinewald assisted us on accounting and financial issues.

We thank Peter Johnston of PSC Consulting for his aid to the computer-illiterate among us in preparing and printing the various drafts of the manuscript as they took shape. Wendy Smith of Print Doctor designed the cover and formatted the entire manuscript, with grace and efficiency, and we thank her for so generously sharing her prodigious talent with us.

Gwen Massie fielded phone calls and guarded the door on innumerable occasions, allowing our writers to go about their tasks, often at her inconvenience.

Beyond Edmonton, we want to thank those patient souls who guided us through the business of copyright permissions. Darlene Smith, our non-alcoholic contact at Alcoholics Anonymous World Services, Inc. in New York, and Anne Golob at Merriam-Webster, Inc. never seemed to tire of answering yet another fax or phone call. Diane Aronson at HarperCollins Publishers in New York gave us invaluable direction in preparing our bibliographical references.

Special thanks go to the staff of Friesens Book Division, and in particular Jim Beckel, Donovan Bergman, and Brad Schmidt, for their assuredly professional, yet altruistic, ministrations to A.B.A. Without their notable proficiency, resources, and technological wizardry, this work could not have been converted from manuscript to book. We are grateful to Ruth Linka at NeWest Press for connecting us with these good folk.

Finally, and most importantly, we offer thanks to the true Author of this book, the Higher Power who prompted us to write it and kept us sober throughout the process.

To ALL who may find healing through this work

and

to THE POWER that inspired it.

CONTENTS

Part II: Here Are Our Stories / 197

Preface

WE, OF ANOREXICS AND BULIMICS ANONYMOUS, are a group of individuals who have recovered from what appeared to be a hopeless condition of physical deterioration and mental obsession. Many of us were pronounced incurable or even untreatable by our doctors and therapists. Yet we have stumbled across a way out of our malady that is simple and deeply effective.

We came to believe that our eating disorders are addictions, parallel in every respect to alcoholism and drug addiction. We learned about the Twelve-Step Program originated by Alcoholics Anonymous, and we followed it. To our amazement, it worked! As we walked through the Twelve Steps we found authentic and lasting release from our preoccupation with body weight and shape, with food and purging, and with exercise. Many of us were virtually raised from the dead to live happy and productive lives, liberated from the obsessions that once dominated our thinking and dictated our actions. By following the Twelve-Step pathway, we have been restored to sanity. We have become walking miracles, acknowledged as such by those who knew us when we were the walking dead.

Ten years ago we formed a Fellowship that meets frequently in the city of our origin and is gradually spreading out from there. Until now, the message we have carried to other anorexics and bulimics has been spread mainly by word of mouth. We now believe the time has come to put what we have learned into writing, for two principal reasons. First, we wish to preserve the integrity and clarity of information that we regard as vital to recovery. Secondly, we hope to reach many more anorexics and bulimics who could benefit from our approach. We earnestly hope that someday no one will die of these diseases without having heard of the Twelve-Step Program as a way out.

It is critically important to be aware that our approach to recovery from anorexia and bulimia is intended to complement, not replace, treatment by professional health care providers. These diseases are serious and potentially fatal conditions whose physical manifestations must be corrected before there can be any hope for recovery from their spiritual aspect. The Twelve-Step Program is a purely spiritual approach to the spiritual component of addictive disorders, and is no substitute for ongoing supervision by qualified medical professionals. We strongly warn any anorexic or bulimic readers to ensure they are receiving such supervision before delving into the content of this book.

Until now our basic textbook of recovery has been the book *Alcoholics Anonymous*, also nicknamed the "Big Book."[1] Published in 1939, this remarkable work remains today as foundational to Twelve-Step recovery as when it was first published. Once we crossed out the words "alcohol" and "drinking" and substituted phrases like "restricting our food" or "bingeing and purging," we discovered that the book was written for us and about us. Once we similarly altered Steps One and Twelve to make them relevant for anorexics and bulimics, we found the Twelve Steps to be a perfect pathway to healing.

For these reasons we wish to make it clear at the outset that this textbook is in no way intended as a replacement for the Big Book in the recovery path of our Fellowship. Rather, it is intended to be used as a supplement to it, as a storehouse of specialized information that is both unique to the disorders of anorexia and bulimia and of critical importance to recovery from them. We strongly encourage every anorexic and bulimic who desires healing to use both the Big Book and this volume as twin vehicles of recovery. Both are indispensable.

We also wish to emphasize that any comments found in these pages regarding alcoholism, Alcoholics Anonymous, the Big Book, the Twelve Steps, and the Twelve Traditions are strictly the opinion of our authors. They are not in any way endorsed or approved by Alcoholics Anonymous World Services, Inc., nor do we wish to imply such endorsement. Moreover, we have altered the Steps and Traditions to bring gender-neutrality to all references to Higher Power or God, and these changes are strictly our own.

One other important point about the wording of this book. Just as the Big Book uses the masculine pronoun throughout, for the simple reason that in 1939 the overwhelming majority of recovering alcoholics were male, so we shall employ the feminine pronoun throughout because our current membership is mainly female. Nevertheless, we believe that anorexics and bulimics of both sexes and of any race or creed may find something useful in these pages.

The text is divided into two main sections. Part I contains all the information that we consider essential to recovery from anorexia and bulimia using the addiction model and the Twelve-Step Program. A number of anecdotes are woven into the text of Chapters 3 through 8 for purposes of illustration. The names of the people in these examples and many identifying details about their lives have been altered to thoroughly camouflage their identities and safeguard their anonymity. Part II comprises a collection of personal narratives of recovery written by some of our members, each in their own words. We trust that these revealing accounts will help those who could benefit from our approach to identify with us, thereby finding hope that they too can recover.

We have included a chapter specifically addressed to the family because we regard eating disorders as family diseases that, like alcoholism, profoundly affect everyone around the sufferer, and in particular those who love her the most. We hope such people will find understanding, consolation, and hope, not only from Chapter 15 but also from the entire content of the book. ***We must, however, warn any families of minor children with eating disorders to avoid relying on this book. Anorexia and bulimia at this early age are a grave problem that need to be handled by qualified professionals, in particular pediatricians and psychiatrists experienced in eating disorders. Our approach to recovery is useful only in more mature age groups.***

A comprehensive Glossary follows Part II to assist the reader in understanding the terminology used throughout the book. It includes an explanation of medical terms and also of such words as "sober" and "drug" that we use with a specialized meaning different from common parlance. As a general rule, terms defined in the text itself are not repeated in the glossary.

With regard to references, occasional footnotes are scattered throughout the text where direct quotations from other sources have been used with the permission of their publisher. Additionally, a lengthy Notes section follows the glossary, acknowledging particular concepts derived from other writers and mentors. The numbers in this compilation correspond to the bracketed numbers found throughout the text. A select Bibliography, preceded by an essay entitled "Suggested Readings," is the last word in this volume. Using all these methods, we have attempted to give credit where it is due: to as many as possible of those spiritual guides who have heavily influenced us, assisting the Creator in the work of transforming our minds as we recover from anorexia and bulimia.

We do not, however, mean to imply that all our members have personally accessed all these other sources of wisdom, nor that we have compiled an exhaustive list. Nothing could be further from the truth. As we follow the A.B.A. Program, each one of us engages in her own quest for spiritual growth and discovers the written sources that speak to her as an individual. This is both our prerogative and our responsibility. The authors of this text possess what wisdom they have only as a result of their own experience in recovery from anorexia and bulimia, and often their spiritual guides have both catalyzed their experience and given them the language to name it. Although our authors remain anonymous, they bear the ethical and moral duty of crediting the sources of their ideas wherever possible.

An Index has been appended to the text as an aid in locating specific topics. This is intended as both a study tool and a convenient guide for discussion topics during A.B.A. meetings.

We do not believe that we have a monopoly on the path to recovery from the psychospiritual component of anorexia and bulimia, that we have found the only solution that can work. We have met people who found a different road to health, and we are happy for them. We, however, found no deep healing until we reached this Program, and we wish to offer our experience to anyone who desires to hear it. We sincerely hope that, if you identify that you are one of us as you read this book and have as yet found no way out of your disease, you will choose to join us on this journey of recovery.

PART I

The Program of Recovery

A Doctor's Viewpoint 1

I AM a family physician who for more than a decade has worked with people suffering from eating disorders. In this work I have had the great advantage of being a recovered anorexic myself. I was fortunate not to die from this disease, which has claimed the lives of others whose clinical pictures resembled my own. Instead I have recovered, and the story of my personal healing journey is detailed in Chapter 2.

In this first chapter I have been asked to contribute some information from a purely medical perspective, and I am honored to do so. I need issue one caveat, however, at the outset. I have found the approach of Anorexics and Bulimics Anonymous to eating disorders to be useful only with patients who have reached a level of maturity and autonomy that allows them to accept full responsibility for their illness and their recovery process. It is not appropriate for children or for young adolescents, who cannot possibly have attained such maturity. In my practice I refer all anorexic and bulimic patients in this age group to a psychiatrist skilled in dealing with their special needs. I never attempt to treat them myself. Readers who are concerned about minors with eating disorders are cautioned to use the content of this book with discretion. Although it may facilitate a deeper understanding of the problem of eating disorders, it is unlikely to provide any useful information leading to their solution in the case of the younger patient. In particular, parents of minor children with eating disorders are strongly advised to consult experienced medical professionals about their children.

THERAPY OF ANOREXIA AND BULIMIA NERVOSA

Current Therapeutic Approaches

The twin disorders of anorexia and bulimia nervosa have baffled and confounded medical practitioners for decades. An impressive body of literature has developed alongside a vast array of therapeutic approaches—including medication, forced feeding measures, gastrostomy, parenteral nutrition, behavior modification, confinement in hospitals and asylums, outpatient meal-support, electroconvulsive therapy, and a host of psychotherapeutic techniques.[1] Therapists in many fields have tried variously coaxing, coddling, convincing, and coercing their patients to eat in a healthy manner. They have tried reason, explanation, gentle persuasion, drugs, threats, and even physical force to control these peculiarly obstinate patients who seem bent on self-destruction.

Results of The Usual Methods

My own experience is that many of these approaches are effective for a time and that none of them work in the long run. Through the application of these methods, individuals with eating disorders may eat normally, attain a healthy weight, feel better physically and emotionally, and even come to fully understand how and why they originally developed their maladaptive behaviors. In most cases, however, they are not released from the central crux of the disease: their mental obsession with weight, food, body image, and exercise. This leaves them predisposed to relapse. Some patients may achieve release from their obsession, only to find themselves using alcohol, drugs, overwork, sex, relationships, or gambling instead. Anything to alter their minds so they can face their lives. Often in such cases, the substitute method of psychic alteration eventually itself becomes a compulsion fueled by a mental obsession, and as self-destructive as the eating disorder ever was.

Is Recovery Possible?

Given these facts, we are faced with a crucial question: Is true recovery from eating disorders even possible? Many of my colleagues in this field, battle-weary and jaded by their heartbreaking experience with these recalcitrant patients, shake their heads sadly at this question. No, they say, the most we can hope for, at least in chronic cases, is to help these patients cope with their dreary existence until death mercifully ensues. This opinion is remarkably similar to universal medical opinion regarding chronic alcoholism in the early 1930s, prior to the advent of Alcoholics Anonymous.

I believe that my disillusioned colleagues are correct. These patients *are* beyond human aid once their minds are fully occupied by the anorexic or bulimic obsession. I have seen hundreds of patients who languished in the misery of their illness for decades in spite of the best treatment by dedicated practitioners. Many experience temporary reprieves, and with each relapse sink to ever greater depths of despair. I have witnessed the deaths of many of these patients, at least half of these from suicide. No amount or combination of antidepressant medication can relieve the pernicious self-loathing generated by the entrenched obsessions of these individuals.

Nevertheless, in the past ten years I have witnessed truly miraculous, enduring recoveries in the anorexic and bulimic population. I have seen people completely restored to physical health, liberated from their obsession with their bodies, free to eat normally without having to think constantly about food, free to live their lives and do their jobs and raise their families. Such recoveries have become so commonplace in my practice that I am no longer surprised by them. And it seems that such a favorable outcome is entirely independent of the age of the patient and the duration of their illness. Patients aged eighteen and sixty recover. Those who have been ill for six months and thirty years recover. Employing the approach outlined in this book, virtually *anyone* can recover, even patients with coexisting mental illnesses.

Coexisting Mental Disorders

As an important aside, the recovery approach detailed in this book deals only with the disorders of anorexia nervosa, bulimia nervosa, and allied eating disorders, not with any accompanying mental illness. In my experience, such coexisting disease is frequent in the anorexic and bulimic population. Particularly common are major mood disorders, including bipolar disorder; personality disorders, especially ones with borderline and obsessive-compulsive traits; dissociative disorders; and posttraumatic stress disorder, often resulting from childhood sexual abuse and other disruptive events in the early lives of these patients. Obviously, these concomitant mental disorders require appropriate treatment in their own right, and psychiatrists and psychologists have a vital role to play in this regard. Appropriate medication and a variety of psychotherapeutic methods can be helpful, and many anorexics and bulimics in the A.B.A. Fellowship undertake such therapy in conjunction with their Twelve-Step work. We never discourage them from doing so. Furthermore, we ensure that every individual entering the rooms of Anorexics and Bulimics Anonymous understands that our program is only intended to help her find recovery from her eating disorder and from the havoc it creates in her life.

ESSENTIAL COMPONENTS OF DEEP RECOVERY

The key elements in the remarkable recoveries I have witnessed have been simple and consistent from one case to the next. All these individuals first needed to risk letting go of their pathological eating, purging, and exercise patterns. They had to admit complete personal defeat by their disease, then come to believe that a spiritual Power greater than themselves could restore them to sanity. They needed to establish an ongoing relationship with that Higher Power and live according to its guidance. They were required to follow a simple program of action to deal with their own emotional and spiritual ruin and with the harm they had caused others through their disease. They needed to work with other anorexics and bulimics who wished to recover, passing on their personal experience and strength. *Most importantly, they needed the support of others walking the same recovery path. No one in my experience has healed in isolation.*

The Physical: First Things First

Of course, anorexics and bulimics always need medical treatment to restore their physical well-being before they can follow the Twelve-Step plan outlined in this book, and the need for such treatment should never be overlooked or minimized. All of us in Anorexics and Bulimics Anonymous are aware of the physical devastation caused by these diseases. When newcomers walk through our doors, much of our early work with them is directed toward connecting them with the medical help they need. We know there is no point in talking about the spiritual message of the Twelve-Step Program to someone whose body has been compromised by starvation or by bingeing and purging, because the words would fall on deaf ears. As you read on in this book, you will notice again and again the top priority we place on physical "sobriety"—defined as adherence to nutritionally sound eating practices and initiation of return to healthy body weight—as a prerequisite to working the Twelve Steps. All are welcome, of course, to attend our meetings, no matter how sick they are. The only requirement for membership in our group is a *desire* to stop unhealthy eating practices. Some people attend for months or years before they finally surrender to healthful eating and become physically well enough to begin the work of psychospiritual recovery through the Twelve Steps.

We frequently refer our newcomers to physicians outside our Fellowship to obtain the medical treatment they may urgently require. Sometimes we accompany these sick members to a hospital or clinic where they can be treated for their physical complications. I have the utmost respect for physicians who are willing to treat these difficult patients, because they demand extraordinary patience, wisdom, and compassion. Many in the medical field give their all and deserve the highest commendation for their efforts. They play an essential role in the physical treatment of individuals with eating disorders.

The Spiritual: The Core of Recovery

However, for anorexics and bulimics to be healed mentally and spiritually, to be released from their deadly obsessions with food and with their bodies, I have found the usual medical and psychological interventions to be of limited use. A spiritual path of recovery is needed to heal a spiritual malady, and the Twelve-Step Program is one such itinerary. Furthermore, it is a well-trodden route, having proven effective for millions of people suffering from a variety of addictive disorders. In the Fellowship of Anorexics and Bulimics Anonymous, individuals who become physically sober are then able to work through the Twelve-Step Program, using the guidance of more experienced members. This Program leads them to profound emotional, mental, and spiritual healing.

Why Powerlessness?

Some of my medical colleagues object to the First Step of our Program because it requires an admission of personal powerlessness over the disease of anorexia and bulimia. "What about the individual's responsibility?" they say. "Why not teach the patient that she truly possesses the power to make better choices for herself?"

Let me respond to these objections by stating that the remaining eleven Steps of the Twelve-Step Program are all about *empowerment.* They lead the individual to assume full responsibility for her illness and her recovery through an intensive program of action. As she works through these Steps, she discovers deep within herself a spiritual Power greater than anything she could have imagined, a Power that not only allows her to eat normally and that stops her deadly obsessions, but also one that shapes and informs every aspect of her life.

The great paradox is that she can arrive at this amazing personal power only through admitting the truth about her disease: that she is powerless over it (Step One). She can then reach out for and accept the help she needs to begin recovery. Our individual members must themselves assume full responsibility for undertaking the actions needed for recovery. No one can do this for them...*and* they don't need to do it alone.[2]

USE OF TERMINOLOGY IN THIS BOOK

Role of the DSM-IV™

Before concluding this discussion, I wish to clarify for both lay and medical readers some of the terminology found throughout this book. I am fully conversant with the precise definitions of eating disorders found in the DSM-IV™.[3] (For the information of the lay reader, this designation refers to a highly respected publication of the American Psychiatric Association that is widely used as a trusted handbook by psychiatrists and other medical doctors throughout the world.) However, I have found the DSM-IV definitions of eating disorders to be of little practical use to my work in this field over the past decade. Some people I have seen meet all criteria for anorexia nervosa or bulimia nervosa, while others who are just as sick do not. For example, some anorexics whose entire lives have been decimated by their disease have never met the weight-loss standards in DSM-IV. Some bulimics do not binge and purge frequently enough to earn the label of bulimia nervosa. And then there is the largely uncharted territory of compulsive eating disorder, an entity yet to be named by psychiatric texts. Of course, the DSM-IV does identify the new diagnosis of "eating disorder not otherwise specified," a catch-all category that encompasses everyone who does not fall within the parameters for anorexia or bulimia nervosa. However, this vague diagnosis seems to be rarely heard by patients or, if heard, it is trivialized and regarded as proof of no significant pathology.

The Dangers of Diagnostic Criteria

I believe that the distinctions found in DSM-IV are not only unnecessary but potentially harmful to patients. I have interviewed many people who sought treatment for their eating disorder years earlier, only to be reassured by their physician because they did not fulfill all the qualifications for anorexia or bulimia nervosa. Regrettably, some of these individuals concluded that they were not sick after all and then went on to become more deeply mired in their disease, often devoting another decade or two of their lives to its practice before pursuing further help.

Others fled to the arms of practitioners with little or no knowledge of eating disorders who, though well-meaning, understandably missed the diagnosis in these patients. Often such therapists recommended costly and sometimes harmful approaches for the physical symptoms that resulted merely from untreated eating disorders. I have met full-blown anorexics who were prescribed highly restrictive diets to treat their fatigue and abdominal symptoms, thus aggravating their anorexic obsession and leading to dangerous further weight loss. Some patients were existing on handfuls of supplements instead of on food when they first consulted me.

We physicians might prevent such unfortunate chains of events by using broader margins in our diagnostic process. The statisticians and researchers must, of course, adhere precisely to DSM-IV, yet I wonder whether we front-line clinicians might consider approaching patients differently. Perhaps we could validate that the patient before us is truly ill even if her condition has not yet progressed to meet all DSM-IV criteria. It is generally agreed that anorexia and bulimia nervosa have the highest mortality rate of all psychiatric disorders. It therefore seems wise to find every possible means to help a patient face her disease squarely while it is still at an early stage.

What Is She *Thinking*?

Anorexics and Bulimics Anonymous recognizes that the essence of eating disorders is neither body weight nor outward eating behavior per se, but rather the insanity of the mental obsession that fuels pathological eating and purging behaviors. *Anorexia and bulimia are defined by what is transpiring in the mind regarding food and body image, not by the outward appearance or behavior of the individual.*

A.B.A Encourages Self-Diagnosis

Furthermore, all who come to this Fellowship identify for themselves whether they belong here or not. No one weighs them at the door or demands a tally of their binges over the past week before letting them in. They are anorexic or bulimic if they say so. If they lack the true mental obsession of anorexia or bulimia nervosa, they will shortly identify this for themselves and not return to meetings. And if they *do* have the mental obsession, they will feel at home among us regardless of their present body size or current eating practices. Most importantly, they will have the opportunity to recover *now*, instead of waiting until they have lost enough weight or binged and purged enough to earn the psychiatric label. Surely this is a desirable outcome, especially for a disorder whose prognosis deteriorates rapidly with elapsed time, and in this fiscally responsible age when early intervention is regarded as one of the highest ideals in health care.

Our members identify themselves as "anorexic" if they act out their obsession through restriction of their food, as "bulimic" if they binge and purge, and as "anorexic and bulimic" if they do both. We don't care in the least whether these labels are diagnostically correct. All that matters to us is that all people begin to be honest with themselves about their pathological behaviors, because that is what they will need to give up in sobriety. We have also happily observed that many who identify themselves primarily as "compulsive eaters" (because currently their preferred behavior is periodic bingeing or daily overeating) have found a home with us and have successfully followed our pathway to recovery. How this is possible will be made clear in Chapter 4.

WHY WOULD A THERAPIST READ THIS BOOK?

I believe that this textbook of recovery has the potential to be helpful to great numbers of people, both now and in the future. We in Anorexics and Bulimics Anonymous have stumbled across a unique approach to recovery from eating disorders that really does work. Miracles abound. Yet they rarely occur in solitude, for the Higher Power behind them works most commonly through human beings. Anorexics and bulimics need one another as well as aid from outside sources to achieve deep healing. Physicians, psychologists, dietitians, and other therapists are all vitally important. I invite all such readers to proceed through the book with open minds. You may be greatly enriched by what you are about to read.

This textbook may provide professionals with fresh insight into the true nature of eating disorders. It will also suggest novel, practical methods of intervention conducive to full recovery. Much of what you will find within these pages has never before been recorded in any medical or psychological or self-help book. I encourage everyone interested in the field of eating disorders to read this book, as it may assist many who have hitherto been groping in the dark. I trust that what follows in the next fourteen chapters will provide new light for therapists, as well as guidance and hope for those afflicted with the disorders and for their families and friends.

Joan J., M.D.

Joan's Story 2

I WAS not born an anorexic.

I clearly recall being free of the web of addiction prior to school age. I knew how to take care of myself, how to feel my feelings, how to stay connected with myself and everything else. When hurt or fearful, I knew instinctively that being with the trees and rocks in the woods behind our home was what I needed. I could hear the murmurs of a loving Creator in the rustling of leaves and the chatter of bluejays; feel the tender embrace of my Mother Earth in the cool needle-packed forest floor and in the tall meadow grasses when I lay on my back to watch the changing wonder of the world's ceiling; smell God in the nearly unbearable sweetness of cool moss and jack pine and the west wind after rain; taste the Creator in the spice of spruce gum and the chilled magic of falling snow on my tongue; see the hand of the Master in the extravagance of northern lights and lavish scarlet sunsets and whipped cream clouds in azure skies.

In all of this I possessed an innate wisdom stretching beyond the language of a child. I knew that I was in the care of Compassion itself; that all was right with the universe, including me; that fear was a scandalous waste of energy. I experienced no separation between myself and all of creation, and I knew that everything flowed from and to the Creator in an unbroken stream of energy that was the dance of Life itself. I was simply myself, and I was enough.

Everything changed, as irrevocably as a rose touched by frost, in the autumn of the year that I was seven. On one never-to-be-forgotten day, my mother summoned me to the living room and dispassionately informed me that Daddy would not be living with us anymore. "I'm telling you this because you're old enough to understand and to help me with the little ones from now on. Aren't you?"

In the next ten seconds I made the decision that altered the course of my life. I decided to lie. To hide from my mother the strangling clutch of sheer terror erupting like bile from my belly to my throat. To pretend that the earth had not just opened beneath my feet, that I was not tumbling headlong into the deepest, blackest chasm I had ever known. Instead, I opened my mouth and stammered my untruths. "Sure, Mommy, I can do that. Sure, Mommy, I understand."

I had no means of knowing that in this moment of calculated deception I began painting the backdrop for my addictive drama, for the disease that would ultimately dismember my life and swallow me alive.

For the next twelve years I proceeded to weave my tangled web of deceit. I put away my dolls and became Mommy's indispensable assistant. I minded the little ones, scrubbed the floors, washed the dishes, and peeled the potatoes. I learned that smiling sweetly and meekly obeying every rule secured the rewards I wanted, so I perfected my favorite con: The Good Little Girl.

I fooled most of the people in my life, including Mommy and my teachers. But I couldn't fool myself. I knew that it was all a sham, that my compliant exterior was merely the lid over a foul cesspool bubbling with unnamed and unnamable emotions. The deep aching loss of my father, a grief that outlasted all the desolate tears my pillow could absorb. Murderous rage toward the woman, my mother, who had somehow caused him to leave, a feeling far too dangerous to allow into consciousness. And, above all else, the spectral terror that stalked my dreams: the fear that if I were not good enough, then she too would leave me.

By my teen years this growing dissonance between my outer disguise and my inner reality led to a profound sense of disconnection from others. I was mysteriously different from my peers. I knew that, I accepted it, I puzzled over it, and I variously attempted to hide it or to revel in it. I noticed that other people seemed to know how to live in the simplicity of daily life and to enjoy mundane activities. I found this baffling. I could not explain how they achieved this enjoyment, no matter how keenly I observed it or how logically I analyzed it. In the end, I decided that everyone else in the universe was privy to the secret of how to be happy and that I had been uniquely ordained, from the womb, to remain in the dark.

I was distressingly ashamed of these thoughts so, instead of sharing them with anyone, I merely worked harder at concealing them. I lived in profound spiritual isolation. On occasion, I made feeble attempts to act as if I were a "normal" person. But, deep in my soul, I knew that I was not.

In the autumn of my twentieth year, I entered medical school. There I began to long for acceptance by my classmates, for an end to the wrenching loneliness of my inner life. One day I chanced to weigh myself, discovered that I had gained a few pounds over the summer, and decided that I was fat. Losing a few pounds would surely make me more acceptable to my peers, so I resolved to go on a diet.

In this I was remarkably successful. Eliminating a few highly caloric items from my daily food intake, I began to lose weight. I stepped on the scale every Saturday morning, and no words can capture my experience as I watched those numbers drop. I felt a sense of inner power that no prior accomplishment had ever produced. *I* was doing this, I and I alone. No one had told me to do it. It was my project and my achievement. I could do what apparently no one else could do: adhere to a diet and keep losing weight. This was something far better than feeling equal to others, for it assured me that I was *better* than them, indeed superhuman.

And I was hooked. Eight months later and thirty pounds lighter, had I been capable of honesty with myself, I would have been able to admit that I had a problem, that I was in the grip of something beyond my control. My dietary restrictions became increasingly severe and my menstrual periods ceased. My poor mother grew frantic as she watched my body shrink, yet I countered every urgent plea she made with still greater rigidity. Eventually, however, I secretly agreed with her assessment that my bones were protruding, that I had lost enough weight. I decided to ease up on my diet.

But I could not. One day I tried adding a dinner roll to my plate and found my arm paralyzed by overwhelming fear. I believed that eating one roll would strip away all my hard-won control, that I would then overeat and quickly regain all the pounds I had lost, and more. In that moment, I knew in my gut that I was no longer on this diet by choice. I couldn't stop.

Starving to death is a highly unnatural experience for any living creature, and everything in our being is mobilized to combat it, to sustain life by any and all means. One such means is to become preoccupied with the pursuit of food to the exclusion of all other mental activities. All my thoughts now revolved around food, calories, exercise, and weight. I began lying to escape eating and the social events that included food. Planning and organizing my alibis consumed much time and energy and, more importantly, generated dreadful guilt in my essentially honest soul. That harrowing guilt never left me.

By my second year of medical school I ostracized myself and became a social recluse, hiding in my room to study and eat the bizarre foods that I permitted myself as a reward for starvation. My chief source of comfort became ginger-snap cookies, which were so low in calories that I could afford to eat a large number every day while still slowly losing weight. Thus I existed for the next three years.

I graduated in 1972 at the head of my class, having earned two gold medals and having lost forty-five pounds. This proves that intelligence and scholastic brilliance provide no protection from the disease of anorexia nervosa. In truth, they could more accurately be regarded as its prerequisites.

I left home for an internship in the Atlantic provinces, and it was there that I arrived at the pinnacle of my insanity. I worked grueling sixteen-hour days while living on a daily intake of thirty-six ginger snaps, supplemented with one ounce of meat and a handful of lettuce to balance my diet.

I still maintained that nothing was amiss in my life, that the obscure passage in my psychiatry textbook entitled "Anorexia Nervosa" did not describe me. However, one day near the end of my internship year my denial was shattered when I could not climb the stairs due to the wasting in my quadriceps muscles. I now tipped the scale at seventy-eight pounds, having lost a total of almost sixty pounds. In a rare moment of clarity, as I clung to the banister and dragged myself up the stairs, I heard a whisper in my mind. "You're going to die if you continue doing this." And I knew it was true.

I also knew I didn't want to die. I wanted to recover. Thus, after completing my internship one month later I returned home to western Canada, determined to do whatever was necessary to conquer this demon that I had finally claimed as my own. I tried using willpower to make myself eat normally, and that worked for two days. I tried a combination of prayer and willpower, and that worked for one day—until I stepped on the scale and registered an increase of two pounds. I panicked, certain that the next day I would weigh two hundred pounds. I consulted a psychiatrist and consented to hospitalization. There I took medication, submitted to behavior therapy, engaged in psychotherapy to determine the origins of my disease, and ate.

Unfortunately, I was sober in my eating for only the first three days in hospital. I ate everything placed before me, while surrendering all control over what food was served and over the portion sizes. On the fourth day, the dietitian visited me. "I'm Carrie, and I'm here to help you, Joan. I'm so glad you're eating again, and I'd like to make this as easy for you as possible. What foods do you like?"

Yes! My anorexic heart bounded with delight. Once again I had some control over my food. I told Carrie exactly what my anorexic mind liked and didn't like, and she graciously accommodated my requests. Chicken instead of pork. Jelly on my toast instead of butter. Baked potato instead of French fries. And so on.

Although I gained twenty pounds during those two months in hospital, my mental obsession with food and my fear of getting fat remained as intense and irrational as it had previously been. My need to control what I ate, and my fear of losing that control, diminished not at all. And in spite of the doctor's pronouncement of "cured" at the time of my discharge, I knew the truth.

Slowly and inexorably I slipped back into the full stranglehold of anorexia, and I stayed there for a further nine years. However, I did strike an unconscious compromise with my disease: "I'll do what you say as long as you let me maintain my weight. If I lose what I've gained I'll end up in hospital again, and I can't pretend my life is fine if I'm lying in a hospital bed." It worked. I ate precisely one quart of ice cream every day instead of ginger snaps, and my weight stabilized at ninety-eight pounds for the next nine years.

For the first four years after leaving hospital, I attempted to control my disease. I tried getting married, and three years later I tried getting divorced. I tried taking trips, going on retreat, losing myself in my work as a family physician, changing my field of specialization, reading a library of self-help books, seeing another psychiatrist, and taking more pills. I tried prayer—but my prayer was always the same: "Oh God, please remove this crazy thinking from me…but don't make me get fat!"

Nothing expelled my anorexic obsession, so for the final five years I gave up the struggle. I admitted that my condition was hopeless, that no one could alter the insane preoccupation that was the center of my life, that I would have to live out my remaining days in the torment of my obsessions, that anorexia was my master and I might as well accept it.

But in the recesses of my mind I always believed that I *should* be able to stop. I was certain that if I really wanted to, I would be able to stop living in such a self-centered manner. I never once truly grasped that I was sick. I thought I was simply bad. And the guilt engendered by this conviction kept me sick, for I experienced such intense self-loathing that I was compelled to escape from it. The most effective painkiller I'd ever found was to think about food, count another calorie, skip another meal, swim another lap. Truly a vicious, unbreakable cycle. I endured solitary confinement in a prison more secure than any ever constructed out of concrete walls, barred windows, and razor wire.

Meanwhile, I maintained the external trappings of life as a successful young physician. A thriving practice, an excellent reputation, the adoration of my patients, money in the bank, a good car, and a comfortable home filled with baubles and trinkets—all of these I clung to with increasing desperation. The good little girl had grown into an ageing little woman, but my con was unchanged from childhood. And so was my isolation and my need to hide the inner workings of my mind from everyone around me.

Loneliness and guilt copulated and gave birth to despair and at last, in January of 1983, my soul disintegrated. I could go on no longer. I could not look another patient in the eye and pretend for one more minute that I was okay. I admitted the whole truth to myself at last, that not only was anorexia my master, but that it also made life unliveable.

Never before or since have I known such pain as I endured in that chasm of nothingness when I faced the entire truth. I was utterly without hope that I could ever be freed from the bondage of my anorexic obsession. And yet, I could live with it no longer. I was unable to work. I was thirty-three years old and my life was over. I prayed blindly for help and longed for death, yet suicide was not an option, for I was also afraid of eternal damnation for the degenerate fashion in which I had lived for fourteen years. The fact that I believed I would be harshly judged by a cruel and punishing God reveals how far I had strayed from my instinctual childhood connection with the Creator. It reveals how little I really knew about my God.

I did not know that in facing the truth and admitting total defeat by my anorexia I had just taken the First Step of the Twelve-Step Program. After eight weeks in that rock-bottom place I took a small action that proved to be the next move in the direction of wholeness. To help pass the time in that winter of discontent, I volunteered to work for a few hours in a skid row mission. In the workers there, I felt the presence of Something I called God, and I experienced inner peace. Having had no peace for fourteen years, I was deeply moved by it. When I left the mission that day, the staff invited me to come for lunch before my next afternoon of work, and without conscious thought I accepted the invitation.

Walking home I was horrified. What had I agreed to? How could I escape this commitment? I agonized over that question for the next two days. In the end I made the most life-altering decision I had made since that day when I lied to my mother twenty-six years earlier. I decided that, in exchange for another taste of the wondrous peace I had felt, *I could surrender control of my food for just one meal* and eat what I was given. After all, no one except I would know what I was doing. No one would expect me to eat another meal. I could return to my anorexic rituals the following day.

In other words, I made the momentous decision to get sober. I went to the mission that day, ate the meal set before me, then began ironing linens and scrubbing floors.

What occurred during the next four hours is testimony to the love of the Creative Power at work in the universe, a Higher Power that I frequently refer to as God. That Power led my newly sober mind through a meditative process that I now identify as Steps Two through Seven of the Twelve-Step Program. I came to believe that I could be healed of my insanity by a God who can and will do anything except control me. I made a decision to turn over my mind and my life, including my weight, to this loving God. I identified what needed to be changed in my thinking if I were to move forward with my life in peace and wholeness. I admitted all this to myself and to God. I became entirely ready to let God do psychic surgery on me. I got on my knees and humbly asked, with no conditions attached, to be made whole in whatever way God decided was best for me.

Five minutes later I experienced a miracle. The entire "tape" of my anorexic thinking was expelled from my mind, just as a videotape is ejected from a VCR. The madness was over. I no longer *wanted* to be thin or to control my food. I wanted to eat anything and everything, to gain weight and to live my life fully. I was whole, I was free, and my eyes were finally opened to the truth. I saw that I had been mortally ill, sleepwalking in a sort of enchanted state for fourteen years, that now I was awake, and that God had effected this wondrous change.

Washed free of all guilt and overjoyed, I felt God's presence all around me and in me. I knew that Presence had always been there, that I was the one who had been disconnected from it by the hypnotic trance of my disease. As I walked home in the gathering dusk of that late winter day I saw God in the fading scarlet streak of the western horizon; inhaled God in the musty aroma of last autumn's leaves under melting snow; heard God in the twittering sparrows perched on overhead power lines; felt God in the caress of the southwest wind. I was seven years old again, I was alive, and all was well in the universe.

I had never heard of the Twelve-Step Program in 1983, yet for the next three months I intuitively worked its final five Steps. I immediately saw how much harm I had done to others, especially my family, through living as an active anorexic for fourteen years. I approached each of these people and told them of my healing, thereby making what amends I could for what I had done. I began writing my story as a means of making amends to my patients and to others whom I had deceived and harmed over the years. I sought to live each day in communion with the Creator, spending time in prayer and seeking guidance to do God's will in my life. I flew to a distant city to find a young anorexic girl who had passed through my medical practice several years before. I visited her in hospital, we went for a walk together, and I carried the message to her. "Janice, I was anorexic too, and God has healed me. This is my story. If God did this for me, then most certainly God can do the same for you." When she returned home some months later, I started working with her in an attempt to pass on what I had received.

During this three-month period I became physically well as I ate without restriction, gained fifteen pounds, and began menstruating again after my fourteen-year hiatus. Unfortunately, I had no inkling of the concept that as an anorexic I was a full-blown addict and that, in order to maintain recovery, I would need to take daily action to align my will with God's will, one day at a time, for the rest of my life. Although I was now in conscious contact with my Higher Power, *I had no human support* in my life for that Power to work through. No sponsor, no group, no meetings to attend, no others in recovery to consult when life presented challenges. And I had no idea that my very life depended on my continued working of the Twelve Steps.

So, in the fourth month of recovery my life again drastically changed. I met an eligible man and immediately experienced a desire to marry him, bear children, and live happily ever after. On our first date I picked up a drink to help me relax. Then another and another and another. Alcohol loosened my inhibitions and I became someone else, a self-styled *femme fatale*. I drank that way for a year.

I had no idea that in diving into a sea of alcohol I returned to a life driven by self-will instead of by ongoing surrender to God's will. I had no idea that my emotional and spiritual healing would halt abruptly with that first drink, nor that this new chemical method of escape from myself would shortly trigger a relapse into anorexic behavior.

At the end of that year I became pregnant and abruptly quit drinking. I stayed dry for six years to bear and breast-feed three children, but I retreated to the sanctuary of anorexia following the birth of each child, becoming obsessed with returning to my pre-pregnancy weight, dragging my exhausted body out of bed to exercise early each morning, and developing new eating rituals that I clung to with mounting desperation.

Meanwhile my life deteriorated in a number of ways. My marriage disintegrated as I was emotionally unavailable and incapable of intimacy. I lived in fear and resentment and self-pity, and I increasingly turned to excessive work as a drug to boost my crumbling self-esteem. As I became a full-blown workaholic my life spiraled further out of control. I made promises that I couldn't keep, I lied about the hours I worked, I regarded myself as a hopelessly inept mother, and I became so self-centered that I believed my children would benefit if I were dead. For the last two years of that turbulent time I took pills to dispel the thought of suicide from my mind.

In rare moments of quiet I wondered what was wrong with me. At times I concluded, as I had in childhood, that I was impossibly flawed as a human being, that I was destined to live a life devoid of lasting joy and peace. I had no idea that I was trapped once more in the web of addiction.

Finally, mercifully, I reached another bottom. My poor spent body collapsed and I could no longer work. I felt battered by life itself. Having exhausted my own resources, I remembered the God who had heard my prayer ten years before, and I dropped to my knees. I said simply, "Please let me know the truth."

A wise man once said, "Ask, and you will receive" (Matthew 7:7). Within a month of beginning to pray for help, I was guided to a Twelve-Step group who taught me that I am an addict, that I will always be an addict, that left to my own devices I will most certainly self-destruct, and that I have the option of recovery if I choose to accept spiritual help and do the necessary work to cooperate with it.

I do choose. When I first read the Twelve Steps in 1992, I instantly recognized them as the pathway out of anorexia that I had intuitively followed a decade earlier. With this knowledge to guide us, I and two other women with anorexia and bulimia united early in 1993 to support one another in recovery. We were joined by still others and soon began calling ourselves "Anorexics and Bulimics Anonymous." The frequency of our meetings has increased over the ten years of our existence, as has the clarity with which we define sobriety and the tools we use to maintain it.

I am now part of a large network of people who share my anorexia and other addictions and are recovering from them. Through the grace of God and the eagerness of others to give away what they have received, I continue to heal. I attend Twelve-Step meetings frequently, work the Steps under the guidance of a sponsor, study the relevant literature, pray daily for knowledge of God's will in my life and for the power to carry it out, and serve the Creator to the best of my ability.

I have relapsed into anorexic behavior a number of times through the years, and each relapse was preceded by an insidiously subtle shift in my thinking. Sometimes I became complacent and believed I no longer needed to devote as much time to my recovery. Sometimes I felt like a victim of anorexia, complaining that I can't live like normal folk, that I need to attend meetings every week and work with other anorexics and bulimics. Sometimes I lied to myself, deciding that I was too busy with work or family to pray or call my sponsor. Sometimes I let resentment fester in my gut instead of dealing with it promptly. Sometimes I was arrogant, seeing myself as wiser or more enlightened than others in the Fellowship.

After a variable period of thinking along these lines, my perception of my body generally changed and I saw myself as unacceptably "fat." I then proceeded to plan how I might alter my body through a small change in my eating or through more exercise. Or, without conscious planning, I simply omitted bread from my next meal or pushed myself to go for a swim when I was tired or unwell.

After each relapse I awoke to the truth about what I had done, then received the humility to call my sponsor and share the truth with her. That action opened a channel of grace to become sober again and to move forward with my recovery. Furthermore, each relapse offered me the possibility of learning something new about myself and about my powerlessness over anorexia, as well as about the goodness of my Higher Power. God will always be the only solution for my disease, and that fact needs to reverberate continuously in my being, like the pulsing of my soul. Otherwise I have no means to stay sober.

My life has changed radically in the past decade, and these changes have occurred slowly. Food has assumed its proper place in my life; I don't have to think about it unless I'm shopping for groceries or preparing a meal. I love my aging body and tenderly nurture it with wholesome food, rest, recreation, and occasional exercise. I have not stepped on a scale in many years, nor do I care about my weight or about the size of my clothing. What I weigh is none of my business; it is God's business.

Through working the Twelve Steps I continue to learn about who I am and to love myself, body and spirit, so I no longer need to alter my feelings through any of the quick fixes that my various addictions once provided. I am learning to participate in healthy relationships, to love and be loved. I have more true friends than I can count, and I know today that we are all the same and all different. I have received the gift of knowing that I am not unique. I experience peace of mind as I feel bonded to others by the invisible threads that connect all of creation.

I have tools today to deal with the slings and arrows that an outrageous fortune sometimes hurls in my direction. I no longer respond to all that is uncontrollable in life by focusing on my body, jumping on a scale, or starting on a diet. I passionately love my life, and I love the Source of it with a greater depth than ever before. Best of all, I am gifted with the privilege of working with others recovering from anorexia and bulimia and of watching a loving God perform miracles of healing before my eyes. My joy in these experiences is indescribable.

Ultimately, in the paradox that always characterizes the spiritual life, anorexia has proven to be both mortal enemy and best friend, and I am profoundly grateful for it. For although I needed to forfeit myself, body and soul, to the torture of my disease for a time, yet having lost my self I had nothing left to lose. With nothing to lose I had nothing to fear. Without fear I was able to face the awful truth about myself, about what I had become. And that truth has set me free.

About Eating Disorders 3

THE MEMBERSHIP OF A.B.A.

THE FELLOWSHIP of Anorexics and Bulimics Anonymous is composed of a true cross-section of the anorexic and bulimic population, some of whom were once just as sick as Joan. The precise details of our stories vary somewhat, but our underlying pathology was remarkably identical. All of us acquired a peculiar mode of thinking about our bodies and acted out these ideas in a truly bizarre fashion through abnormal eating and purging behaviors and through compulsive exercise.

Many of us regarded ourselves as hopeless, and so did those who loved us. And yet we have recovered. We found a solution for our deadly disease. That solution and the pathway we trod to find it are the principal subjects of this entire textbook, and they are fully explored in subsequent chapters. However, before we can utilize a solution we must know the exact nature of our problem, and that is the substance of this chapter and of the three that follow.

DO YOU SUSPECT YOU ARE ANOREXIC OR BULIMIC?

Perhaps you are reading this book because you wonder whether you are anorexic or bulimic. Other people may have suggested such a diagnosis to you. You may have dismissed their concern or even become angry with them, yet secretly dreaded that they are correct. We invite such a reader to approach what follows with an open mind. We hope you will identify with what you read, that you will find yourself in our stories. If you cannot identify with some of the specific details of what we did with food and exercise, then perhaps you will relate to our feelings and thoughts and attitudes. Such identification can pour the foundation for recovery as it generates hope that you are no longer alone, that others have been where you are now and have moved on to full recovery.

Is Your Case Mild?

Or perhaps you already know that you are anorexic or bulimic, but you think your problem is very mild, that it has not reached the extreme degree that you have seen portrayed in magazines or on television. Maybe you still enjoy being thin or regard vigilance over your weight as essential to your career in modeling or dance or sales. We welcome all such readers and assure you that you need not progress any further down the scale before beginning your recovery. If you can identify to even a slight extent with what follows in this book, then we believe our approach to recovery can work for you too.

WHY DO WE DO IT?

Anorexia and bulimia are incomprehensible to people who think normally about food and about their bodies, as we who are afflicted know only too well. We frequently heard those who love us ask us *why* we acted as we did. Why in heaven's name do we not eat when any fool can see that we are too thin, when even the scale proves we are too thin? Don't we like food anymore? How can we be so bright and energetic when we look like walking skeletons? Or, as we get sicker, do we *like* fainting in the street? What is so pleasurable about self-induced vomiting? Why not quit before the dentist starts pulling out our teeth? Are cramps and diarrhea fun? Why do we go into debt to buy food for our binges? Why risk criminal charges by stealing food and laxatives when our credit runs out? Don't we care about our children? How can we set such a terrible example of self-abuse for our daughters? How can someone so smart do something so stupid to herself? How can we be so self-absorbed? Are we just looking for attention?

When we heard such questions our hearts sank, for many of us asked ourselves the same things every day for years. We analyzed and speculated and tried to figure out why we acted in these ways. Most of us sought professional help to assist with our self-analysis. Frequently we came up with plausible explanations and were certain that surely *now* we would change.

But we did not. Despite understanding all about how food was controlled by our domineering mothers, or about how our peers teased us for our prepubescent fat, or about the helplessness and terror we experienced while our drunken father broke dishes and bones in the next room, we continued to survive on salads and count fat grams or to devour the Hallowe'en candy we stole from our children and vomit it into the nearest toilet.

Or perhaps we couldn't find any reasonable explanation for our behavior. We may have come from wonderfully secure homes where we were loved unconditionally, treated respectfully, and given every encouragement to develop our independence and make decisions for ourselves as we matured. We were taught to value ourselves for who we were rather than for what our bodies looked like. In these cases our behavior with food placed an even heavier burden on our conscience. How dare we have an eating disorder when we couldn't even find a cause for it?

CLASSIFICATION OF EATING BEHAVIOR

The first thing we need to grasp is that there is an unbreachable chasm separating what we will call "normal eaters," "casual dieters," and "serious dieters" from real anorexics and bulimics.[1]

The Normal Eater

Normal eaters eat in order to live, paying little or no attention to food or to their body size. They instinctively adhere to the principles of good nutrition; prepare appealing and balanced meals that they eat with pleasure; and spend little time between meals thinking about food, unless they are shopping for groceries or planning a dinner party. They occasionally miss a meal because they are too busy, in which case they often compensate by ingesting more at a later time, usually without conscious awareness of what they are doing. They sometimes overeat at a family feast, groan and loosen their belts, then sit on the sofa in pleasant conversation waiting for their discomfort to pass; the next morning they eat less for breakfast, simply because they are not hungry. Normal eaters absolutely trust their internal appetite and satiety mechanisms and have usually paid no attention to this biological phenomenon. They accept their bodies as they are, may joke about being too plump or too thin, but this worries them not in the least. They exercise because they enjoy playing tennis with a friend, or because they like walking in the outdoors or feeling their bodies move rhythmically through water.

The Casual Dieter

Then there is the casual dieter. This is the woman who decides to shed a few pounds because her favorite skirt is tight around the waist. She stops eating dessert, buys low-fat mayonnaise, and goes out walking for half an hour after dinner most days. A few weeks later she may or may not have lost the pounds she aimed for, but in either case she smiles or shrugs and goes on with her life, the diet forgotten by the following month after she has bought a larger skirt. She knows her body is fine and doesn't care what the current fashion models look like. She is much more interested in her children's grades and in weeding the garden than she ever was in losing weight.

The Serious Dieter

The serious dieter is common in our society today. She is chronically dissatisfied with her body and has an ongoing desire to alter it, believing that she will find happiness and success by losing weight. She often feels at war with her body and drives herself through punishing exercise routines. She regularly places herself on the latest fad diet, enlisting all her willpower to adhere to it, and yet rarely can she stay committed long enough to reach her desired weight. She frequently chides herself for her lack of willpower. Sometimes she attains her goal weight, then rewards herself with a celebratory phase in which she regains the pounds she has just shed. Most serious dieters lose and regain the same twenty pounds many times over. The serious dieter deeply cares about how fashion models appear, buys clothes that conceal the despised areas of her body, and may even try purging as a method of weight control. She often tells her friends that she wishes she could become anorexic for a few weeks.

However, the serious dieter doesn't really *like* the feeling that she gets from dieting.[2] She therefore has no desire to continue doing so any longer than she believes she must, and she can moderate or stop dieting if she has sufficient reason to do so: family pressure, traveling, eating at a restaurant, hunger, boredom, or ill health. Furthermore, although thoughts about food and calories and weight occupy much of her mind when she is actually dieting, such thoughts dissipate quickly when she is not. Like the normal eater and the casual dieter, she perceives her body shape and size fairly accurately, without distortion. She does not lie about her dieting practices or hide them from others. And she generally does not use her eating practices as a means of altering her feelings.

The Real Anorexic

But not so for those of us who are real anorexics and bulimics. We have virtually all started out our lives as normal eaters, according to our mothers. We may or may not have been casual or serious dieters for a certain period of our lives. But at some point along the way, if we are bound for the anorexic path, we acquire an intense and unceasing preoccupation with the appearance of our body. We are tormented by an unwavering conviction that we need to alter our weight or our shape. We begin restricting our food, and within a few months we are living on grapefruit and rice cakes. We may exult in feeling lightheaded and empty, as we delight in our clothes hanging loosely on our shrinking frames. We get up at five o'clock in the morning to run ten miles before dining on dry toast and black coffee, and we ignore the shin splints we develop. We feel invincible.

We become annoyed when our families express their concern, and we repay them with the silent treatment as we skip another meal. Then we start lying about our behavior to allay their fears. We hide the potato in our pocket, feed the pork chop to the dog under the dinner table, and dump our milk into the potted plant when no one is watching. We may vomit our food or take laxatives if we can't avoid eating, and we go to great lengths to conceal this from others. Some of us take diuretics to dispose of real or imagined water from our bodies.

By this time we notice that most of our thoughts now revolve around food and weight, or calories and grams of fat. We become conscious that our minds are elsewhere when we're watching a movie or reading our sociology textbook or conversing with our friends, and we try to hide our inattention. We may notice that our emotional natures have changed, that we are moody or irritable or depressed, and that we are less sociable than before. We might observe that many things in our lives are becoming problematic: We aren't sleeping well; our close relationships are suffering; we can't get our school assignments done as easily as in the past; we're having trouble getting up in time for work; we forget to do important things unless we write them down. We may not yet attribute these problems to the way we are eating. Rather, we turn to our restrictive diets even more, because we need to feel in control of *something* when everything else in our lives is going downhill. Sometimes we use these life problems to justify what we are doing with food and exercise.

However, eventually we do wake up and admit to ourselves that our diet has gone awry. We then try to modify it or stop completely. But our entire willpower is to no avail, because by now we have developed an overwhelming terror of getting fat. A reading of ninety pounds on the scale fails to allay our anxiety, because we fear that at any moment we will lose all control and eat everything in sight. Finally we begin to consult doctors to help us, and we take the medicine they prescribe to reduce our fear before meals. Then we start needing the pills to get through the day. We agree to be hospitalized for treatment, then pull out the feeding tube and do jumping jacks in the bathroom. One day we overdose on the pills to find relief from our torture.

The Real Bulimic

Those of us who are bulimic walk a slightly different path. We may or may not start off with a desire to alter our weight or shape as did our anorexic sisters. Many of us do as they did, but after three months of dieting we're tired of feeling hungry all the time. We read a magazine article about bulimia or learn about it in school and decide to give it a try. A year later we are bingeing and purging three times a day. Our parents put a lock on the refrigerator and listen at the bathroom door. We lie to our boyfriends in restaurants to get away from the table and purge. Our spouse questions why the grocery bills are so high, and the plumber has to be summoned to unblock sewer lines clogged with the undigested food we have vomited.

Eventually our judgment becomes so impaired that we resort to bingeing out of garbage cans and vomiting into plastic bags in the garage or under the bed. Our dentists comment on the state of our teeth, and our guts are in knots from the laxatives we take by the handful. We beg our friends to help us by handing them our binge foods, then curse them when they won't relent and give them back. We walk three miles to binge on ice cream, but are too weak to get out of bed. We consult our doctors and take heaps of antidepressants. Then we vomit blood for the first time and end up in hospital with a plastic tube in our arms. We are so weak we cannot stand, but still we must crawl to the kitchen to binge. The carving knife looks more and more attractive as a way out of our pain.

PROGRESSIVE DISEASES

As individuals no one of us looks precisely like either of the above descriptions, but we can all identify ourselves in some of these behaviors. After reading these sketches of anorexia and bulimia, you might be saying to yourself, "I'm not *that* bad. Sure I watch my waistline and am a little fussy about what I eat, and my family is worried about the weight I'm losing, but I certainly haven't gone to the extremes that these people have!" Or you may be thinking, "Good heavens, just because I lose control of myself and binge once in a while, and then have to throw up because I feel so full, it doesn't mean I have a serious problem. Clearly these people in Anorexics and Bulimics Anonymous are much worse off than I am. I don't belong with them."

If you are thinking such thoughts right now, let us assure you that we all found anorexia and bulimia to be progressive diseases.[3] We all started out at one place and ended up at quite another. In the beginning we really liked dieting and exercising or bingeing and purging. We felt good as we did it, and these behaviors appeared to occupy a small place in our lives. We felt remarkably in control of ourselves and experienced no guilt about what we did with food. The behaviors were *working* for us. Life was good, in fact much better since we had begun to diet and exercise or to binge and purge.

However, as time went by, all of that gradually changed. We anorexics needed to eliminate more and more foods from our diet and to spend increasing amounts of time thinking about what to eat or how to avoid eating. We felt compelled to increase the intensity, frequency, and duration of our exercise. Our fear of getting fat grew ever more extreme. The bulimics among us found ourselves bingeing and purging with greater frequency. We spent more and more time wishing we could binge, thinking about and planning our binges, obtaining the food we needed, and carrying out our binge/purge cycle. Most of us, both anorexic and bulimic, began to feel embarrassed or guilty about our eating behavior, so we became skillful at lying or hiding it from others. We organized our work and play activities around our eating, and our days gradually became controlled by what we needed to do with food. It wasn't much fun anymore, so eventually we decided to stop—then discovered to our dismay that we could not.

Attempts to Control the Downhill Slide

It took most of us a very long time to admit we were no longer in control of our behavior, and even then we were certain we would be able to control it if we just fought harder, used more willpower, or changed our circumstances.[4] Some of us tried frontal assaults on our disorder, many of which have been alluded to in the descriptions of the real anorexic and bulimic. We anorexics tried forcing ourselves to eat our forbidden foods, broadening the scope of our vegetable intake or daringly ingesting a morsel of our child's birthday cake. We paced the floor until nightfall so we couldn't go running. We bulimics tried limiting the size of our binges, thus convincing ourselves that purging was unnecessary.

When the direct attack on our disease failed, we often opted for the rear approach. We anorexics tried visiting friends for the weekend, acquiring a roommate, joining a religious community, or finding a husband, reasoning that if other people were around we would be forced to eat like normal people. We tried canceling our membership at the gym, discarding our running shoes, or praying for a broken leg. The bulimics among us tried throwing everything edible in the house into the trash, selling the car, moving far away from the fast-food restaurants, asking our spouse to keep our credit cards and cash, taking the bathroom door off its hinges, finding a hypnotist, reading the latest self-help book, or scaring ourselves by reading stories about rupture of the esophagus.

When even these tactics failed to make us quit our crazy behavior, many of us elected for the geographic cure, fleeing from the battlefield altogether. We tried leaving home or moving in with a sibling, finding a new boyfriend or breaking up with the old one, changing our job or going back to school, vacationing in Australia or climbing Mount Everest, moving to an ashram in India or returning to the town we grew up in, joining a new church or finding a new therapist, having another baby or getting a divorce, taking up needlepoint or learning to skydive. And so on.

Regrettably, nothing worked. Sometimes these measures gave us brief or lengthy reprieves from our pathological thoughts and behaviors; but our obsession always prevailed, driving us back to our diet and exercise or to bingeing and purging. We became increasingly discouraged with ourselves as time went by, felt more and more alone and depressed, until we simply couldn't face life anymore.

Early Anorexia and Bulimia

Therefore, if you think you are not one of us because your anorexia or bulimia is not as severe as ours, be assured that it almost certainly will progress with time. If you are not miserable and depressed because of your eating disorder, you eventually will be. If you haven't yet wished you were dead, by next year you may be there.

Furthermore, you are welcome among us even if your case is mild, even if you only recently developed your eating disorder, even if you're not certain that you are one of us. We are happy to report that many of us felt that way in the beginning and yet were able to use the support available in this Fellowship to get well. The Twelve-Step Program worked for us, no matter what point we had reached in the progression of our disease.

Variations Among Us

In fact, we are quite a varied lot. Our stories have many superficial differences. For example, some of us remained functional in our lives for long periods of time, sometimes for decades, before beginning to decompensate, while others were desperate for help within a year of onset of our symptoms. A great number of us managed a home, marriage, childrearing, and career for many years before someone confronted us with their suspicion that we had an eating disorder. Others were unemployable or confined to a hospital or psychiatric ward before a year of anorexic or bulimic behavior had elapsed. Many of us developed our problem in adolescence, while others began at a much later age. Some of us, without conscious intent, masqueraded our anorexia as intolerance of specific foods and had no overt desire to control our weight, at least in the beginning. Many of us who are bulimic did not vomit after a binge but rather took laxatives or diuretics as a method of purging, or simply fasted for a period of time or engaged in exercise to compensate for the food we ingested.

SO, WHY DO WE DO IT?

All of this returns us to the question posed at the beginning of this chapter: *Why* do we act this way? Many of us are excellent scholars, the pride of our families, pursuing brilliant careers as lawyers and teachers, nurses and politicians, dietitians and architects. Yet we end up losing our jobs and our marriages, our health and our fortunes—all because we will not eat like normal people. Why? What is wrong with us?

In truth, we are just as baffled as everyone else about our sick behavior. Most of us have no idea why we do what we do with food and exercise. Sometimes we come up with credible reasons, but they seem paltry and pitifully inadequate in the face of the devastating consequences that result from our antics, consequences that are blindingly obvious to anyone with even a modicum of common sense. Years of psychotherapy have led some of us to splendidly logical explanations, yet even then we cannot master our preposterous behaviors. *The grim truth is that all of us have long ago lost control of our pathological eating behavior. We have lost all power of choice about what we do with food and exercise. We simply cannot stop.*[5]

Although we can't explain our condition, we have come to believe that we are suffering from a two-fold disease that consists of a physical anomaly in our bodies coupled with a mental obsession so powerful that reason and willpower are useless against it.[6] Let's take a look at these two elements.

The Two-Fold Disease: Physical Allergy…

We often refer to our physical abnormality as a craving or an "allergy," but as far as we know there is no immune basis for it. Perhaps it is genetic. Perhaps it is linked to the alcoholic tendency in some way. We don't know. What we do know is that once we begin restricting our food, exercising, or bingeing and purging, we experience an overpowering need to continue doing so. This need is not a psychological desire but rather a *physical compulsion* strikingly similar to the withdrawal reaction experienced by the chemically dependent when their drug is unavailable. Indeed, we believe that our symptoms *are* a true withdrawal state. The cells of our bodies seemingly vibrate if we are prevented from repeating the pathological behavior. We crawl out of our skin, pace the floor, tremble, sweat, and cannot sleep. As soon as we can restrict our food, exercise, or binge and purge again, these symptoms abate for a time. Most of us can manage to live a few hours or even a few days without repeating the behavior, but then the physical signs of withdrawal mount and we must succumb to our craving.

It should be obvious that if we never started dieting or exercising or bingeing and purging, then our physical quirk would not be activated and we would not be compelled to continue. Why then do we start?

...and Mental Obsession

The answer to this question lies in the second component of our disease, our mental obsession. This term refers to *any thought that leads us to begin acting out in the first place*. It may assume the form of believing that we are fat or that we need to get our bodies in better physical shape. We may believe what we read in a magazine or hear in a television commercial: "Fat is bad for you and should be drastically cut from your diet." We may compare our weight to societal norms on a height/weight chart and conclude that we are too heavy. Our obsession may center around exercise as we become convinced that "working out" is essential to good health. At other times our mental obsession may consist of the simple thought that we are not hungry or that we can't afford to purchase food. We may start a binge with the seemingly harmless idea that we deserve to have a second serving of lasagna because we ate sparingly at lunchtime or took a long walk before dinner. Or we may trigger the bulimic cycle by convincing ourselves that we need to binge and purge only once, just to relieve our emptiness tonight, and we'll never do it again.

We can best understand the interplay of our mental obsession and physical allergy by looking at examples of it in the experience of some of our members.

Mental Obsession and Physical Allergy: The Story of Jane

Jane was a twenty-six-year-old bulimic who had recently completed a stint on a psychiatric ward following a suicide attempt. For about four weeks she ate normal meals and refrained from bingeing and purging. She was feeling physically well for the first time in many years, her self-esteem had improved, and she was beginning to understand and work through many of her underlying issues. She was highly motivated to continue getting well. While in hospital she learned about our Fellowship, attended a meeting, and expressed interest in what we shared about our disease. However, she saw no need to attend further meetings, since she was eating normally and had no desire to binge and purge.

Following her hospitalization she began dating a young man who was introduced to her by a mutual friend. A few weeks later they decided to spend Saturday night together in a hotel. They woke up the next morning in a great mood and passed the morning talking and relaxing.

When Jane arrived home, she realized that it was almost noon and she had "forgotten" to eat breakfast. She decided to have lunch instead, but was feeling so elated she had little appetite. She ate an apple and a cookie, then started cleaning her apartment. By six o'clock she was suddenly voraciously hungry. She phoned out for an extra-large pizza, intending to eat half and leave the remainder for her roommate, who had been absent all day. When it arrived she began eating rapidly while watching television, then discovered she had eaten the entire pizza. She completed her binge with two bowls of cereal, then purged.

Thus began a month-long relapse for Jane, at the end of which she was eager to learn more about our program. Later, she was able to look back to the beginning of her relapse and identify the pathological thinking that initiated it. She admitted that in the hotel room on Sunday morning *she had thought about breakfast, but was reluctant to suggest to her friend that they order it through room service. He had said he wasn't hungry, and Jane was embarrassed to eat in front of him. Besides, it would be costly and she was on a tight budget.* All these excuses Jane used to avoid eating constituted her mental obsession. Once she had skipped breakfast, her physical allergy became activated and she experienced no appetite for lunch. By that evening her body now fully craved her favorite means of acting out: bingeing and purging.

Once an Anorexic or Bulimic, Always an Anorexic or Bulimic

This example illustrates how our physical allergy and our mental obsession interact with each other. Our problem as anorexics and bulimics is that we have a body that cannot tolerate any restriction of food or bingeing and purging (because we cannot stop doing it once we start), coupled with a mind that invariably creates ideas that prevent us from adhering to normal eating practices. Our disease is relentless. Left to our own devices we will *always* lapse into restriction or into the binge/purge cycle, no matter how long we have been eating in a healthy manner. *Once an anorexic or bulimic, always an anorexic or bulimic.* The experience of our members has painfully confirmed this fact again and again.

Mental Obsession and Physical Allergy: The Story of Sally

Sally was a thirty-year-old chronic anorexic who had successfully completed a five-month treatment program at a center that employs our approach to eating disorders. She had reached her normal weight and had recovered sufficiently to choose and prepare her own food while living independently for a whole year. She was happy, had returned to her work as a nurse, had begun dating a fine man, and was fully committed to her recovery. She attended meetings, worked with a sponsor, sponsored others, and was a wellspring of hope in our Fellowship. For many months she had been free from all obsession about her body or about food.

An altruistic and adventuresome woman, Sally decided to take a leave of absence from her job and travel to a third-world country where she would devote six months of her life to helping the poor. While there she would be billeted with a local family and work in a ghetto with impoverished children. She took a crash course in the language of that country, and off she went.

Upon her return we were shocked at Sally's appearance. One glance at her gaunt frame told us she had relapsed. She started attending meetings again and a few weeks later admitted to herself and us that she was in relapse. She took steps to get sober once again and later was able to relate her story.

"To be honest with you, I had been feeling sorry for myself for a while before I left. I hated the thought that my life depended on my continued attendance at meetings. I wanted to live like a normal person again, and I had been free around food and comfortable with my body for so long that I couldn't believe I would ever go back to the way I was before treatment. I didn't tell my sponsor any of this. Going away was my means of testing the waters, of proving to myself and to all of you that I would be fine on my own.

"In the beginning I was fine. I prayed and read our literature every day, and I ate everything my host family served. But when I started working in the ghetto, *I felt guilty that I had all the food I needed while our kids had nothing. I started giving them most of my lunch, keeping only the fruit for myself.* Then a few days later the thought popped into my mind, out of the blue, that I should lose weight. I was shocked. I prayed to my Higher Power for help, and I was sure that I was eating enough to keep my weight up. I never skipped a meal. I couldn't believe it when I stepped on the scale and saw the low number. I thought the scale was wrong. Now I know it wasn't.

"I'm grateful for my relapse, because it has convinced me that I will have this disease lurking in the background for the rest of my life. I know that I need God's grace and all of you in this Fellowship for my Higher Power to work through. On my own, without support, I don't stand a chance of staying sober for long."

Sally's story is interesting because it demonstrates how insidious our disease is. Her relapse began as an emotional and spiritual one, with self-pity and dishonesty operative for months before she physically relapsed. She told no one what she was thinking or about her true motive for going abroad. Once there, without a human support system easily accessible to her, her mental obsession took shape in the insane thought that started her full-blown relapse: "Because others have no food, I don't deserve to eat what my body needs." She acted on this thought by giving away her lunches. Her physical allergy then took over, ensuring that she continued restricting her food intake below what her body required. Her later thought about losing weight was merely reinforcement for the relapse already initiated. Weight loss was inevitable, because Sally's method of acting out was anorexia, restriction of her food intake. Anorexics in relapse generally lose weight.

Our Uncontrollable Disease: Beyond Human Power

We believe that anorexia and bulimia are true diseases and are chronic, progressive, and potentially fatal. Our mental obsession and physical allergy are core components of the disease, and we cannot control either one. Furthermore, we cannot eradicate them from our minds and bodies, nor have we found any human power that can do so.[7] We did not cause our anorexia or bulimia, nor did anyone else. We believe there is a genetic element involved, for most of us come from families where others suffer from addiction of some kind. In addition, many of us have also engaged at times in other addictive behaviors, as we shall see in Chapter 5.

To reiterate: *To be an anorexic or bulimic means that we have a body that cannot deviate in safety from sober eating practices, coupled with a mind that ensures we cannot stay sober.*[8]

Before we explore the solution we have found for our disease, we need to look at our problem in still greater depth. That is the purpose of the next two chapters.

The Loonie Theory 4

ALL EATING DISORDERS ARE ONE

SOME PEOPLE regard eating disorders as a spectrum of pathological eating behavior. We have developed a similar yet somewhat different view of them. This unique perspective is derived from our own experience with insane eating practices, and we call it "The Loonie Theory." The term originates from the Canadian one-dollar coin, which is embossed with a loon on one side. When it was first minted, Canadian citizens somewhat irreverently nicknamed it "the loonie."

We believe that all eating disorders constitute one entity, like a loonie. We who are afflicted with the disorder carry the loonie around in our pockets, and every time we take it out we hold it with either heads or tails up. We all have a preferred way of holding the coin, yet most of us flip it over from time to time. The Loonie Theory is illustrated in figure 1.

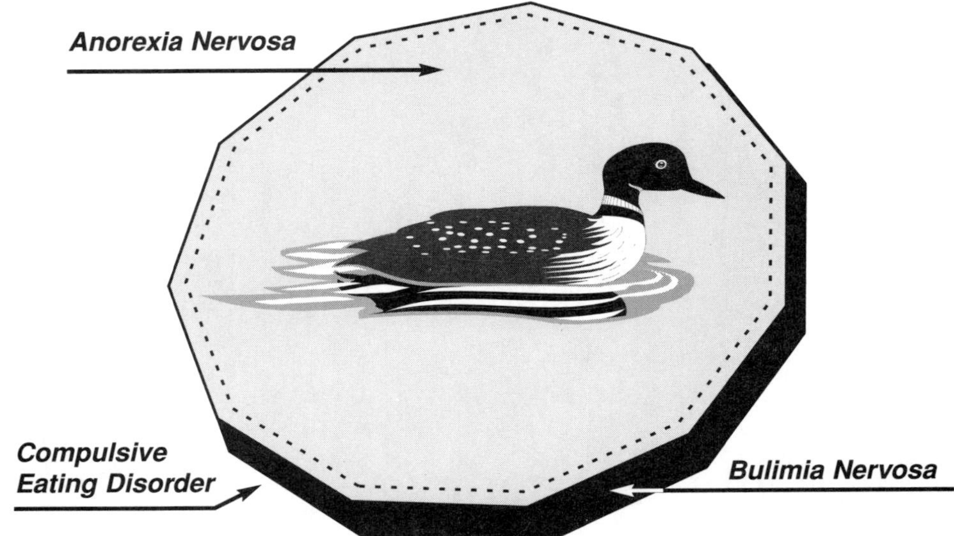

Figure 1: The "Loonie" of Eating Disorders

Heads or Tails? Anorexia vs. Compulsive Eating Disorder

One side of the coin is anorexia nervosa with its intense fear of getting fat, well described in the last chapter. The opposite side we shall call "compulsive eating disorder," or C.E.D., although it has also been termed "binge-eating disorder"[1] or "compulsive overeating."[2] These are the folks who appear to use the act of overeating in itself as a drug to alter their feelings. Because of their physical allergy, the drug then takes control of them and they cannot stop using it. Our bulimic members identify with this but, unlike bulimics, compulsive eaters do not purge to rid themselves of ingested food. Additionally, some compulsive eaters do not binge in discrete episodes, but rather overeat every day. They may be completely unaware that they are consuming more than their bodies require and may even believe they eat sparingly.

C.E.D. Behavior

Compulsive eaters behave like the mirror image of anorexics in that they are insanely fearful of being empty. They eat more than they need for lunch because they're afraid they may not get enough for dinner. They carry food in their pockets or handbags just in case that hollow feeling strikes them in the middle of a business meeting or while they're stuck in a traffic jam on the freeway. They may have recently eaten a satisfying meal, but an hour later that dreaded emptiness strikes and they *must* eat, although logically they know they cannot possibly be hungry.

C.E.D. Progression

As they become overweight and later obese, they are ashamed of themselves and exert every ounce of willpower to change. Only they cannot. They hide in closets and public toilets to devour chocolate bars. They keep licorice in their desk drawer at work and eat it when their co-workers break for coffee. They conceal the chocolate chip cookies behind the flour in their cupboards, lest their spouse discover them or their children eat them. They consult a dietitian but cannot adhere to the diet. They go to the doctor and get diet pills, lose ten pounds, and regain twenty. They join diet clubs, lose fifty pounds, then regain seventy. Increasingly desperate, they may have their stomachs stapled surgically, lose a hundred pounds, then regain it all and more. They loathe themselves and their bodies, although they maintain a brave front as the office clown. They become diabetic, but still they cannot lose weight. Their knees wear out and surgical joint replacement looms ahead. Then they have their first heart attack, are prescribed a low-fat diet, but stop on the way home from hospital to buy a large bag of potato chips.

Compulsive Eaters Flip the Coin

All of the compulsive eaters' attempts at weight loss look remarkably like anorexic behavior, and indeed we have come to regard them as temporary flips of the coin for compulsive eaters. But because the C.E.D. side of the loonie works better for them, they almost always revert to it, although they may spend months or even years on the other side. Some of our members identify themselves as both compulsive eaters and anorexics and have been able to use our approach to recovery with great success. They tell us that at various points in the course of their disease they switched to anorexic behavior, usually as an attempt to control their compulsive eating. However, when a compulsive eater enters an anorexic phase and begins to lose weight, she often reacts with intense fear, particularly as her body becomes more curvaceous and attracts male attention. This fear may catapult her back to her preferred side of the coin.

The Middle of the Coin: Bulimia

Perhaps you are wondering where bulimia fits on this loonie. We believe that it lies sandwiched horizontally down the center of the coin, in that it resembles both faces. Those of us who are bulimic binge in a similar fashion to the compulsive eater, but then experience our anorexic sisters' terror of getting fat and must purge our food in order to regain a sense of being in control of our weight. This we do through self-induced vomiting, large doses of laxatives or diuretics, self-administration of enemas, vigorous exercise, or rigidly controlling our intake or fasting for a period of time following our binge. Some of us are more subtle in our purging methods. For example, some diabetics among us tried to rid ourselves of our binges by reducing our intake of insulin below what was required to control our blood sugar, having acquired the brilliant notion that if we let our blood sugar skyrocket, then our kidneys would dump the extra calories into our urine, sparing us the bother of vomiting. (This, by the way, is one of the more immediately lethal ways to practice bulimia.) Others among us, on thyroid replacement therapy, tripled our dose of medication in a vain attempt to speed up our metabolism sufficiently to dispose of our binges.

We bulimics do harbor a fear of getting fat, but this fear is not as intense and overwhelming as that of anorexics, nor do we usually perceive our bodies with such extreme distortion. Most of our bulimic members are of fairly normal weight, although some are underweight and others are overweight or even obese. This is determined not only by the size of our binges and the efficiency of our purging, but also by the manner in which we eat when not bingeing and purging. Some, being more skewed to the anorexic side of the loonie, eat very little or nothing in between our binges and consequently lose a good deal of weight. Others, favoring the very center of the loonie, eat normally when not bingeing and purging and thereby maintain a normal weight or even become overweight. Some of us lean so far toward the C.E.D. side of the loonie that we don't purge every time we binge, because we have grown tired of the time, effort, and planning that purging requires. In this case we usually become overweight or obese.

Moving Around Within the Loonie

In Anorexics and Bulimics Anonymous, most of our members indicate that we did not adhere rigidly at all times to one side of the loonie. Almost all of us anorexics experimented with flipping the coin over to compulsive eating, or plunged down into the loonie's center, into the realm of bulimia. Many of us who identify primarily as bulimics fervently wished to control our bingeing and purging by becoming purely anorexic; and often, when we succeeded in doing so for a time, we thought we were cured. Sometimes we moved from one place on the loonie to another for a few hours or days, cycling rapidly back and forth from anorexia to bulimia to C.E.D. over and over again. Sometimes we dwelled in other regions of the loonie for months or years.

A few stories may assist in our understanding of the loonie concept.

Primarily Compulsive Eater: The Story of Martha

Martha was a high-ranking government executive in her early fifties when she first reached out to us for help. At that point in her life she perceived herself as a compulsive eater and had been attending a Twelve-Step group for the past five years, with intermittent success in maintaining healthy eating practices. She continued to obsess about her body shape and size and about food. She possessed no inner peace.

Martha told us that her illness began in her teens with classic anorexia nervosa, although no one diagnosed this at the time. She recalled her family doctor prescribing a tonic for her pallor and thinness, and some thyroid powder in a futile attempt to restore her menstrual periods. Tired of starvation by her late twenties, she lapsed into full-blown bulimia for about ten years. Her spouse confronted her about her purging, so she stopped doing it. She could not stop bingeing, however, and gained seventy pounds over the next year. Desperate to regain control, she attended a diet clinic and was given an eight hundred calorie diet. Not one for half-measures, Martha ate two hundred calories daily and exercised vigorously.

At the pinnacle of this phase, at the age of forty-one, Martha suffered a major heart attack. While recuperating in hospital, she was able to face the truth about herself and sheepishly confessed to her doctors that she had caused her heart attack through dieting. They dismissed this notion because her weight was still twenty pounds above normal. Nevertheless, following her discharge she was afraid to diet again and lapsed into compulsive eating behavior, which she had been battling ever since.

Martha identified with our stories, became sober in her eating, followed the Twelve-Step path, and today is at peace with her body and with food. Her case is an excellent example of flipping the coin around and also demonstrates how some compulsive eaters have found what they need in our Fellowship.

Men Find the Loonie, Too: The Story of Frank

Frank also has a fascinating story. He was a thirty-four-year-old lawyer when his wife approached us for help, ostensibly for herself. Eventually she confessed that she did not have an eating disorder, but had been too ashamed to admit that her husband did. By that time he had dropped about forty pounds in weight, was running ten miles every day, and had become fanatical about eating only "healthy" foods. His obsession had progressed over the past three years to the point that he now lived on steamed rice, seaweed, tofu, and raw vegetables. Frank watched in disgust as his family dined on meat and potatoes, although usually he went out running at dinner time and prepared his own food when he got home. His wife wept and told us that she was losing her husband, could no longer talk to him about anything, and feared she would soon be a widow raising their ten-year-old son.

It was more than a year later before we actually met Frank. After he began to feel comfortable he shared more of his story with us. He had been a normal eater when he joined the military after graduating from college. He enjoyed the discipline of the army, and for a time all went well. Three years later a tour of duty took him to the Middle East, and he was soon involved in active combat. He was deeply traumatized by some of his experiences, and when he returned to Canada was unable to readjust to life at home. One day he tried inducing vomiting after eating a large meal. He was unable to recall why he did this, or even where he got the idea. Nevertheless, he was soon bingeing and purging three times a week.

Frank felt such intense shame about his behavior that he couldn't imagine disclosing it to any of his military friends, and certainly not to his wife. He tried leaving the army and entering law school, hoping that the change would expunge his insane behavior. He consulted a doctor for depression, never mentioning his bulimia, and began taking medication. Under its influence he was able to limit his bingeing and purging to approximately once a week, still successfully concealing it from his family.

Following his bar admission he joined a large firm and practiced corporate law. Frank did not enjoy his work there, but felt compelled to stay to recoup the money he had spent on law school. About six months later he decided to "get fit," joined a health spa, and launched into a personal training program that included running. He quit bingeing and purging and developed a great interest in nutrition, reading a number of books from the health-food store. He started taking vitamins and eliminated many foods from his diet. He never thought of losing weight, but rather was interested in building up his fitness level. His obsession had assumed control of his life and was destroying his marriage, yet he was powerless to stop it.

It was difficult for Frank to admit he was anorexic, yet eventually he did so and began his recovery. Today he is a changed man with a very grateful family. His story contains the important lessons that men too can develop anorexia and bulimia and, more importantly, can successfully use our approach to recovery.

Traversing the Coin, and Beyond: The Story of Tess

Let's look now at the story of Tess. She developed anorexia at the age of twelve, within a year of her parents' messy divorce, and by fourteen was in serious trouble from starvation. Her mother dragged her to a doctor, who sent her to a dietitian and prescribed medication. She managed to stay alive for the next year, but did not recover mentally. At fifteen, Tess returned to her doctor.

To his surprise she had gained a good deal of weight and was now somewhat plump. When he inquired about her current behavior, she replied, "Oh, I've still got my problem, Doctor, but I'm not anorexic anymore. I'm tired of starving. Instead I'm just eating a lot. I sneak downstairs after my mother is asleep and eat a whole loaf of bread. Stuff like that. I know I'm fat now, but I don't care. I like it this way a lot more than anorexia, because I've got a life now. I can go out with my friends for pizza and have fun."

A year later Tess was at a normal weight, and her "fun" had progressed to partying every weekend with her friends, smoking drugs, and drinking. Under the influence of these chemicals she cared little about her appearance and paid no attention to food. By twenty-one she was in her first treatment center for drug and alcohol dependency. There, clean and sober from chemicals, she lapsed into bulimia. She spent the next eight years careening between bulimia, alcohol and drugs, and treatment centers. She encountered trouble with the law for shoplifting laxatives as well as for drunk driving, was unable to hold down a job, and subsisted through public welfare funding. During every period free from drugs and alcohol, Tess tried her best to work the Twelve-Step Program, but was unable to heal because she loathed herself for continuing to act out in bulimia.

At twenty-nine Tess became desperate enough that she sought admission to a treatment center specializing in eating disorders. There she was introduced to our Fellowship and attended meetings regularly. Unfortunately, Tess could not accept what we told her from our own experience: that the process of recovery requires an intensive commitment of time and energy. Nor was she ever able to reveal her innermost self to a sponsor. She could not stay sober in her eating, even while in treatment, and was eventually expelled from the center. All of that was two years ago. To our knowledge, Tess is still alive today—drinking, taking drugs, and practicing bulimia.

Is One Side Better Than The Other?

These are only three stories that illustrate the Loonie Theory. Almost all of us have experienced many more examples. In the final analysis it is often difficult or impossible to know whether we were anorexics lapsing into bulimia, bulimics aspiring to anorexia, compulsive eaters experimenting with anorexia and bulimia, or anorexics and bulimics falling into C.E.D. Nor are these distinctions of any significance, for *ultimately it makes no difference whatsoever where we prefer to dwell on the coin of eating disorders. We all eventually die from our implacable disease unless we recover.*

OTHER FELLOWSHIPS FOR THOSE WITH EATING DISORDERS

Other Twelve-Step Fellowships exist primarily to help people with compulsive eating disorder to recover.[3] These groups also usually welcome anorexics and bulimics. We encourage readers who cannot relate to our stories to explore these options, and others. And, we have had many compulsive eaters join our Fellowship who in the past had clearly been anorexic or bulimic. They identified with our stories, felt at home with us, and were warmly welcomed to our groups. Most importantly, they have recovered by following our pathway to wholeness.

The Iceberg Theory 5

ADDICTION-SWITCHING

THE STORY of Tess in the last chapter leads into another critically important area of our experience, that of addiction-switching, or "cross-addiction," as it is sometimes termed. Tess used alcohol and drugs to suppress her feelings, and throughout her addictive career switched back and forth from her eating disorder to these mood-altering chemicals. At times she used both avenues simultaneously.

Eating Disorders and Chemical Dependency

Many of our members had similar experiences. In fact, few of us clung exclusively to our eating disorder as a means of escape from ourselves. All of us, however, can identify our "drug of choice"—the substance or process that altered our inner state more effectively than anything else. For most of us, that drug was anorexia or bulimia, but many of us also identify ourselves as full-blown or potential alcoholics or drug addicts. A number of our members sobered up from chemical dependency, sometimes with the support of other Twelve-Step Fellowships, only to slide immediately into anorexia or bulimia. We may or may not have suffered from an eating disorder prior to our alcohol and drug careers.

Our Fellowship has been approached by a number of chemical dependency treatment centers, requesting information to help them understand our disease. They have long observed that many of their clients withdraw from alcohol and drugs—only to promptly quit eating, live on coffee and cigarettes, and be emotionally unavailable to do their healing work. Or else their cooks notice that large quantities of food are missing from the kitchen, and the sewer lines in their facility become mysteriously blocked.

Some of us traveled the opposite direction on the addiction path, letting go of anorexia or bulimia because they had become too painful to endure any longer, only to plunge headlong into an abyss of alcohol or drugs.

Eating Disorders and Other Addictions

Whatever our individual stories, it is clear that our eating disorders and our other addictions—whether to chemicals or overwork or compulsive gambling or abusive relationships or destructive sex—were but symptoms of a much larger problem, much as the tip of an iceberg is merely the surface manifestation of a massive hidden monolith with the power to kill. The Titanic did not go down by striking the *tip* of the iceberg that fateful day in the North Atlantic.

Experience First, Then Theory

We call this the "Iceberg Theory" of addiction, a theory emerging from our personal experience. This hypothesis, illustrated in figure 2, explains many things that are otherwise perplexing, and in particular the phenomenon of addiction-switching. We believe that our disease is itself an iceberg and that all our visible addictive behaviors and substances, all the chemicals and processes that effectively altered our feelings, together comprise the barest tip of the iceberg. It is also abundantly clear that if we do not attend to the underwater part of this monster, we will inevitably switch to another tip when we sober up in anorexia and bulimia.

THE BOTTOM OF THE ICEBERG: INSANITY

What is the hidden, underwater aspect of our disease? It is nothing more than the insanity in our minds, the pathological way we think as active addicts. In other words, *our main problem as anorexics and bulimics centers in our minds, rather than in our bodies.* Because of the insane way we think, we are compelled to act out in our addictive behaviors, not the other way around. That is, anorexia and bulimia do not cause our insanity, but rather our insanity causes anorexia and bulimia. Put yet another way, *anorexia and bulimia relieve the pain of being insane. Therefore, to fully recover from anorexia and bulimia without switching to another addiction, we absolutely must change our insane manner of thinking.*

Some anorexic or bulimic readers might object to the idea that they are "insane." The word means nothing more than "lacking soundness of mind." Who among us can claim soundness of mind if we take an honest look at our past behavior? Is it sane to starve ourselves to the point of malnutrition? Of shutting down our reproductive functions? Of hospitalization? Is it sane to hide in our basement or our car to gobble up a bag of cookies or a dozen doughnuts? To spend hours roaming from one restaurant to another in a feeding frenzy? To waste thousands of dollars on food that we promptly throw up?

No, these behaviors and many others that we could name are obviously the actions of people who lack soundness of mind. We now need to delve into that mind, into the bottom of the iceberg, and explore the thinking that leads to such outrageous behavior. We will examine the essential aspects of our insane thinking processes, aspects referred to by the Twelve-Step Program as "character defects" or "shortcomings" or "the exact nature of our wrongs." All of us can identify with some of these insane modes of thinking, and many of us can identify with all of them.[1]

THREE PRIMARY COLORS OF INSANITY

Self-Centeredness: Grandiosity

Self-centeredness was the taproot of our insanity.[2] We perceived the universe as comprising two components: ourselves, and everything else. More disastrous still, we saw ourselves as the hub around which everything else revolved. Everything that happened was about *us*. Our kids got sick in the middle of the night because they knew we had an important meeting early in the morning and needed a good sleep. Our parents were conspiring to make our lives miserable. Even the weather was inclement because the universe was against us. People were plotting against us at work, trying to get us fired. We were overly sensitive to imagined nuances in the behavior of others. If our boss failed to greet us in the morning, we were crushed and our day was ruined. When we entered a room, we were certain that a hush fell. Everyone noticed us because we were at the forefront of everyone's thinking. When we weren't present, surely others were thinking and talking about us. What were they thinking? What were they saying? All this self-centered thinking can be summed up as grandiosity: having an inflated opinion of ourselves, of our place in the universe.

Self-Centeredness: Worthlessness

Then five seconds later we flipped to the opposite pole of self-centeredness: worthlessness,[3] having a deflated perception of ourselves and of our place in the scheme of things. We knew we had no value. We never had any value. God made a mistake when we were created. Nobody noticed us; we were invisible. When we entered a room, people looked right through us. Nothing we said was heard. Nobody cared about us at all, and rightly so. Nobody ever took any notice of our opinions, so we might as well not bother voicing them. We made unilateral decisions without considering that others were affected by them, then were stunned when a furious spouse confronted us for not consulting him. We didn't need to bother calling to say we weren't coming to the party, because nobody would notice that we weren't there. If we killed ourselves the family would go on without blinking an eye—in fact it might be better off without us. We were incapable of seeing a situation from the perspective of others, of putting ourselves in their shoes. Sometimes we tried to compensate for this deficiency through exaggerated solicitude or a profusion of apologies that sorely tried the patience of those around us.

Reading this account of our twisted thinking in print, we grin uneasily or laugh in disbelief. How could anyone who is not seriously emotionally disturbed or even frankly psychotic think such thoughts? Actually, no one could. We anorexics and bulimics were truly that disturbed, that psychotic in our thinking. We usually managed to conceal our thoughts well enough from others that we were not carried off in strait-jackets to padded cells, but we were profoundly insane in our self-centeredness. It is clear that thinking in this way ensured our unceasing misery.

The Illusion of Control

Closely related to self-centeredness was another main root of our sick thinking: our *illusion of control*, a term used frequently by Anne Wilson Schaef, Ph.D.[4] We clung to a primitive belief that we actually had the power to make others feel, think, speak, and act. From the time we were children, if we saw someone weeping we would think, "What did I do to cause this?" It was our job to keep our mother happy, to make our father quit drinking, to stop the fights between them. Our parents divorced because we hadn't been good little girls. Our uncle molested us because we wore that short skirt or looked at him

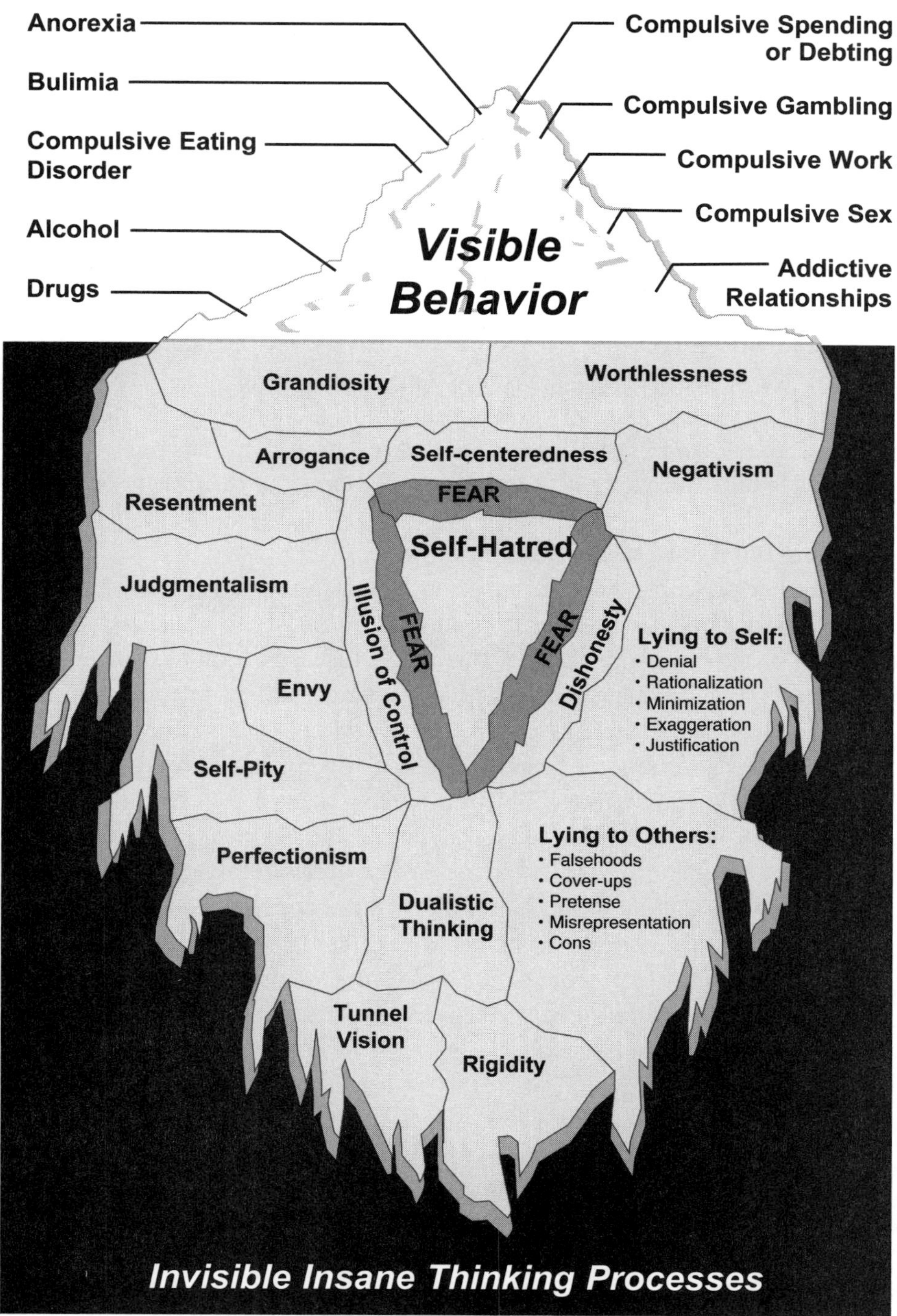

Figure 2: The Iceberg Theory of Addiction

seductively. Mom was in a bad mood because we hadn't scrubbed the floor well enough or had the right music playing when she got home from work. We could make our boyfriend happy by listening to him attentively or by drinking with him. If we acted in the right way, we could convince everyone that we were truly exceptional people. If our husband wasn't treating us well, it was because we hadn't yet found the magic formula, so let's keep trying.

Operating perpetually out of this illusion of control was physically exhausting and emotionally debilitating. Being the puppet-master of the universe was a big job, and it lay heavily on our shoulders. We needed to be constantly vigilant, watching for cues, assessing the evidence to see if we were managing things correctly or not. We became exhausted, but slept poorly. We often had headaches and backaches and stomach pains caused by the enormity of our task.

Dishonesty: With Others...

Another principal root of our insanity was our *dishonesty*. Many of us have been shocked by the extent of our dishonesty, because as young children we never could tell a lie. But as this disease corrupted our minds we became consummate liars. We told fibs and little white lies: When asked how we were feeling we said, "Fine," when we were in fact sad or angry. We invented bigger lies and alibis, always justified by the best of intentions: "I'm not hungry." "I don't like potatoes." "I'm allergic to sugar." "I've already eaten." "I can't come for dinner." In the end we progressed to the colossal untruths: We neglected to mention to our fiancé that we were anorexic or bulimic. We pretended to be available for conversation with a friend when all we could think about was how to escape in order to binge or exercise. We made love with our spouse, feigning intimacy, while our soul huddled behind the barricade of our shameful secrets. We concealed our binge foods, denied that anything was troubling us, sneaked out of the house in the middle of the night, cheated on our income tax to get extra money, stole food from supermarkets and cash from our children's piggy-banks, wore baggy clothing to hide our emaciation. We bluffed, denied, distorted, pretended, covered up, fabricated, rationalized, and minimized everything.[5]

...and With Ourselves

And at the root of all our dishonesty with others was the convoluted mass of endless falsehoods we told to ourselves and ultimately believed[6]: I'm fat. Nobody will love me unless I look good. I can't trust anyone. I'm fat. People will shun me if I tell them what I'm thinking. I don't need to eat. I'm fat. Feelings are a sign of weakness. I don't need anyone. I'm fat. I'm bad because I'm still anorexic after thirty years. If I really wanted to control this bulimia, I could. I'm fat. I'm not good enough. Nobody loves me. I obviously must not care about anyone else. I'm fat. I'll be happy if I lose some weight. I deserve to die. I'm fat.

Our every thought gradually became contaminated with our dishonesty, until we were utterly incapable of distinguishing between what was true and what was false.[7] All our perceptions were distorted by our disease, and we were slowly and painfully reduced to a vibrating mass of terror and despair.

THE SECONDARY HUES OF INSANITY

Perfectionism

Out of these three fundamental aspects of our insanity sprang a number of other insane characteristics, much as primary colors can be mixed by the artist to yield secondary ones. One of these defects was *perfectionism*.[8] Nearly all of us set impossibly high standards for ourselves and, when we failed to measure up, felt like dismal failures. We often thought in this vein from early childhood. We were dissatisfied if we achieved a mere eighty percent on our physics exam. Why didn't we get ninety? Or if we got ninety, why not 100 percent? Or if we got 100, why didn't we get 100 percent in history also? We might have been satisfied with our academic performance, but not with our athletic abilities. Or, if both scholar and athlete, why were we not musically inclined as well? We gazed at our reflection in the mirror and were oblivious to the lovely smile and sparkling green eyes that gazed back, because all we could see was that ugly pimple on our left cheek, or the red hair that we wished to be blonde. We had more boys asking us for dates than we could count, but felt miserable because the captain of the football team had not yet called. Clearly, our perfectionism doomed us to exist as chronic malcontents.

Judgmentalism

Then there was our *judgmentalism*.[9] Beginning early in our lives, virtually all of us compared ourselves to others. Sometimes we judged ourselves to be better than others, sometimes worse, but more often we were both. The girl who sat next to us in seventh grade wore designer clothing—but we were on the honor roll. The people next door had a bigger car than we did—but we had a far more imposing house. Our best friend had much friendlier parents than our own—but we made the basketball team. That stranger we passed on the street looked like a bag lady—Poor thing, so much worse off than us. Our co-worker put on airs because the boss commended her and gave her a raise—but God sure shortchanged *her* in the beauty department. That man we had married was an arrogant bastard—Thank heaven we had learned to be humble. Our psychology professor had a rump resembling the broad side of a barn—Wasn't it wonderful to be thin?

A deadly aspect of judgmentalism was the reality that by judging another we made ourselves into subject and the other person into object. Such objectivism is deadly to everything in the realm of the spirit because it creates the illusion of separateness, leading to self-imposed isolation. Even if we merely judged ourselves, without reference to another person, we made ourselves an object to be admired or despised. We separated ourselves from ourselves. That was our most lethal flaw of all, for it led to inner fragmentation.[10]

Resentment, Self-Pity, Envy, Arrogance

On and on we went in this judgmental mindset, progressing to the point that we operated in this manner in every waking moment, in every situation we entered. Our judgmentalism was a fertile breeding ground for seething *resentment*, *self-pity*, *envy,* and *arrogance*. Furthermore, making these constant judgments about ourselves and others resulted in profound isolation. It was impossible to be intimate with other human beings when we believed ourselves to be one-up or one-down to them, for such beliefs generated hatred of ourselves and of them. Healthy, respectful, mutually loving relationships were impossible. We felt increasingly alienated from the rest of the human race as we grew older, and we became lonely and miserable creatures.

Negativism

Another pervasive aspect of our insane thinking was our *negativism*.[11] Beginning in early childhood, we anticipated the worst. Events would turn sour; it was merely a question of time. If we felt happy one day, we tried to hide it lest we tempt fate to send a catastrophe sooner. A black cloud hung over the brightest day. If someone was kind to us, he must have had an ulterior motive. People who said they loved us were lying, or at least badly misguided. Thinking in this fashion guaranteed perpetual dissatisfaction. Over time we became cynics and pessimists, completely incapable of joy and hope.

Dualistic Thinking…

An overriding characteristic of all our insanity was our *dualistic thinking*.[12] We conceived every thought in terms of polar, mutually exclusive opposites. Black or white. Good or bad. All or nothing. Right or wrong. If we ate even one bite of a doughnut, we would end up weighing three hundred pounds. It was no use going for a run unless we made it ten miles. If we weren't the thinnest woman in the room, we were worth nothing. We've taken the first bite of our binge now, so there's no point in stopping until the cupboard is bare.

…Caused Tunnel Vision and Rigidity

Dualistic thinking gave us *tunnel vision*,[13] making it impossible for us to see the endless possibilities available to us everywhere. It locked us into *rigidity*.[14] We had no way of seeing any options other than the two opposite poles in front of us. And, in fact, our diseased minds created those poles; they were illusions, mirages, with no basis in reality.

FEAR: THE SHADOW OF INSANITY

And then, there was *fear*.[15] As the disease of addiction incubated in our minds, a miasma of fear seeped into every level of our thinking, oozing into every nook and cranny and empty space, displacing all trust in the essential goodness of life and of the Creator. Most of us were unaware of how fearful we truly were until we got sober and began working the Twelve-Step Program. We were afraid of people and terrified of being alone. We feared being abandoned, and frightened when others came too close. We were scared of rejection and alarmed when we were accepted. We were afraid of not being loved and of being loved too much. We were fearful of being noticed and of being overlooked. We were apprehensive about death, and equally afraid our crazy lives would go on and on. We were terrified of losing control of ourselves, and frightened that we would never achieve spontaneity. We were afraid of God and afraid there was none. We dreaded pain and were alarmed when feeling nothing. We were fearful of being empty, and anxious when we were full. We were horrified of others controlling us, and uneasy with the freedom to make our own decisions. We were afraid to fail and terrified to succeed.

In short, we became exceedingly confused people as our fearful thinking progressed. For most of us this litany of dualistic fears operated at an unconscious level, casting a shadow of low-grade terror that dictated our actions and controlled the course of our day. At times fear erupted into panic attacks, which we labeled as a discrete entity and often medicated away. In the end we were fully conscious of only two dominant fears: the fear of getting fat and the fear of getting caught, of someone discovering what we did with food and forcing us to stop.

SELF-HATRED: THE BEDROCK OF INSANITY

Early Origins

Finally, and most importantly, we need to examine the character defect that formed the core of all the others: *self-hatred*.[16] This treacherous quality in our thinking was so insidiously pervasive that most of us anorexics and bulimics were unaware of it before we began to recover. Who among us is aware of oxygen as a discrete component of the air we inhale? Of carbon in the ground we walk upon? Of hydrogen in the water we drink? Of blue in the light radiating from the sun on a clear summer day? Self-hatred is like that. Somewhere, somehow, early in our lives every one of us acquired the entrenched belief that we were not good enough. Not good enough to deserve praise or attention or success or acceptance. Not good enough to be loved. Unnamed and unrecognized at a conscious level, this idea grew and grew like a fungus in the dark, subverting all existing sanity. In time we were not good enough to deserve new shoes or a pretty blouse or a good haircut or time off for a vacation. If we acted in ways contrary to this belief, we experienced uneasiness or outright guilt. We were not good enough to know happiness or joy or peace of mind.

Finding a Tangible Reason for Self-Hatred

As we approached the onset of our anorexia or bulimia, we transferred this hidden self-hatred to a tangible level and projected it onto our bodies. *They* were not good enough. We were too fat or too short or too tall or too ugly, or our thighs were too large or our buttocks too flabby or our bosoms too generous. What a relief to finally be able to name the demon that had tormented us all our lives! We became convinced that once we altered our bodies we would feel good about ourselves, would like ourselves, and then we would be happy at last.

Unfortunately, it didn't work out the way we had planned. Something was not following our script; for as we flung ourselves headlong into anorexic and bulimic behavior, we could never quite achieve the goal we had set. We always needed to lose just another few pounds or to make our thighs just a little firmer. If we did feel happy for a while, these feelings were ephemeral and marred by our fear of losing control of things, of getting fat once again. And our experiences with bingeing simply validated those fears.

A Vicious Cycle

As our disease advanced and we began to lie to people and spend most of the day planning and carrying out our crazy eating and exercise routines, we had new reasons to hate ourselves. Look at how self-centered we were! Look at what liars we had become! We deserved to be hated, rejected, tortured, and killed. So we carried out the verdict and punished ourselves. The punishment took the form of still greater deprivation in our eating, ever more painful bingeing and purging, larger doses of laxatives, more grueling exercise routines, and deeper feelings of misery.

Generator of Other Defects

It should be clear to the reader that this pernicious self-hatred spawned and fed all our other character defects. To begin with, self-hatred itself was inherently dishonest, based on a lie: that we were not good enough. This lie generated another, and another, and another, until we were hopelessly deluded. Believing we were not good enough, we became massively self-centered because we needed to figure out precisely *how* we were flawed so we could fix ourselves. That required much introspection and self-absorption. We needed to think about ourselves a great deal. We also needed to launch a major campaign to control other people, for if we could make *them* think well of us, then perhaps we would begin to accept ourselves. Thinking we were never good enough laid the foundation for perfectionism and was also in itself a judgment. In judging ourselves, we simultaneously judged others.

INSANITY: WEB OF LIES

It is obvious to us who have recovered from anorexia and bulimia that all these aspects of our aberrant thinking were interconnected threads, woven together by our disease into a tenacious web in which our minds became impossibly entangled. As noted above, self-hatred was inherently dishonest and led to self-centeredness and to the mistaken belief that we could control others, as well as to perfectionism and judgmentalism. The deadly root of self-centeredness gave birth to fear. Our fears were dualistic and negative, generated more judgmentalism and perfectionism, fueled our illusion of control, and necessitated further dishonesty. All these qualities in turn fed back into self-centeredness and deeper self-hatred.

An endless loop thereby dominated our deranged minds, ensuring that we lived in a state of chronic discontent, joylessness, loneliness, and terror. Inner peace was unknown. Trust in anything or anyone was impossible. Hope was gradually extinguished. Barricaded within the fortress of our insane thinking processes, we could not love or be loved. Intimacy was a foreign concept. The life source within us was slowly strangled and its corpse disintegrated. No wonder suicide often became such an attractive option.

It is equally clear to us that many of these aspects of our insane thinking predated our anorexic and bulimic behavior. For most of us, the sinister seeds of our madness were planted in our minds as very young children; as we grew older they took root, sprouted, blossomed, and bore the vile fruit that nourished our thinking and drove out the original blessings of trust, love, freedom, and peace that were endowed by the Creator as our birthright.

THE BOTTOM OF THE ICEBERG PRODUCES THE TIP

We see now that living with ourselves in this disordered state—our minds a contorted ruin of disharmony and chaos crystallizing beneath the surface—the pain of our existence eventually became unbearable, and we erupted into the tip of our iceberg. We discovered the addictive behaviors that relieved this pain. Starving intoxicated us with the illusion of power: We felt as if nothing could touch us or hurt us as we floated over the surface of life in the empty, featherweight shells of our bodies. Compulsive exercise drugged our minds and calmed the low-grade anxiety in which we lived, as it eased our terror of getting fat. Bingeing and purging blunted our consciousness and often allowed us to pass out, thereby fleeing for hours from the pain of being ourselves. At last we were in control of something.

Many of us were hooked right from the beginning, from the first day we dieted or exercised compulsively or binged and purged. These activities provided us with a means to get out of our skin, out of our minds, which had become too painful for us to bear as a result of our demented thinking. Anorexia and bulimia were reliable. We learned that we could trust them to invariably make us feel at ease and comfortable in our own skin, or at least anesthetized. They worked for us, and they became our best friends. Most of us also discovered alternative friends that worked almost as well, to which we could turn if our best friend was temporarily unavailable. Alcohol and drugs worked. Compulsive work practices worked. Fixation on another person and on sex worked.

THE TIP OF THE ICEBERG QUITS WORKING: BOTTOMING OUT

However, the disease of addiction is progressive. Gradually, imperceptibly slowly, our best friend turned against us. It quit working, and in reality it gave rise to more pain than was ours to begin with. Still we pursued it, chasing that elusive relief it had once provided. We are enormously persistent people. We don't give up easily. We couldn't admit that our feelings of control were a hollow parody of freedom, a cruel joke orchestrated by some invisible jester. We were certain that if we just kept trying, we could recapture that magic of the early days.

But the day came when we could not. No matter how rigidly we controlled our food or how many times we binged and purged, we felt no relief—not even oblivion. That was the day we woke up. We saw the meaningless mockery of a number on a scale. We looked around and saw the devastation of our lives, saw our damaged bodies and our broken relationships and our sad children and our wasted fortunes. We looked within and saw the remains of our integrity and our values and our dreams rotting in the grave of our despised bodies. We saw the awful truth, the horror of our lives, the obscenity of throwing away everything in the pursuit of nothing, and we believed to our very core that we had done all of this to ourselves. That was the day we either executed ourselves or fell to our knees and begged for help. That was the day we hit bottom.

Step Zero 6

WE SPENT the last three chapters examining in depth the nature of our problem as anorexics and bulimics. We saw how our essential problem was the utterly insane way we learned to think early in our lives, and how our unholy alliance with anorexia and bulimia provided a faulty solution for the pain engendered by this way of thinking. We saw how our subversive disease sunk its claws into our minds, casting them into anarchy and dragging us down to destruction. We saw how this disease operated out of a mental obsession that compelled us to restrict our food or to binge and purge, coupled with a physical allergy that ensured we could not stop restricting or bingeing and purging once we had begun. We saw how our pathological behavior eventually quit working for us and how we reached the day when we could no longer do it, nor could we stop doing it.[1] *Alcoholics Anonymous* has termed that bottoming-out process "the jumping-off place" (p.152), and that is truly what it is, for it is the day when we either jump off a thirty-storey building or else jump into recovery.

SOBRIETY FIRST

When we hit bottom and joined our Fellowship, all of us learned that the process required for recovery was a simple one, although not easy. *Our first priority had to be physical sobriety.* In other words we had to take the risk of letting go of the tip of our iceberg before we could deal with the submerged part of it. It should be self-evident that no alcoholic can ever recover from alcoholism if she continues to drink, nor a cocaine addict if she continues smoking crack, nor a heroin addict if she continues to shoot up. These facts are so obvious that it seems foolish even to mention them.

Attempts to Avoid Sobriety

Yet when it came to eating disorders, how many of us intuitively grasped that *we had to quit doing the insane things we did with food before we could recover from anorexia and bulimia*? In fact, practically none of us did, and in this we were often unwittingly abetted by the very people we approached for help. Most of us consulted psychiatrists, psychologists, counselors, family therapists, and spiritual advisors, hoping their techniques would allow us to ferret out the reasons for our behavior. We fervently believed that if only we could work through the abandonment issues in our childhood well enough, or could process the pain of our sexual abuse fully enough, or could resolve our enmeshment issues with our mothers thoroughly enough, or could analyze our dysfunctional families cleverly enough, then surely we would have no further need to restrict our food or to binge and purge. How we clung to this notion! When a year of primal scream therapy with one expert failed to produce the magic key, we raced off for two years of inner child work with the next.

Many of us took our quest for understanding one step further. We quit focusing on other people and conceded that our problem lay within ourselves, in our twisted mode of thinking, and then searched for the therapist who could help us change that. If only we could repair our low self-esteem and find empowerment, or quit worrying about what other people thought of us, or put an end to that damnable feeling that we had to take care of other people, or stop looking negatively at everything, surely *then* we would quit doing anorexia and bulimia. So we devoted three years to cognitive therapy, followed by six months of chanting positive affirmations, followed by four years on an analyst's couch. After we had exhausted every conceivable avenue of change and were still living on carrot sticks, running ten miles, or bingeing and purging five times a day, we gave up, now thoroughly convinced that we were hopelessly flawed and beyond redemption.

The Value of Understanding

We do not mean to imply that these good therapists and their remedial methods were of no value. Nothing could be further from the truth. Exploring the roots and understanding the origins of our disease ultimately proved to be one important ingredient in our full healing process, and many of us are immeasurably grateful to those women and men who walked so patiently and compassionately with us through our process of coming to this understanding. We owe them more than we can ever repay, and we are now aware of how blindly and viciously we fought some of them. *The critical point here is that understanding how we came to acquire anorexia or bulimia will never provide us with the power to relinquish it.*[2] *Sobering up must precede our inner healing work, not follow it.*

Fear of Letting Go

This central fact is so vital to our recovery that we will risk belaboring it. Some of us had always known, deep in our guts, that we would have to quit restricting our food or bingeing and purging in order to get well. That's why we took so long to admit our problem and seek professional help. We equated letting go of our insane eating practices with getting fat, and our fear of that held us back. So when we discovered therapists who would treat us without requiring that we sober up first, we were delighted. Anything to delay that dreaded day when someone would make us stop doing what we wanted to do—or, more precisely, were compelled to do—with food and exercise.

HITTING BOTTOM

First, Avoidance...

Some of us had to hit bottom before we reached out for any help at all. Many more used the appearance of getting therapy as another tactic to avoid hitting bottom. In other words, we could tell ourselves and others that by visiting our doctors we were truly doing everything we could to bring about change, when in reality we were not ready to let go of any aspect of our insane eating, purging, and exercise behaviors. We used our therapists as reinforcement for our denial, and we later owed them amends for that.

...Then, Willingness

"Hitting bottom" is a vitally important concept, the true meaning of which has precipitated much debate. We will not enter into that controversy, because in practical terms for all of us it meant one thing only. It was simply arriving at that point in the painful progression of our disease where we could honestly say to ourselves and others, "I can't do this anymore, and *I'm willing to go to any lengths to quit*."[3] We were in such unmitigated inner distress that we were willing to pay any price, spend whatever time was needed, quit our job, leave our marriage and our children, move out of our home and community, and commit any required energy to be released from the prison of our merciless obsessions. We even had to be willing to gain weight if the process of recovery mandated that.

Some Never Make It

Some of us required an exceedingly long time indeed before we reached this place of surrender. Others arrived there within a year of first becoming anorexic or bulimic. We have known still others for whom death was their bottom: They were willing to die rather than quit doing anorexia and bulimia. Or perhaps they died in order to quit doing it.

Finally, Open to Change

Reaching a bottom was the only way we could become open to change, so great was the power of our addictive disease and the stranglehold it had on our minds. Anorexia and bulimia maintained a reign of terror over us, so in order to change we had to reach the day when our fear of letting go of our sick behaviors was exceeded by the pain of holding on. On that day we could admit defeat, ask for help, and be humble enough to do what was suggested to us by others.

Some of us were truly at our bottom when we arrived at the doors of Anorexics and Bulimics Anonymous, and for us it was a blessed relief to be handed A.B.A.'s clear-cut instructions regarding the process of recovery. Others had not yet reached their bottom and were quite annoyed at our insistence on sobriety first. But most of us, being the peculiar creatures that we are, felt both relief and annoyance. Eventually, as we continued to come back and to witness the miracle of recovery in those who had found sobriety, we received enough hope and strength to surrender also.

One of Us Talks to Another

Herein lies the key point for us. *Because these others had been where we were, had personally experienced the torture of anorexia and bulimia, because they clearly knew what they were talking about, we were willing to listen.*[4] They were not sanctimoniously preaching at us, and they had nothing to gain except a deepening of their own recovery. That caught our attention. Only equals can truly connect, as we saw in the last chapter, and our equality as anorexics and bulimics allowed us to connect at the deepest level with one another. The shock waves of that bonding cracked open the walls of our prison and allowed the light of hope to filter in. Then, gently pulled forward by the love and compassion we experienced from those who had recovered, we were able to step through the breach and begin recovery ourselves.

And so the day finally arrived when we were willing to go to any lengths to get sober, because we heard again and again from our recovering sisters that this had to be our priority, that without sobriety we could not recover from anorexia and bulimia. But what exactly did "sobriety" mean for us with this disease?

WHAT IS THE DRUG?

We often humorously refer to this question as "Step Zero," a term we use to denote the process of identifying the "drug" of our addiction. It was obvious to us what was the drug for an alcoholic, and it seemed to us that sobering up was pretty simple: the alcoholic needed to put the cork in the bottle. Similarly we could see that the heroin addict had to leave the cap on the syringe, the amphetamine addict flush the pills down the toilet, the crack addict refrain from striking the match. Some of us indulged in self-pity as we compared ourselves to those suffering from chemical dependency. We judged that they had a pretty easy job of getting sober, whereas our task seemed obscure and nearly impossible.

The Feeling of Being in Control

But then we learned what our drug in fact was. We discovered that it was not food in itself, nor restriction of food, nor bingeing and purging, nor loss of weight, nor exercise. We learned that it was nothing more or less than the *feeling of being in control* that was induced in us when we restricted our food, or purged following our binges, or exercised. In reality this sense of being in control was an illusion, a mirage, a cruel travesty, for we all knew at some deep level the distressing truth: We were not really in control at all, because we had no choice about doing what we did with food and exercise. We had to do it, we couldn't stop doing it, we were acting under compulsion.

Compulsive Eating is Control? Nonsense!

Some of us, in particular those who were compulsive eaters when we got to the doors of our Fellowship, argued vehemently about this definition of our "drug" because we couldn't identify feeling in control of anything. The scale and the empty cupboard and our family doctor all reproached us with our *lack* of control, with our pitiful lack of willpower. Where, we wailed, was our "feeling of being in control"?

To answer this question, we needed to ask these members to describe their inner state prior to and just after a binge or a too-large meal. "Well," they replied, "that's easy. We're just plain hungry. We might have eaten only an hour ago, but we're hungry anyway. And it's not the sort of hunger we can ignore or delay in responding to. We absolutely have to eat, and it better be quick! Once we've eaten, the hunger goes away and we feel great, at least until the guilt sets in."

In Control of Our Feelings

We who trod this path of compulsive eating needed to consider the possibility that this "hunger" we felt may not have been hunger at all, but rather something else rumbling around in our guts, and that if we were to refrain from eating at these times, we might actually experience a *real* feeling. We might erupt into tears or howls; we might start to tremble or drive our fist into something; we might scream obscenities until we are hoarse; we might whimper and curl up in the fetal position for a week. These alarming prospects we could avoid by eating, by stuffing down whatever it is that was coming up. *We could stay in control of our feelings by doing what we did with food.*

So we saw that our drug of feeling in control operated on many levels simultaneously. On the surface we anorexics felt in control of our food and our weight as we experienced the emptiness behind our navels and the lightness in our heads and gazed at the number on the scale. We bulimics felt out of control of our food as we binged, but *in* control of our weight once more when we saw the food floating in the toilet bowl or felt the wonderful rush of laxative-induced diarrhea or stepped on the scale after an eight-mile run. We compulsive eaters felt out of control of food as we consumed the chocolate cake, but *in* control of that gnawing "hunger" in our bellies. We should note that at this level, usually unconscious, all of us—whether anorexic or bulimic or compulsive eater—experienced being in control of our feelings by doing whatever it is we did with food and exercise. As anorexics we starved out our feelings or ran them off, as bulimics we threw up our feelings or defecated them out, and as compulsive eaters we stuffed them down.[5]

In Control of *Something*

Additionally, in some primitive place in our psyches, *all of us felt in control of our lives because we were eating the way we wanted to eat* instead of in the way someone else wanted us to eat, whether our mother or the doctor or the dietitian or our spouse. "I'll show *them* if they think they can control me," we grumbled to ourselves. "I'm going to eat what *I* want." And what we anorexics wanted was bean sprouts and lettuce, not meat and potatoes. We bulimics wanted to binge on cereal and ice cream, then purge. And we compulsive eaters wanted warm biscuits with plenty of butter and a chocolate bar for dessert, not the salad and tuna that the dietitian had suggested.

At this level all of us with eating disorders felt in control because we were doing what we wanted to do with food instead of what others wanted us to do.

So it was that all our members eventually saw our real drug as the sense of being in control of *something*, whether of food or weight or body shape, or of our deepest emotions. We saw that we actually created this feeling of control within ourselves through the act of restricting our food, or bingeing, or purging, or exercising, or some combination of these.

SOBRIETY IS SURRENDER

At this point it became clear to us what we needed to do in order to be sober from this drug. *We needed to surrender all feelings of control over our food and our weight and our exercise and our body shape in order to be sober in eating disorders.* But to whom were we to surrender? And how exactly were we to do this?

To Whom?

Let's look at the first question first. We saw that in acting out in anorexia and bulimia we had been eating out of self-will. We had been intoxicated on the powerful feelings induced in us by eating exactly what we wanted to eat, when we wanted to eat, and how we wanted to eat. In some of us, self-will drove us to eat nothing at all, or some type or amount of food that was pitifully inadequate to meet our body's needs. In others, self-will compelled us to eat large quantities of food and to sometimes purge it through vomiting, laxatives, fasting, or exercise. Operating out of self-will, not one of us practicing this disease ever adhered to the principles of healthful eating, of regularly nurturing our bodies through balanced meals. *Not one of us ever consistently ate in the way that human beings are intended to eat.*

We saw other species feeding themselves as the Creator ordained. We watched squirrels gathering nuts and robins pulling worms out of the lawn and mosquitoes feasting on our blood. Never once did we see a squirrel draw back from the nut out of fear that it was getting fat. Nor did we ever see a robin gorge itself on chickweed and purge before returning to its nest. And no mosquito in our acquaintance ever did push-ups to burn off the blood it had just ingested. We watched normal members of our own species effortlessly eating corn flakes for breakfast and sandwiches for lunch and ham and potatoes for dinner. But never could we allow ourselves to do that for any sustained period of time. Our self-will was enslaved by the mad tyrant that ruled our minds from the day we contracted our disease.

Reflecting on this, we knew what we needed to do to be sober. We simply needed to surrender our eating practices to the principles followed by normal humans, and to surrender our body weight and shape to the way we were created to be. We needed to bring our self-will into line with the Creator's intention for us. *To be sober in anorexia and bulimia we needed to surrender all control of our food and our exercise and our body weight and shape to the Creator, or Higher Power.*

And How?

Very simple, but clearly not easy. We come now to the second question posed above: Just how were we to accomplish this surrender? Exploring the answer to that vital question will require a chapter in itself. For getting sober is the key to everything else that follows, the key to our entire healing process.

Getting Sober 7

NO ONE CAN DO IT ALONE

ONCE WE identified that we needed to surrender our food and our weight to a Higher Power in order to get sober in anorexia and bulimia, we all faced the puzzling question of what sobriety would look like in practical terms. First, most of us saw that we could not do this alone. After two or twenty years of insane eating and purging practices, almost none of us could even *think* about food without distortion, without believing countless lies we told ourselves about it. We could not distinguish truth from fiction. We were far too ill to be able even to plan a sober meal, let alone prepare it and eat it.

Can God Cook?

Furthermore, it seemed highly unlikely that the Creator would have bacon and eggs sizzling on the stove when we woke up the next day or, with a cheery goodbye, hand us our lunch in a brown paper bag as we headed off to work. We couldn't imagine God sending an angel to prepare spaghetti and meatballs and to serve it when we arrived home for dinner.

Obviously, we needed to allow some human agent to plan, prepare, and serve our meals for us. We needed to trust this individual, this meal-support helper, to carry out the Higher Power's intention for us for that meal. We needed to put the food placed before us into our bodies, exactly as it was served, and to keep it there, without purging or going for a brisk walk afterward to burn it off. We needed to relinquish all decisions about what food was served, how it was prepared, and how much was on our plate.

SURRENDER OF FOOD

Most of us initially reacted with horror to the idea of another person arbitrarily deciding what we would eat. What if they gave us something we didn't like? Something harmful to us? Something that gave us a stomach ache? Something that triggered a binge? What if they gave us too much or too little? Something our bodies couldn't tolerate? Indeed, many of us had acquired very rigid ideas about what we could tolerate. We thought that wheat was bad for us, or sugar, or red meat, or fat, or fried foods, or preservatives, or anything that came out of a can, or anything that wasn't "organic."

We were only minimally relieved to learn that the person preparing our food would respect any true allergies or medical conditions in our bodies, such as celiac disease or diabetes or a high cholesterol level, and that our physician and a dietitian would be consulted in this regard. Many of us were convinced that certain foods were bad for us, even though our doctors dismissed the idea after appropriate tests had failed to confirm our suspicions.

Despite our misgivings about relinquishing control of our food to someone else, that is precisely what virtually all our members needed to do to get sober. Some concrete examples of this process will follow later in the chapter.

SURRENDER OF BODY WEIGHT

When we ate in this fashion, one meal at a time, day in and day out, our body weight sometimes changed. All of us who were low-weight anorexics and bulimics gained weight, kept gaining until our weight was normal, then stopped, contrary to our greatest fear: that we would blow up like balloons and become obese. Those of us who were of normal weight were certain that we would put on weight when we ate three normal meals a day, and were shocked to discover that we did not. Those of us who were overweight eventually shed our excess poundage, usually following an initial hiatus during which we learned to eat normally and stop our yo-yo dieting.

When we get sober and stay sober, all of us end up at the weight we were created to be. What that number is, is not our business to know. It is the Creator's business. *It is not wise for any of us to weigh ourselves or even to know what our weight is if someone else is monitoring it.* Seeing the number on the scale fuels our mental obsession and places us at high risk for relapse. If the number has increased, we get scared. If decreased, we are delighted or frightened, depending on our mental state at the moment. If the number is unchanged, we experience a rush of self-will to keep it there or change it. In every instance, reacting to the scale consumes precious time and energy that would be better spent on recovery work. We have learned that eating disorders are not about weight. The sooner we truly grasp that fact, the sooner we heal.

SURRENDER OF EXERCISE

In addition to our food and body weight, we needed to surrender our exercise to the Creator. In early sobriety none of us could safely exercise at all, even when we were convinced that we had not been doing it compulsively. It was far too slippery an area in which to dabble, because many of us had used exercise as a means of taking control of our weight, or at least of our body shape. One clue to help us determine whether exercise had become a mood-altering drug for us was to notice how resistant we felt to the idea of giving it up. Some of us cried out in dismay, “But I like swimming! I love the way my body feels in the water, and I feel so good. Surely God wants me to feel good!” Others declared, “If I have to gain weight I want it to go into muscle. If I quit running, it will turn into fat.” Still others were terrified that if they quit doing sit-ups, their bellies would be flabby within days. With all these folks we shared our experience: Continuing to exercise in early recovery almost always sabotaged our healing process. It kept us at least mildly intoxicated and prevented us from connecting with our Higher Power so we could be restored to sanity. *Sobriety requires absolute surrender of our body to the Creator. Only with sobriety first can we recover from anorexia and bulimia.*

SURRENDER TAKES WORK

The word “surrender” may carry a passive connotation, conjuring up visions of a limp noodle floating in a pot of soup. Let’s dispose of that misunderstanding right here. As we will learn in a later chapter, the act of surrender is entirely volitional, wholly intentional, and requires intensive work on a daily basis. We will need to use every tool within our grasp to remain in an attitude of surrender to a Higher Power.

HOW LONG DOES IT TAKE?

When we first sobered up, we wondered how long we would need to allow another person to prepare our meals and serve them to us, how long before we could end our physical inactivity and don our running shoes again. The simple answer to this question is that we do these things until we no longer need to do them, until we have been restored to sane thinking about our bodies and about food. We have all discovered that when we stay sober physically and work the Twelve-Step Program as outlined in the next four chapters, we arrive at a place of deep spiritual and mental wellness. We awaken, slowly or suddenly, to the consciousness of a Higher Power at work within us restoring our thinking to healthy modes, melting the bottom of our iceberg. As this occurs we begin to love ourselves, body and mind and spirit, and to deeply desire for ourselves everything that is nurturing and wholesome. This healing process takes as much time as it takes!

Until We Are Free

Once this complete psychological change has occurred, this profound spiritual transformation, this pervasive shift in our attitude toward ourselves and others, then we have no desire to escape into the tip of our iceberg. In other words, we no longer perceive or believe that our body weight and shape require alteration. As a result of this shift, we are no longer compelled to restrict our food or to binge and purge or to shape up our bodies through excessive exercise. A Higher Power has accomplished the change in our thinking that we could never bring about ourselves through years of intensive therapy. When this longed-for time arrives, we can begin selecting and preparing our own meals and decide to exercise or to not exercise. We are given back the power to freely determine how we shall eat and whether we shall exercise on any given day.

The amazing paradox is that when we surrender our eating and our exercise to a Higher Power, followed by the vigorous action of the Twelve-Step Program, then this Power returns our eating and our exercise to us, but with freedom attached![1] No longer are we compelled to eat a low-fat diet or to consume more than our bodies need. Now some of us return to vegetarian eating as a truly spiritual or ethical choice. Now we can run in the river valley or swim laps because it really is good for our bodies, not because we are driven to keep ourselves in shape. To all of us anorexics or bulimics, who had hitherto known only compulsion, this liberation of our minds is miraculous indeed. When we were still enslaved by our deadly obsessions, such freedom was only a dim memory from our past or an impossible dream for our future. Now, with sobriety first, it becomes a glorious reality of our present.

To better understand this theoretical framework, let's look now at some concrete examples of what early sobriety looked like for some of our members.

ANY LENGTHS: THE STORY OF VICTORIA

Victoria was an eighteen-year-old anorexic who had been sick for three years when she first arrived at our meetings. She looked like a walking skeleton, yet was living on rice cakes, apples, and low-fat cheese and was running five miles every day to keep in shape. She had been hospitalized for treatment six months earlier, after collapsing on the volleyball court at school. In hospital she was encouraged within one week of her admission to make her own food selections from the hospital menu. Given this "choice," she had opted for the foods that appealed to her: all the lower-fat items and, whenever possible, vegetarian entrées. Of course, she lacked the power to choose otherwise. After three months of weight gain and psychotherapy to explore her family-of-origin issues, she was discharged with outpatient follow-up. Within two days, she was running the stairs again and screaming at her mother when a fried food was served for dinner.

Victoria was a tortured soul and desperately seeking release from her prison. After attending our meetings for seven weeks, she surrendered, burst into tears, and asked us to tell her what she had to do. She was so enmeshed with her family that she could not allow them to prepare food for her. One of our members, a bulimic with two years of sobriety, offered to be Victoria's meal-support helper, someone who would prepare and serve all her meals. Victoria accepted this generous offer and moved into her home. There Victoria began eating everything placed before her: three meals and three snacks daily as directed by an informed dietitian. The size of her meals was gradually increased over the first week to a level that resulted in a steady weight gain of two pounds per week, and this was monitored by her physician.

The first three weeks were difficult for Victoria. When she faced food, she often felt waves of nausea and needed to eat slowly with her helper present to offer gentle support. At times she felt such rage that she could not eat until she had processed this, screaming and weeping on her bed for an hour or more. Sometimes she ended up eating her dinner at midnight for this reason. She discovered, as we all do, that when we get sober we begin to feel and that our feelings are often uncomfortable. Nevertheless she continued, one day at a time, to surrender control of her feelings, and her food, to her Higher Power, whom she called God. She trusted that God was placing the food before her and was directing her feelings where they needed to go. She honored her feelings and did not run from them. As she processed them, she came to many new learnings about herself and her past relationship with her family. These she would share with her meal-support helper, her doctor, and her sponsor.

At first Victoria continued attending school, but she found concentrating on her studies to be impossible, so consumed was she by the process of staying sober. At times the additional stress of schoolwork reinforced her obsession with her body, which she continued to perceive as "fat" for the first four months of sobriety. So she surrendered her schooling to her Higher Power, trusting that one day she would be able to return to it as a changed person.

Victoria needed to refrain from all exercise for the first nine months of her sobriety, and that aspect of surrender triggered many feelings within her. She continued to process these feelings, one at a time, as they came up.

Victoria relapsed twice, once by running the stairs at her apartment building and once by pouring her milk down the sink, and these slips she promptly admitted to her sponsor and to others in recovery. We listened, acknowledged her honesty, reminded her that recovery is a process that no one does perfectly, and encouraged her to seek the lessons from her relapses and continue on her path.

As she stayed sober and worked the Twelve-Step Program, Victoria changed before our eyes, physically as well as emotionally and spiritually. Within six months her weight returned to normal, she radiated an aura of peace and vitality, and her previously haunted eyes sparkled with joy. At the four-month point she was sane enough to begin selecting some of her food and preparing some items for herself, and by six months she was planning and preparing all her own meals. She was fully restored to sanity by her Higher Power.

Victoria was unable to return to her parents' home in early recovery except for visits of up to one week at a time. While there, she was usually able to allow them to prepare food for her without becoming angry at them. They have been astonished and delighted by the depth of her recovery and frequently express their gratitude to our membership. The daughter whom they had been certain would die has been restored to them, healthy and whole. She needed to leave school for only one semester. When she returned, she achieved top honors. Today Victoria is working on an undergraduate degree at university and is engaged to be married. She recently celebrated six years of sobriety and continues to be an active member of our Fellowship.

Victoria's story contains a number of important lessons. It reveals the lengths to which we need to be willing to go to sober up. When she surrendered her food and her running, her home and her schooling to her Higher Power, Victoria had no way of knowing whether she would ever get these things back. She deeply feared that she would become fat if she got sober. She took the risk blindly, on the basis of our testimony, and she was able to do that solely because of the level of her desperation, because she had been utterly defeated by her disease.

Her story also illustrates the high level of personal responsibility that each of us needs to assume for our own recovery process. No one watched Victoria eat or followed her to the bathroom, nor did she have a bodyguard when she left the apartment to attend her doctor's office or meetings. There were times when she needed to ask her meal-support helper or others for an intensive level of support, but it was her job to do so. She was responsible for picking up the tools of recovery daily and using them to stay sober. She needed to pray and meditate, attend meetings, read the Big Book, call her sponsor, and work the Steps. When she did these things she was given her life back, one day at a time. She was also responsible for processing her feelings as they came up and for getting whatever support she needed to do so. She chose to join a healing circle, where she deepened her understanding of herself and her childhood experiences. Today she has forgiven everyone, including herself, and is grateful to be an anorexic.

Perhaps the most important aspect of Victoria's experience is the revelation it contains about the essential goodness of her Higher Power. That Power sustained her through all her pain by providing the grace she needed each day to stay sober, as well as the people she needed to connect with for support at any given moment. Clearly, that Power loves her passionately and wills for her to be happy, joyous, and free. Her story demonstrates that her Higher Power was the only match for her disease, the only force in the universe that could deliver her from her enslavement to anorexia. Within a month of sobering up, Victoria experienced a conscious awareness of her God's presence and realized that this Presence was actually inside her body as well as outside her in other people. Today her relationship with that God is the center of her life.

Victoria had possessed a lifelong faith in a loving God that stood her in good stead in her sobering-up process. Let's look now at another member's experience to see that such faith is not a prerequisite for recovery.

AN ATHEIST SOBERS UP: THE STORY OF DIANE

When we first met Diane, she was a twenty-two-year-old bulimic who had started her career as a restrictive anorexic at the age of eleven. By fourteen she was so tired of fasting all day that she began bingeing and purging two or three times daily, from the time she got home from school until bedtime. She concealed everything from her family. At fifteen she attempted suicide, and her bewildered parents took her to a psychologist for help. She was not yet ready to tell anyone her shameful truth and got nowhere in therapy. She graduated from high school with honors, despite her daily battle with bulimia. She then embarked on her dream of becoming a world-class figure skater, moving to another city to do so. Two years into her training Diane passed out on the ice one day, her body spent from the ravages of bingeing and purging five or six times every day. She told her instructors the truth and was sent home to get well.

Next came a fruitless search for someone or something to help her. Her physician gave her medication, and she ran the usual gamut of psychotherapists that most of us have tried. After two years on this quest she sank into despair, knew she was dying, yet felt a deep desire to live. She heard about our Fellowship and turned up at a meeting, broken and desperate. After a month of attending meetings, then going home to binge and purge, she fainted on the street and was transported to a hospital Emergency Room. From there she called one of our members, pleading for help, now ready to do whatever was needed to get well.

We visited Diane at the hospital and told her, from our own experience, what was needed for sobriety. She had been a fervent atheist since the age of sixteen, having rejected her parents' fundamentalist religion and the idea she had formulated as a child of a harsh and punishing God. We encouraged her to pray on her knees out loud and ask a Higher Power for the capacity to surrender to the hospital food, one meal at a time. Diane was appalled by this suggestion but, because of the level of her desperation, was willing to follow it. She went into the washroom where no one would see her, dropped to her knees, and asked for help, even though she possessed no belief that anyone would hear her prayer. To her surprise, she was able to eat lunch ten minutes later. Following her meal, she waited for the compulsion to purge to overtake her as it always had, but to her further shock it did not come.

Thus began Diane's sobriety. Our members visited her daily at the hospital, sometimes sitting with her while she ate. She relapsed once during a stressful day of group therapy, but told us about this immediately and continued her journey. She discovered that her appeal for help to an unknown Higher Power before every meal gave her the power to eat and keep it in her body. She was amazed at this, and gradually she came to believe that Something or Someone heard her prayer and loved her enough to respond. Her psychiatrist gave Diane permission to attend our meetings, and she began working the Twelve Steps with the support of a sponsor.

After one week on a medical ward, followed by six weeks on the psychiatric unit, Diane was discharged to her parents' home, somewhat apprehensive. She was not yet sane enough to plan or prepare her own meals and needed someone to do this for her. Thus far the hospital dietitian had been willing to do all the meal planning, and Diane had accepted that arrangement with relative ease. But would she now be able to allow her mother to cook for her? Using her newfound faith, she asked her Higher Power for help and, meal by meal, received the grace to eat what her mother set before her. Two weeks later she had been restored to sufficient sanity that she could begin selecting her own breakfast and snacks, and two months later she could cook for herself and her family when it was her turn to do kitchen duty.

Today Diane remains a committed member of our Fellowship. At seven years of sobriety, she continues to participate in meetings and to guide others. Over the years, the Higher Power shining through her has provided a ray of hope to many a desperate newcomer.

Diane's case is important for at least two reasons. First, it illustrates the important fact that pre-existing faith in a Higher Power is completely unnecessary to the recovery process. *All that is needed is a willingness to take action, regardless of what we think about the issue.* Diane's initial prayer was, "I certainly don't believe you exist, but here I am, asking for help. If there's anyone out there listening, please help me eat my lunch today, because I know I can't do it by myself." The words of our prayers don't matter. What does matter is our willingness to say them, to humble ourselves and ask for help.

Secondly, Diane's experience demonstrates how many of us need extensive outside support to get sober. Her family physician and psychiatrist, the nurses at the hospital, the dietitian, her fellow patients, and the hospital itself all contributed to the safe environment Diane needed in order to begin eating again, after eleven years of not eating normally. Many of our members are deeply indebted to the medical community for their patience, their willingness to help us, and their provision of a safe place where we can sober up.

A CHRONIC BULIMIC SOBERS UP: THE STORY OF GINA

Let's look now at Gina's story, which is somewhat different. Gina was forty-three years old when she came to us, and had been bulimic for twenty-seven years. She had sought professional help a number of times in her twenties and early thirties and had been hospitalized twice for intensive therapy. When everything failed to resolve her problem, she gave up and for the past ten years had simply resigned herself to her fate. She had an advanced degree in home economics and was employed teaching nutrition to medical and nursing students at a local university. She had never been anorexic and had focused surprisingly little on her body weight throughout her disease. She ate a normal breakfast and lunch every day, then began her binge while preparing her family's evening meal. She usually binged and purged once or twice more before bedtime, although in the past eight years she often substituted alcohol instead. Gina noticed that when she drank she could control her bulimia. Her alcohol intake had gradually escalated to one or two bottles of wine in the evening, two or three times each week.

Gina was married to a patient man who had tried everything to help her over the twenty years of their marriage. She had achieved only one sustained period free of bulimia: the nine months of her only pregnancy. Their twin daughters, now ten years old, knew their mother was bulimic, but never talked about it. Her husband had abandoned all hope that Gina would ever change, but nonetheless had expressed his concern about her drinking, which he noticed was getting worse and which he believed was harming their family more than her bulimia. He issued an ultimatum that unless she got help for this problem, he would leave her and take their daughters with him.

Gina's fear that she would lose her family brought her to our meetings. Her rock-bottom came quietly, without any drama, when one day she knew she was prepared to do anything to get well. We suggested she deal with her drinking first, and she was willing to do that, even though she did not initially perceive herself as an alcoholic. She quit drinking and joined Alcoholics Anonymous. Not surprisingly, her bingeing and purging escalated when she stopped drinking, yet Gina continued to hope that she would eventually recover.

Because she had always possessed a deep religious faith, it was not difficult for Gina to pray and ask for help every day, and a mere three months later she knew that her Higher Power would keep her sober that day. Instead of bingeing and purging that evening, she ate a normal meal with her family and left the house for a meeting without having purged.

In this manner Gina entered sobriety. One day at a time, employing prayer, the guidance of an understanding physician, and the support of two Twelve-Step Fellowships, she remained sober in her bulimia. With the guidance of a sponsor she worked the Steps. Gradually, Gina healed. She had three or four relapses in her first year, each of them related to cutting back on the intensity of her personal recovery work, and from each of them she learned something important about herself and her disease. After a time, she decided to undertake therapy with a psychiatrist to gain a deeper understanding of the roots of her disease. Today she is approaching five years of continuous sobriety in our Fellowship and six years in Alcoholics Anonymous. Her relationship with her husband is more joyful and authentic than ever before, and her teenaged daughters are delighted to have their mother emotionally available to them. Her family attended her first anniversary celebration and expressed their gratitude to us.

We can glean some important lessons from Gina's story. First, the fact that she had been ill for nearly three decades did not diminish her prospects for healing. This has been the experience of many of our members. On the contrary, perhaps our long history in some cases contributes to our willingness to go to any lengths for sobriety. Secondly, Gina rarely focused on her weight, had never wanted to lose weight, nor did she use bulimia to control her weight. Perhaps that explains why she required no outside meal-support in her process of getting sober. She knew how to prepare nutritious and appealing meals and had never restricted her food as anorexics do. So when she sobered up, she needed to go no further than her own extensive knowledge of nutrition to learn how to eat normally. She saw her knowledge as a gift from her Higher Power and was able to humbly surrender to it each day, using the strength provided by that Power.

CREATIVE SOBERING-UP: THE STORY OF BARBARA

We will look at one more member's experience before concluding this discussion of getting sober. Barbara was in her mid-thirties when she first came to us, and she had been anorexic and bulimic for nineteen years. Her disease had progressed to a degree of physical incapacity that had forced her to leave her job as executive assistant to the CEO of a major oil company. She was forty pounds underweight, appeared gaunt and emaciated, and over the years had exhausted all the usual channels of therapy, including hospitalization, medication, and psychotherapy. She starved all day, then binged and purged every evening, and she couldn't stop.

After hearing our message about "Sobriety First," Barbara sat down with a few of us to discuss what sobriety might look like for her. She was married to a compulsive gambler and knew that her home was a dangerous place fraught with tension and discord, with both her and her husband engaged in mutual deception. She knew she could not prepare and eat a single sober meal for herself, and she was willing to go to any lengths for recovery.

Barbara's psychiatrist agreed to admit her to hospital. There she met with the dietitian, telling her what she had learned from us about physical sobriety. The dietitian was willing to select all her food for her, and Barbara ate it, using phone calls and visits from our members to support her eating. Her doctor gave her passes to attend our meetings. Slowly, Barbara gained weight and grew physically stronger. She asked one of our members to sponsor her and began working the Twelve-Step Program.

When it was time for her discharge three months later, Barbara was terrified of returning to her husband, who remained in the throes of his own addiction. Furthermore, still obsessed with the desire to lose weight, she knew she continued to lack the sanity to prepare any meals for herself. She spent her first month out of hospital living with one of our members, who prepared and served all her food. During this time, Barbara became clear about separating from her husband. She decided that she needed a home of her own, found an apartment, and moved in, while continuing to eat all her meals with the meal-support helper from our Fellowship.

Shortly thereafter, the helper became unavailable, and Barbara sought other options. By this time she was able to plan and prepare a simple breakfast and snacks for herself, but even thinking about the other meals cast her into a state of confusion and panic. In the short term, she went to the food court of a nearby shopping mall and bought her lunch and dinner from the kiosks there, rotating from one to the next as they were laid out geographically. Lunch one day was pizza from the Italian counter, dinner was four items chosen randomly by the attendant at the Chinese booth. Lunch the next day was the first entrée listed at the Greek kiosk, dinner the "special" at the Ukrainian one, and so on.

Meanwhile a family member suggested a community of nuns who lived near her apartment, and Barbara approached them about meal-support. Two days later she began attending the convent for her evening meal, which the nuns prepared and served for themselves and for her. When she left each evening, they gave her a paper sack containing her lunch for the following day. Barbara reimbursed them for the cost of her food.

This arrangement worked well for the next four months. Barbara enjoyed eating with the nuns and getting to know them, and she appreciated the prayerful atmosphere of the convent. During this period she met with a psychologist twice each week to deal with her emotional issues as they came to light. Now sober for the first time in nineteen years, she was able to do this emotional healing to a depth and effectiveness never before possible.

Gradually, Barbara got well. She continued gaining weight and felt better physically than ever before. Her emotional healing process was difficult as she uncovered memories of childhood sexual abuse and also admitted the wounds she sustained in growing up behind the Iron Curtain and emigrating to Canada at age eleven. Much of her deep healing work surfaced at night, and she often awoke drenched in sweat from terrifying nightmares, then cowered and wept in her bed for the rest of the night. As a result of all this, she remained unable to work throughout this period.

When summer arrived, the nuns experienced a change in their community and needed to terminate their arrangement with Barbara. She was still completely unable to cook for herself, but by this time was able soberly to select and prepare her own sandwich and fruit for lunch. What was she to do about dinner? One day she learned that her neighbor, an elderly woman in a nearby suite, had been recently widowed and was desperately lonely. They discussed their mutual needs. Her neighbor enjoyed cooking and agreed to prepare and serve an evening meal for both of them. For the next six months, Barbara went to her neighbor's suite every evening for dinner and gradually, almost without noticing it, began to assist with preparing the meal and even shopping for it. Eventually she realized that she was now capable of planning and preparing all her own meals, completely liberated from her old obsessions about weight. This process had required a total of fourteen months of surrender to her Higher Power through an outside agent, one meal at a time.

Barbara's story illustrates the creativity that some of us needed in order to find our pathway to get sober and stay sober. Hospital, a fellow member's home, the food court at a local mall, the convent, her neighbor's kitchen—each of these in turn provided Barbara with a sober milieu and people to assist her. Furthermore, as each door closed Barbara discovered that another one opened. She needed willingness and open-mindedness each time to look around for options and to voice her needs with honesty and humility. Doing so required great courage, especially when this entailed revealing her eating disorder to normal folk.

As Barbara stayed sober, attended meetings, and worked the Twelve-Step Program with a sponsor, she acquired a deep and unshakable faith in a Higher Power. She recognized this Power both guiding her to find options for meal-support and giving her grace to accept them. In the end she discovered that this Power compassionately removed her deadly obsessions. Her newfound faith enabled her also to surrender her emotional healing process to her Higher Power, and today Barbara is a changed woman. The damage from her past has mended. She has discovered long-buried artistic talents, is operating her own small business, and at six years of sobriety is a spectacular witness to the Power that can heal us all.

BEYOND EARLY SOBRIETY

All the women in the examples above gradually reached the stage where they could sanely plan and prepare their own food and decide when and how they would exercise. We must emphasize that in so doing they continued to surrender all control of their food and exercise to their Higher Power, who now clearly guided them from within. All our members who have become sober and stayed sober can attest to this experience. As we remain sober and work the Steps, we develop a clear sense of a newfound Power deep within us directing our decisions about food and exercise. To surrender to this Power becomes effortless and virtually automatic.

In Control Now?

To an outsider, it might appear that in such advanced recovery we are assuming control of our eating and exercise in the same manner a normal eater controls these areas of her life. But we are not. We cannot. For us anorexics and bulimics, to take control over our food or exercise choices is deadly, no matter how long we have been in recovery. *At every stage of recovery, and for the rest of our lives, we must surrender all control of our eating, our weight, and our exercise to our Higher Power.* Otherwise we are no longer sober.

This point is so important we have risked belaboring it. This is not mere semantics. The difference between eating as directed by self-will and eating out of surrender to a Higher Power's will (even if that Power can now guide us through our own appetite and thinking and desires) is infinite. It is the difference between relapse and sobriety. It is the difference between life and death for us.

Self-Will and the Creator's Will Merge

The real miracle is that in time, with sustained sobriety and the psychic change that comes through following the Twelve Steps, our self-will begins to merge with our Higher Power's will for us in all areas of our lives, including eating and exercise. This will be discussed further in the next chapter. Once this point is reached, staying sober feels and appears effortless.[2]

Nevertheless, once an anorexic or bulimic, always an anorexic or bulimic. All of us are capable of relapse, no matter how long we have been sober. Our disease is cunning, baffling, powerful, and exceedingly patient.

Everyone Needs Support

We have explored in depth in this chapter what sobriety looks like and precisely how some of us have proceeded in getting sober. The reader may regard much of the detail as irrelevant and excessive. However, we have learned through sometimes bitter experience that without sobriety true recovery from our eating disorders is impossible, and the most common questions that newcomers ask are, "What does sobriety mean?" "How do I get sober?" "What do I have to do?" We hope this chapter has fully answered such questions. Most importantly, we hope to impart the clear and unmistakable message that *none of us has been able to get sober in isolation. We all needed help from other human beings.*[3]

A Tribute to Alcoholics Anonymous

BEFORE WE plunge into an exploration of the Twelve-Step Program and, later on, of the Twelve Traditions, we need to pause here and look at these Steps and Traditions in the form in which they were originally developed by Alcoholics Anonymous more than six decades ago. For us in A.B.A., this is our ancestry, and we are deeply grateful to our grandparents in Alcoholics Anonymous for the wisdom they allowed to flow through them from the Creator. We have all benefited from their insight and clarity.

In graciously permitting us to reprint and adapt the Twelve Steps and Twelve Traditions for our purposes in A.B.A., Alcoholics Anonymous World Services, Inc. has requested that we reprint them in their original form before we introduce our adaptation of them. We are honored to do so.

THE TWELVE STEPS OF ALCOHOLICS ANONYMOUS

1. We admitted we were powerless over alcohol—that our lives had become unmanageable.
2. Came to believe that a Power greater than ourselves could restore us to sanity.
3. Made a decision to turn our will and our lives over to the care of God as we understood Him.
4. Made a searching and fearless moral inventory of ourselves.
5. Admitted to God, to ourselves, and to another human being the exact nature of our wrongs.
6. Were entirely ready to have God remove all these defects of character.
7. Humbly asked Him to remove our shortcomings.
8. Made a list of all persons we had harmed, and became willing to make amends to them all.
9. Made direct amends to such people wherever possible, except when to do so would injure them or others.
10. Continued to take personal inventory and when we were wrong promptly admitted it.
11. Sought through prayer and meditation to improve our conscious contact with God as we understood Him, praying only for knowledge of His will for us and the power to carry that out.
12. Having had a spiritual awakening as the result of these Steps, we tried to carry this message to alcoholics, and to practice these principles in all our affairs.

Alcoholics Anonymous World Services, Inc.®

THE TWELVE TRADITIONS OF ALCOHOLICS ANONYMOUS

1. Our Common welfare should come first; personal recovery depends upon A.A. unity.

2. For our group purpose there is but one ultimate authority—a loving God as He may express Himself in our group conscience. Our leaders are but trusted servants; they do not govern.

3. The only requirement for A.A. membership is a desire to stop drinking.

4. Each group should be autonomous except in matters affecting other groups or A.A. as a whole.

5. Each group has but one primary purpose—to carry its message to the alcoholic who still suffers.

6. Each group ought never endorse, finance, or lend the A.A. name to any related facility or outside enterprise, lest problems of money, property, and prestige divert us from our primary purpose.

7. Every A.A. group ought to be fully self-supporting, declining outside contributions.

8. Alcoholics Anonymous should remain forever nonprofessional, but our service centers may employ special workers.

9. A.A., as such, ought never be organized; but we may create service boards or committees directly responsible to those they serve.

10. Alcoholics Anonymous has no opinion on outside issues; hence the A.A. name ought never be drawn into public controversy.

11. Our public relations policy is based on attraction rather than promotion; we need always maintain personal anonymity at the level of press, radio, and films.

12. Anonymity is the spiritual foundation of all our traditions, ever reminding us to place principles before personalities.

Alcoholics Anonymous World Services, Inc.®

Three Strikes at the Iceberg— Steps One, Two, and Three

8

SOBRIETY IS BUT THE BEGINNING

ALL OF us who have recovered from anorexia and bulimia learned that physical sobriety as described in the last two chapters was the foundation for recovery, yet by itself sobriety was not enough. Surrender of all control of our food and our body size and shape to the Creator was absolutely essential, but unless we engaged in a psychic healing process as well, none of us was liberated from our fatal obsessions. To use the analogy of Chapter 5, physical sobriety dealt with the tip of the iceberg of our disease, but unless we did something about its submerged bottom, relapse was inevitable.

TWELVE STEPS TO DEEP HEALING

We will now explore, in this chapter and the three following, the Twelve-Step Program that we followed to heal fully from our disease. This pathway was originated by Alcoholics Anonymous and is masterfully detailed in its basic text, *Alcoholics Anonymous*, and in a second important work, *Twelve Steps and Twelve Traditions*.[1] We have no desire to repeat here what is written there, and we strongly recommend that all our members study and follow the instructions in those two texts as they work the Steps. We wish only to add a few comments about each of the Twelve Steps, sharing some of what we in A.B.A. have learned as we walked through them. In examining each Step, we needed to use a dictionary, and we encourage everyone to use one also. It is obviously impossible to carry out a set of detailed instructions if we don't know what their wording means.

We believe that the Twelve-Step Program is purely and simply a spiritual path that connects us with a Higher Power that solves the problem of our mental and spiritual disease. The Higher Power is the only agent we have found that can straighten out our deranged thinking processes, thereby melting the bottom of the iceberg of our disease. We have the power to use the tools and to avail ourselves of the support of others as we prepare to receive the precious daily gift of physical sobriety (tip of the iceberg), but only a Power greater than ourselves can alter the insane way we think. As this humanly impossible task is accomplished, as we are liberated from our self-centeredness and dishonesty and illusion of control, as we begin to truly love ourselves, then we discover that we have also been miraculously released from our insane obsessions about our bodies and about food. The tip of the iceberg has lost all its attraction for us. A Higher Power has succeeded where we could not.

STEP ONE:

We admitted we were powerless over our insane eating practices—that our lives had become unmanageable.

This Step is the basis of recovery from addiction. It is said in the A.A. literature that this is the only Step we can, and must, take with perfection, "the 100 Percent Step."[2] It requires an admission of personal defeat by our disease, and it comprises two separate and equally important components.

POWERLESSNESS

The first half of the First Step is about admitting and accepting that we are utterly powerless over anorexia and bulimia. "Powerless" is a powerful word. *Merriam-Webster's Desk Dictionary* defines "power" as "the ability to act or produce an effect; a position of ascendancy over others; one that has control or authority; physical might; mental or moral vigor;...force or energy used to do work...."* To be powerless is to be without power, without the ability to act, without ascendancy, without control, without physical might or mental vigor, without the energy needed to accomplish a given task. Not surprisingly, personal powerlessness is a very unpopular concept in our culture, based as our

*By permission. From ***Merriam-Webster's Desk Dictionary*** ©1995 by Merriam-Webster, Incorporated, at www.Merriam-Webster.com.

society is on the principles of rugged individualism and personal autonomy.[3]

Admitting Powerlessness

Yet those of us who have been defeated by anorexia and bulimia generally have little difficulty in admitting that we were without power over our own sick behavior. We need only to examine the evidence: all the years we spent living on lettuce or bingeing on chocolate cake long after we had reached the point where we consciously desired to stop, when every shred of our willpower proved useless to make ourselves stop. Powerless is a term that fit us like a glove.

Accepting Powerlessness

However, admitting powerlessness was useless until we *accepted* it, and for many of us this was a huge stumbling block. Many of us said to ourselves, "Of course I can see that I can't change my own crazy behavior with food. Any imbecile can see that I can't change, and I'm not stupid. But I *should* be able to change. If I were a stronger person or a better person, then I would be able to quit doing these ridiculous things with food." Therefore we concluded that we were not strong enough, not good enough. We castigated ourselves, utterly loathed ourselves, for our lack of strength and goodness. This self-hatred, examined closely in Chapter 5, engendered such intense inner pain that we had to seek escape from it, for no human beings can go on living with such conscious feelings toward themselves. And our surest escape route was what it had always been: the loss of another pound, the disposal of another bag of cookies, the completion of another ten laps around the track. *Our anorexic and bulimic behavior provided simultaneously both the escape from ourselves that we needed and the punishment we knew we deserved.*

In other words, our inability to accept the first half of Step One perpetuated our disease. Fortunately for us, however, we all reached the time when our escape route ended in a dead end, when it failed to give us the pain relief we needed. That was when we hit bottom and, utterly defeated, crawled into the rooms of this Fellowship open to hearing how to get well. That was when we became willing to go to any lengths for our recovery and sobered up, as described in the last chapter.

UNMANAGEABILITY

Denial

The second half of Step One requires admitting the unmanageability in our lives that resulted from our addictive behavior. This was another area that proved difficult for many of us, for it meant the death of our denial. "Manage" means "to handle or control; to direct or carry on business or affairs;...to treat with care; to achieve one's purpose."* Many of us lived for decades regarding our anorexia and bulimia as a minor hobby, of no greater significance than knitting or skydiving. We pointed out the external evidence that proved we were handling our lives exceptionally well. Our outstanding grades and doting teachers, our handsome boyfriends, our notable careers and sterling reputations, our college degrees, our imposing homes and impressive cars, our twenty-year marriages, our flourishing children—surely all these things convinced us and you that we were doing just fine at the business of living. Didn't they?

Well, in fact, they did. For a long time we believed that although we couldn't stop doing odd things with food and exercise, our eating disorders were but a trivial problem that barely deserved mention. Even the word "problem" was overstating the case, really. They didn't interfere with the successful pursuit of our business and affairs, they didn't prevent us from achieving our purposes, they didn't affect our ability to handle and control our lives. All this we vehemently told ourselves, albeit with growing desperation as the years trickled by.

Consequences Shatter Denial

So it was that many of us needed to lose many of the external trappings of success before we could admit the truth to ourselves: that anorexia and bulimia had decimated our lives and annihilated everything of value in them. Others saw the truth at an earlier stage, before our husbands left and our employers fired us and the bank foreclosed on our mortgages. We were able to see the devastation of our souls, the erosion of our moral values, the tortured misery in our hearts, and to accurately attribute these things to the monster we harbored within: anorexia and bulimia.

STEP ONE AND WILLINGNESS

It should be obvious that many of us in effect took Step One before or as we sobered up, because it was necessary to admit the truth about our personal powerlessness and the unmanageability of our lives before we could develop the willingness to go to any lengths for our sobriety. However, for many of us these early admissions were unconscious and, once sober, we reneged on them, again unconsciously. Almost all of us who did this eventually relapsed into anorexic or bulimic behavior. In fact, we have come to believe that *relapse in itself is frequently evidence that the one who relapsed had not fully taken Step One.*

STEP ONE AND RELAPSE

To understand this better, let's listen to some folks returning to our Fellowship after a relapse. "I knew what I was doing," says Melanie. "It's true that I hadn't been taking good care of myself, I hadn't been getting to enough meetings, I hadn't been praying enough. But on the day that I first binged and purged, I knew what I was doing. I knew I could call my sponsor instead of bingeing, but I chose not to. I wanted to binge, and I didn't care about recovery anymore, and I just said, 'To heck with everyone at A.B.A. I just want to feel good for a while.' I knew what I was doing. I made a conscious choice to binge and purge. That was three months ago, and now I can't stop. I'm so ashamed of myself. I want to die again. I need help."

Then there is Daria. "I couldn't stand how fat I was getting. I knew what I was doing when I started skipping breakfast a month ago, but I had to do it. I chose to start running again too, because I had to get my weight down. Losing weight is the only thing that made me feel good about myself, and I made a choice to go back to it. Now I'm scared to eat anything again, and I'm afraid I'm going to die. I don't know what to do anymore."

The Great Lie: The Illusion of Choice

Behind these words looms the great lie of our disease: I'm doing this by choice. We saw earlier how believing this falsehood keeps us stuck in the vicious cycle of our anorexic and bulimic behavior, because we have to punish ourselves for making such a dreadful "choice." The Big Book of Alcoholics Anonymous uses the word "choice" extremely rarely, and *never* in connection with drinking except to say that alcoholics "have lost the power of choice in drink" (p. 24).[4] Nowhere does the book tell us they will be given back the power of choice as they recover. In fact, the Big Book's silence regarding the subject of choice is deafening,[5] given that the book is a comprehensive textbook guiding alcoholics to the empowerment to live fully and well, completely free of their insane obsession to destroy themselves with alcohol, for the duration of their days on earth.

We believe that anyone who uses the word "choice" in relation to their anorexic or bulimic behavior has not yet grasped Step One, because to admit powerlessness means to let go of the illusion that we have a choice over our insane obsessions about our bodies and our resultant actions with food and exercise. To admit powerlessness means to know that we lack all ability to change our own thinking in this area, whether by reason or by education or by deep desire or by sheer force of will. To admit powerlessness means to fully concede that, left to our own resources, we have no choice but to act on the basis of these obsessions.[6] *To admit powerlessness means to stop trying to change ourselves.*

It is clear that Melanie deeply believed that had she gone to enough meetings, said enough prayers, talked to her sponsor enough, taken good enough care of herself, then she would have been able to conjure up the ability to stay sober in her bulimia. She would have kept herself sober. This is the antithesis of powerlessness. And Daria hadn't the slightest clue that her perception of her body as fat *was* the mental obsession of her disease and that she was utterly powerless over this obsession. She actually believed she retained the power of choice to eat her breakfast in the face of this powerful obsession. How this disease blindfolds us to the truth!

Powerless, Not Helpless

Powerlessness is not synonymous with helplessness, however. We are anything but helpless. There is much we can choose to do to help ourselves, to engage actively in our own recovery. When we came to A.B.A., we learned about the tools of recovery and quickly realized we are personally responsible for using them. No one else can use them for us. However, when we equate "using the tools" with "keeping ourselves sober," we leave Step One and set ourselves up for relapse.

Giving Up The Fight Takes Courage: The Story of Marla

As we prepare to go to press, one of our newest members, whom we will call Marla, has inadvertently furnished us with a telling example of what we have just discussed. Recuperating from a suicide attempt that narrowly missed its mark, Marla is far too sick to tell her own story, and her story needs to be told.

A chronic bulimic in her mid-twenties, Marla bounced into our midst six months ago and swiftly captured our hearts. Charismatic, open and candid, and totally oblivious to the beauty of her own personality, she has become a glowing ember in our midst, often inciting stodgy oldtimers to deeper levels of honesty and commitment. Having tried for years every means of escape from her bulimia that willpower and intellect could provide, Marla eagerly pounced upon all that she heard from us about recovery and, with the command of a five-star general at war, initiated a campaign to achieve sobriety.

Marla's efforts to defeat her bulimia cast a whole new meaning on the word "willingness." She attended meetings and more meetings. She prayed despite her agnosticism. She journaled, pouring out her deepest self to an unknown Higher Power. She read the literature, made phone calls, and did service work until she nearly collapsed from exhaustion. She listened, she spoke, she told the truth; she wept and embraced others who were suffering. She asked for a sponsor and reached out to her. In short, Marla did everything humanly possible to get sober.

Her towering determination to win appeared to show results. A day free from bingeing and purging: a miracle! Three days here, eight days there. But always the inevitable relapse. Marla redoubled her efforts and continued to try again, applying ever greater ingenuity to her strategic planning. She clawed her way to a deeper level of surrender, letting go of exercise and conspiring with her husband to prepare and serve her meals; together they would outwit this cunning predator. She left her job to free up more time and energy to do her recovery work. She devised new tactics, locking herself out of the house, away from the food that beckoned to her without surcease. She surrendered her car keys, her credit cards, and her cash. She followed her husband around like a fearful puppy, knowing she could not trust herself to be alone.

Marla did everything except give up the battle.

Over time, ever so slowly, Marla's relapses began taking their toll. Her formidable resolve to win at any cost ebbed from her like a receding tide. And yet she continued to tell the truth, expressing her growing hopelessness in meetings. Until that last night when, sleepless, she plotted her ultimate act of defiance, her most daring manoeuver yet. She *would* vanquish the foe, even if it required the sacrifice of her life. In her final insanity, she regarded suicide as the only route to liberation, to victory over this enemy that she finally admitted was otherwise undefeatable. "At least," she told us later, "I could free my husband from the constant anxiety about me that is killing him. And at least I would die on my own terms, controlling the time and the means." At that moment of total lunacy, blindfolded by her barbaric captor, she truly could not see that to kill herself was to play straight into its devious hand; nor that her husband, caught in her line of fire, would be irreparably maimed by her suicide as he could never be by her life, however fraught with problems and pain.

And yet there was still nothing she could control, for her attempt was thwarted. The note she left would be read, not at her funeral, but by a police officer summoned to the scene.

Today, as Marla waits in despair for the next chapter of her life to begin, she continues to languish in the deepest pit of her life, her self-will extinguished. She has finally admitted how sick she is, how powerless she truly is. She is giving up not only the battle but the war. She cannot yet see any light at the end of her inky tunnel. She can as yet feel no joy at hearing our assurances that, paradoxically, she has just taken the first step to recovery. This she cannot comprehend; we might as well be speaking Swahili. She still has no desire to go on living, still feels disappointed that she did not die, still feels that she merits nothing more. She has ceased fighting her bulimia and now simply binges and purges every day. She knows she has no other choice. She knows she cannot stop.

Some may be shocked by these statements, throw up their hands and say, "Then what's the point? We might as well kill ourselves if we're really that helpless, if there's truly no hope!"

The point is that Marla is powerless. She is not, however, helpless. In reality, she is now having to take the bravest action she has ever taken in her life. She must daily make the choice that only she can make: to go on living, to refrain from repeating her suicide attempt. She must do that despite the fact that she has no faith, no belief in a Higher Power to bolster her decision. She must be willing to believe that her nightmare will end one day, simply because we tell her it is so. She must continue to trek through this dark time in her life although she cannot imagine how it will ever change. She must put into her body the medication prescribed by her physician, one dose at a time. She must trudge daily to her doctor's office to check in, phone her sponsor every morning and every evening, continue to attend daily meetings. She must remain ready to be admitted to a psychiatric ward, despite her consuming fear, as soon as a bed becomes available. And, once admitted, she must be willing to surrender her eating and her weight and her body shape to some obscure Higher Power whose help she does not believe she deserves. And she must do all these things blindly, without any real hope.

There is no more daunting challenge a human can face than to take the risk of staying alive without expectation of a future worth living. We commend Marla for her courage in taking on this task, as we commend her to the Power that we know is carrying her through it.

The Power of Choice is Lost Forever

Some of us believed that if we stayed sober long enough, then we would be powerless no longer, that we would be free to choose to eat like normal people. This was a grave error that led many of us to painful relapses. The truth is that once we are anorexic or bulimic, we have forever lost the power of choice in eating that normal people possess. Normal folk are completely free to skip breakfast if they oversleep; omit the butter from their toast if they so choose; fast for a day or a week as a spiritual practice; purposely gorge themselves on pie to win a prize at the county fair; use harsh laxatives as part of a naturopathic cleanse; or drive their bodies through punishing exercise routines in preparation for a marathon. We anorexics and bulimics can never safely take these actions, because of our physical allergy described in Chapter 3. The word "choice" implies a free decision between at least two alternative courses of action. In order to choose, we need to be free to select either option. Since we can never be free to restrict our food or to binge or purge or over-exercise, then we are not free to *refrain* from these actions. This is entirely analogous to the situation of sober alcoholics. To have true choice over alcohol, they must be free to drink or to not drink. Since in sobriety they can never drink, then they have no choice.[7]

The reader may regard this exploration of the subject of choice as tedious hair-splitting, as long-winded haggling over semantics. But for us in recovery it is a critically important First Step issue. Taking Step One to the depth required for continuous sobriety has been a slow process for most of us. After sobering up, we needed the guidance of a sponsor to help us get this Step embedded in our guts, in our bone marrow, in our toenails. Step One requires great humility, and it is a Step each of us needs to take every day of our lives to remain sober. The moment we slide into the delusion that we have the power to *choose* to stay sober today, we are on dangerous ground, and unless a Power greater than ourselves intervenes to awaken us to the truth, we will relapse sooner or later. This is true whether we have one day or three decades of sobriety behind us. We are 100 percent powerless over our fatal obsession, and we remain so for 100 percent of the days of our lives.

And yet there is hope for us. Admitting powerlessness is not a death sentence. Rather, as we will discover in the next two Steps, it is paradoxically the doorway to freedom. And as we progress even further along the Twelve-Step pathway, we will find the dazzling power of true choice to which we are restored in sobriety. More about that in Step Ten.

STEP TWO:

Came to believe that a Power greater than ourselves could restore us to sanity.

STUMBLING BLOCKS

Higher Power: Religion vs. Spirituality

This is the first Step that introduces us to the concept of a Higher Power. In the context of the Twelve-Step Program, the word "Higher" refers to "greater than," in the sense of *more than.* The Higher Power is simply a source of strength or might that is more than we are alone, as individuals. Nevertheless, when we reached Step Two many of us came to a screeching halt. We equated the concept of a Higher Power with that of God, and we were burdened with all sorts of preconceived notions blocking our embrace of the Step. We assumed we were now being asked to "get religion," and many of us balked at that notion. Others had regarded ourselves as pretty religious people all along, and what good had it done us? God hadn't helped us quit doing anorexia or bulimia for even a single day, yet now the Program was asking us to rely on the idea of God. How could we do that? We didn't really trust God anymore, and that was that.

Still others among us continued to devoutly believe in God, had never stopped praying, attended church faithfully, were not angry at God, and yet still were defeated by anorexia or bulimia. We were truly baffled by Step Two, because how could we *come* to believe in God when we already did so? Or, worse still, we decided that we could skip over this Step because we had already done it.

To begin taking this Step, many of us needed to divorce it from religion and to see it instead as dealing with spirituality, the realm of the spirit. The word "spirit" signifies "a life-giving force; the animating principle…."* This was a lot easier for many of us to swallow, since it seemed obvious that every living thing possesses a life force or animating principle. We also saw that our life force was in jeopardy as a result of our anorexic and bulimic behavior; that the animating principle given us by the Creator was being strangled by the ludicrous obsessions that controlled our minds; that our spirits were indeed in need of healing. By thus focusing on spirituality, we were able to let go of the prejudices about religion that stood in our way.

Are We All Prejudiced?

Those of us who are deeply religious encountered another problem. Step Two requires an open mind, a freedom from prejudice. We could see that people who were antagonistic to religion were terribly prejudiced, but we truly could not see that we were also. Our dictionary defines "prejudice" as "…an opinion made without adequate basis."* We religious folk needed to admit that our faith in God to this point had failed to keep us from nearly destroying ourselves with anorexia and bulimia, and that perhaps this failure had less to do with God than with our opinions about God.[8] Perhaps we did not know everything there was to know about God. Perhaps we needed to let go of our existing notions and begin to truly hear what others who were sober had to say about a Higher Power.

Is God Someone Like Us?

As we opened our minds to Step Two many of us, whether religious or not, came to see that our greatest prejudice about the God-concept had to do with anthropomorphizing God. In other words, we had imagined God to be someone like us, only bigger.[9] And that, not surprisingly, had reduced us to a state of quivering trepidation. For we knew what we were like. If God was merely a larger version of ourselves, then God was more callous and judgmental, more arrogant and self-righteous, more demanding and perfectionistic, more jealous and devious, more rigid and unforgiving than we. What a revolting proposition! Small wonder that we approached Step Two with bewilderment, grave misgivings, or

*By permission. From ***Merriam-Webster's Desk Dictionary*** ©1995 by Merriam-Webster, Incorporated, at www.Merriam-Webster.com.

outright disgust. How predictable that many of us had long ago decided to reject this God altogether, hoping we could forever evade the whole issue of spirituality. And how foreseeable too that the religious among us, who may have clung to this God-concept in some stagnant, primeval vault of our unconscious minds, had languished in anorexia or bulimia for decades despite our beliefs.

Clearly, something massive and fundamental needed to change as we grappled with Step Two.

CAME TO BELIEVE

Seeing is Believing

We next looked at the words "to believe" in Step Two. Going to our dictionary again, we found "…to have a firm conviction about something; to accept as true;…to suppose."* The only firm conviction held by many of us was that we were fat and flabby and needed to lose weight. We certainly had no convictions about trusting some obscure, invisible Higher Power to help us. Nor could we suppose that we would merit the attention of such a Power, even if it existed. And yet we *could* accept as true what we saw and heard from other anorexics and bulimics who had gone before us in recovery. They talked about finding a Power who had changed the way they thought about their bodies and about food, and we knew they spoke the truth because we saw the incontrovertible evidence in front of our eyes. We watched in meetings as they ate their lunch without anxiety. We saw their bodies at the shape and size of regular folks, and we knew from their sparkling eyes that they delighted in their physical beings. We heard their message of hope, and we wanted what they had.

Willingness is Enough

That was all we needed to begin the process of Step Two: nothing more than a *willingness* to suppose that whatever had helped our recovered sisters could possibly help us too.[10] We didn't have to take this Step with perfection. All we needed was faint hope and a willingness to take further action on the basis of it.

RESTORE US TO SANITY

As for the final part of the Step, very few of us had any problem

*By permission. From ***Merriam-Webster's Desk Dictionary*** ©1995 by Merriam-Webster, Incorporated, at www.Merriam-Webster.com.

with the idea of needing restoration to sanity. As we saw in Chapter 5, "sanity" refers to "soundness of mind,"* and we knew at the very least that we had been insane when it came to our thinking about food and about our bodies. Some of us could remember a time in our lives when we had thought rationally about food; others could not and were therefore puzzled by the word "restore." But almost none of us knew how seriously deranged we had been in other areas of our thinking. We didn't know that the bottom of our iceberg contained self-hatred and self-centeredness, dishonesty, and the illusion of control. We didn't really know what we were getting into when we first took Step Two.

None of that mattered. All that mattered was that we became willing to believe that something greater than ourselves might be able to deliver us from our insanity, however tenuous our belief and however limited our concept of that insanity might be.

STEP THREE:

Made a decision to turn our will and our lives over to the care of God, as we understood God.

DECISION? OH NO!

Step Three marked another turning point for us. Having made the full admission of our personal powerlessness over anorexia and bulimia, and having come to some kind of fledgling notion of a Higher Power that possesses the power we lack, we now needed to move forward and make a decision. This was difficult for many of us because, by the time we were beaten and crawled into recovery circles, our disease had reduced us to a quivering mass of human cells, incapable of making the simplest decision. Physical sobriety helped a little, but even a few months of that rarely enabled us to decide easily between the blue shirt and the red one when we got dressed in the morning.

To make a decision we need to "decide," meaning "…to make a choice or judgment."* We grasped in Step One that as anorexics and bulimics we have lost the power of choice over our mental obsession with food and our bodies and over the destructive actions that inevitably result from our obsessions. Now in Step Three we discover that we do in fact have a choice: to let the Higher Power into our lives

*By permission. From ***Merriam-Webster's Desk Dictionary*** ©1995 by Merriam-Webster, Incorporated, at www.Merriam-Webster.com.

or not; to take the next reasonable action following upon our fledgling belief that this Power can help us, or not. At Step Three we are given the privilege and responsibility of making this choice. To refuse to make the choice means to choose death, because unless we move forward with the remainder of the Twelve Steps we cannot be freed from our deadly obsessions.

"TURN IT OVER" MEANS SURRENDER

The words "turn over" refer to shifting the burden of responsibility from one party to another. They imply an act of surrender.

Surrender Our Will…

What exactly does it mean to decide to turn our *will* and our *lives* over to the care of a Higher Power? "Will" represents "…the mental powers manifested as wishing, choosing, desiring, or intending; a disposition to act according to principles or ends; power of controlling one's own actions…."* So with this word too, Step Three reminds us that we do have choice, we do have power, we do have control of something. We, and only we, can and must choose *for ourselves* whether to let a God of our own understanding into our minds, into our thinking, or not. We must decide whether to let this God change our mental powers, alter our wishes and choices and desires and intentions, transform our disposition to act and the principles we will act upon, or not. The choice is absolutely ours. No one else can make it for us.

…and Our Lives

The word "life" signifies "…the physical and mental experiences of an individual;…the period from birth to death;…a way of living…."* Thus the second aspect of what we decide here is whether to surrender and let a Higher Power alter our actions as human beings, change our future physical and mental experiences, redirect what the remainder of our days on earth will look like, transform our way of living, or not. A momentous decision indeed.

Stated simply, "will" means "thinking" and "life" means "actions." [11]

At this point in Step Three, we realize that we have already been taking the Step, one meal at a time, since the day we got sober. What

*By permission. From ***Merriam-Webster's Desk Dictionary*** ©1995 by Merriam-Webster, Incorporated, at www.Merriam-Webster.com.

else is sobriety but surrender of our actions around food after coming to realize we can no longer rely on our own thinking in the domain of eating? Our surrender up until now, however, has been solely in the arena of food, weight, and exercise. In order to take Step Three to the depth required to move forward with the remaining nine Steps, we must face squarely the question of surrendering additional areas of our thinking and behavior to a Higher Power.[12] Are we prepared to make this decision or not? And if so, what choice will we make?

SURRENDER TO WHAT?

Care

And to what are we to surrender our thinking and our actions? Not to the Higher Power itself, but rather to the *care* of the Higher Power. "Care" denotes "…watchful attention;…solicitude"* or guardianship. The term implies a sense of concern or interest on the part of the one who is rendering care. So our decision in this Step is about allowing a Higher Power, one who is deeply concerned about us, to oversee and guard our thoughts and actions, to prevent us from harming ourselves and others. That seemed like a good idea to many of us, who had done a pretty poor job of guarding ourselves.

Individual Choice of a Higher Power

Perhaps the most graceful aspect of this Step is the final phrase, *"as we understood God."* With these words Step Three solidifies the personal autonomy to which we were introduced in Step Two and further liberates us to choose our own conception of a Higher Power.[13] It matters not at all what that Power is. All that matters is whether it fits for us as individuals and whether we are willing to make the critical decision to turn our thinking and our actions over to the watchful attention and guardianship of this Power.

Most of us took Step Three, not with dignity and lofty self-sacrifice, but rather with the somewhat ignoble attitude of, "What have I got to lose? I've messed up my life badly through anorexia and bulimia. Why not let somebody else have a go at it? It can't get any worse!" Our attitude doesn't matter in the least to the outcome of taking the Step. All that is important is to make the decision and act upon it by moving on to the following Steps.

*By permission. From ***Merriam-Webster's Desk Dictionary*** ©1995 by Merriam-Webster, Incorporated, at www.Merriam-Webster.com.

Melting the Iceberg — Steps Four through Seven

9

DEFINE THE PROBLEM, SOLUTION, AND PATH TO IT

IF PHYSICAL sobriety pours the foundation for our healing process as anorexics and bulimics, then the first three Steps build the framework within which our healing takes place. Step One serves to define our basic problem: our personal powerlessness over the physical allergy and mental obsession of anorexia and bulimia. It further serves to engender humility by convincing us of the unmanageability of our lives as long as we rely on our own nonexistent power to combat our disease. Step Two presents us with the solution to our basic problem: find some power—and obviously it must be one that is greater than our own! Step Three opens the door on the path we must take to arrive at this solution: a surrender of our thinking and actions to the care of this greater Power. Taken together, Steps Two and Three reassure and remind us of the crucial power we already possess as human beings: the power to believe and the power to make a decision. Moreover, Step Three brings us into an embryonic stage of conscious connection with the greater Power that can solve our problem for us. *It is only by developing a relationship with a Higher Power that we can be healed from the insanity of anorexia and bulimia.* The last nine Steps are about that relationship.

STEP FOUR:

Made a searching and fearless moral inventory of ourselves.

FROM DECISION TO ACTION: SELF-EXAMINATION

Following our decision to let God direct our thinking and our actions, we now must act upon the decision. Otherwise it is useless.

Our first action is to embark upon an intensive examination of ourselves.[1] Step Four is about exploring the bottom of the iceberg of our disease, about uncovering the invisible twists in our thinking that have been the whole root of our problem as anorexics and bulimics. It is not a catalogue of the wrongs we have done in our sickness, but rather a teasing out of the insane threads of perfectionism, self-centeredness, dishonesty, fear, judgmentalism, negativism, dualistic thinking, illusion of control—all of which initially sprang from, and then reinforced, our radical self-hatred. We saw in Chapter 5 how this insanity engendered a need to escape from ourselves through the mood-altering effect of starvation or exercise or bingeing and purging.

Step Four is explored in marvelous detail in the textbooks of Alcoholics Anonymous, and we will repeat none of that information here. What we do need to look at are some blocks that may prevent us from making this thorough self-appraisal. While we do not wish to tell anyone how or when to work this Step, we can offer our experience of its pitfalls in the hope that this will be helpful to the reader.

Timing

Some of us delayed for years before taking Step Four, while others plunged in willy-nilly after one week of sober eating. For many of these folks the cost was relapse. The procrastinators failed, despite staying sober, to find any relief from their deadly obsessions and eventually acted upon them, whether they had taken the first three Steps or not. The overly eager ones had not yet achieved any measure of detachment from their disease; had not grasped the full meaning of powerlessness; had no grounding in a Higher Power, a grounding that results from sustained sobriety and thoroughly working Steps Two and Three. Without this ability to see how sick they were, they had no compassion for themselves and thus used Step Four as yet another instrument of self-flagellation. The result was even more self-hatred and a greater-than-ever need for its diabolical solution: relapse into anorexic or bulimic behavior.

Learning From Relapse

All of us who relapsed, of course, gained from our experience the opportunity to learn something more about ourselves and about recovery from our disease. Recovery is a process, and many of us seemed to need to do it the hard way. What we most often learned was that taking Step Four requires both the humility that flows from truly grasping Step One and the deep rootedness in our Higher Power that can only be acquired by spending sufficient time in Steps Two and Three. No one can tell us when we are ready to take Step Four, but a sponsor who knows us well can often guide us in this matter.

How Can We Be Fearless?

Before doing Step Four, it is useful to look closely at its wording. To fearlessly search is to investigate, to seek and examine while yet remaining free from "fear," or "…anxious concern…."* The paradox here is that while we are investigating our resentments, our sexuality, and even our fears, we need to do so without fear. A Higher Power is the only one who can free us from anxious concern while we examine our anxious concerns! This is another reason why we need to be connected with that Power before undertaking this Step.

In the context of Step Four, to take "inventory" means to make a detailed survey of the specific qualities we find within our psyches at the present time, and to write down what we discover.

"Moral" Can Be a Problem

The word "moral," pertaining "…to principles of right and wrong…,"* was problematic for many of us because it fed into two of our most troublesome character defects: dualistic thinking and judgmentalism. Some of us needed to let go entirely of the idea of right versus wrong, of good versus bad, and instead to regard our psychic characteristics as "sick" or "healthy." However, even these labels imply judgment. It is far better if we can ask our Higher Power for the grace to survey our psychic characteristics without any prejudgment whatsoever, because then we can usually be more thorough.

Calm Noticing

We aim simply to survey ourselves, to notice our twisted thinking processes in a calm and neutral manner, without drama or anxious concern, and to write down what we notice. If we have listened to our sponsor's account of herself and to others who speak at meetings, we are better able to do this, because we have acquired the knowledge that we are no better or worse than anyone else, that we are all sick in our

*By permission. From ***Merriam-Webster's Desk Dictionary*** ©1995 by Merriam-Webster, Incorporated, at www.Merriam-Webster.com.

thinking and all equally in need of healing.

Step Four is about enlightenment, about awareness. It prepares us to be liberated from the destructive patterns in our thinking that have been the source of all our problems as anorexics and bulimics.

STEP FIVE:

Admitted to God, to ourselves, and to another human being the exact nature of our wrongs.

AWARENESS: GROUNDWORK FOR CHANGE

This Step continues the process of awareness begun in Step Four, in which we uncovered a good deal of truth about ourselves. In writing down this truth, we admitted it to ourselves and to our Higher Power. Step Five takes us one stage further as we share all we have learned with another human being. As long as our inventory remains on paper, we continue to be heavily burdened by its content, mainly because we are still telling ourselves self-abusive lies about it. When we read aloud what we have written and experience our confidant's response to it, many of these lies evaporate on the spot, and we walk away unburdened.

"Exact Nature of Our Wrongs"

Notice what this Step asks us to admit: not a litany of our misdeeds from the past, but rather "the exact nature of our wrongs." To paraphrase this, we disclose to another human being the most accurate assessment we can make at this point in our recovery of the qualities within us that led to our problematic actions as anorexics and bulimics. What specifically was directing our minds when we told all those lies to our parents and spouses about what we had eaten? When we stole time from our employers to binge and purge? When we looked into a mirror at our waif-like reflections and incorrectly perceived rolls of fat invisible to others? When we consumed food so ill-suited to meet the true needs of our bodies? When we misgauged so disastrously what we should eat and what we should weigh? When we acted in ways so injurious that we almost died and our loved ones near perished from grief?

Only by distilling the essence from our checkered history, from our disagreeable and often perilous escapades as anorexics and bulimics, can we become fully aware of the fatal flaws in our thinking that led us to act so dreadfully toward ourselves and others. As we disclose those basic flaws to another human being, further light is shed on them, and we leave Step Five closer still to glorious liberation.

STEP SIX:

Were entirely ready to have God remove all these defects of character.

AWARENESS DOESN'T CHANGE US

This Step and the one following are the central ones in the Twelve-Step Program, for they deal directly with the process of change. Steps Four and Five have prepared us to change by making us aware of what needs to be altered in our thinking to liberate us from our disease. But awareness by itself, we soon ruefully discover, is not enough. Many of us left Step Five feeling immeasurably lighter, whistling happily, and noticing for the first time how blue the sky is and how red the roses. Then we got home, walked in the back door, and without missing a beat lied to our parents about where we had been. Or we concluded that our spouse was deficient in love because he failed to cast aside the evening paper and ask how our Fifth Step went. Or we found our children in the throes of an argument and leapt in to control them by ending it, just as we always had in the past.

No, awareness alone avails us nothing. We can be fully conscious of our self-hatred, dishonesty, self-centeredness, crippling fears, and illusion of control, and yet remain impotent to change these defective mental characteristics.

IMPATIENCE DOESN'T CHANGE US

Step Six was a period of intensely heightened awareness of our shortcomings. Everywhere we went, day in and day out, we found ourselves acting out of our faulty thinking like some conditioned laboratory rat. In glorious technicolor our perfectionism and judgmentalism and arrogance were on display. With dismay we watched ourselves think and behave in the same old ways, just as we might watch an actor on a stage—and we didn't know who was directing the play. Only now we were eating like normal people, so what excuse did we have? None at all, we thought.

Sometimes our loved ones thought so too, their patience wearing thin. "Those meetings sure don't seem to be doing much for you. When are you going to stop being so rigid and stubborn about everything?" Or pouting when we don't get our own way. Or complaining when we do. Or arrogantly claiming to know what's best for everyone. Or disclaiming all knowledge when things go wrong. Or continuing to make unilateral decisions, never considering their impact on others. Or strutting about like peacocks, demanding attention. Or wafting in and out like silent ghosts, afraid to look anyone in the eye.

Can't I Do Something?

Step Six contains no action whatsoever, and many of us felt frustrated about that. We wailed to our sponsor, "What can I *do*? I can't stand myself any longer, and I just can't seem to change! Please tell me what to *do*!" Our sponsor merely smiled knowingly, gave us a friendly pat, and told us we were right where we needed to be, to stay with it.

Stay with what? It was then that we looked more closely at the precise wording of the Step. The first word, "were," tells us that we are dealing here with being, not with doing. Step Six occurs on a deep interior plane where we meet our Higher Power. All we can do here is be ourselves, as unsatisfactory as we judge that to be. "Entirely ready" clearly indicates a preparation Step, and somehow our chagrin about our character defects is an important part of its groundwork.

STAGES OF CHANGE

Denial

However, most of us fought the process. We were starting to suspect the awful truth that we are powerless over far more than our insane eating practices. It dawned upon us that we are utterly powerless over our own self-hatred, dishonesty, self-centeredness, and fear; over our entire array of character flaws. This truth was so abhorrent that most of us could not at first face it. Usually we attempted to deny it. We summoned our willpower and tried harder, went to more meetings, doubled up on our prayers, did more service work. We talked to all who would listen about "working on" our pet character defect of the week. We read books on humility, hoping to get the hang of it. We analyzed our fears and tried to talk ourselves out of them. We attempted to dispel our self-hatred by reading books about self-esteem and writing lists of our positive attributes. Surely *that* would convince us that we are lovable!

Bargaining

When denial no longer worked for us, we often tried bargaining with our Higher Power. We begged and pleaded, "Please, God, don't let it be true that I'm powerless to change. I'll do *anything* to change myself. I'll give more money to the Salvation Army. I'll go to church on Tuesdays. I'll meditate for two hours instead of one. Please!" But we walked away from our prayers just as self-centered and fearful as ever. We began to suspect that nobody was listening.

Anger

Then many of us became angry. Why couldn't we change ourselves? What was *wrong* with us? And why had we acquired this stinking disease anyway? What had we ever done to deserve it? It wasn't fair to be doomed to live forever as helpless puppets of our own insane egos, dominated mercilessly by self-centeredness and fear and delusion. What kind of Creator would make us this way? Well, to heck with a God like that. We were better off on our own. In fact, we should never have started this recovery business in the first place. At least when we were starving or bingeing and purging, we were happily oblivious to our many deficiencies.

Depression

Mired in such self-pity, some of us relapsed at this point. But more often we stayed sober and continued doing the footwork of recovery, and most of us discovered that our anger gradually dissipated, to be replaced by a spiritual malaise more painful than anything we had yet experienced in sobriety. We felt empty, bereft of hope as we faced the naked truth. We couldn't avoid it any longer, and none of our old coping mechanisms worked in the least to blunt the searing edge of this pain. We admitted that we were totally incapable of changing ourselves and that we would always remain so, no matter how long or hard we tried. Our self-esteem, which had begun to mend as we stayed sober in anorexia and bulimia, now shriveled again. Our joy withered and died, our energy drained away, our enthusiasm for living was extinguished. We slept poorly, had no taste for food, dragged our exhausted bodies through futile days, and wondered where God had gone.

Some of us remained depressed for a long time. Rarely were we relieved by even a glimmer of insight that all this was part of the process of Step Six. Sometimes we noticed that our current depression was oddly reminiscent of the painful bottom we reached prior to sobering up. Our despair was just as deep as the hopelessness we experienced in Step One, only now our admission of powerlessness was not about eating, but rather about the condition of our psyches.

Acceptance...

Finally our will to resist took its last gasp, the empty shell of our inner being cracked open, and grace flowed in, bringing with it a profound acceptance of ourselves *as we are*. As light finally dawned we accepted our flaws—our self-centeredness, our dishonesty, our illusion of control, our fears, our perfectionism and arrogance and judgmentalism. We deeply accepted our powerlessness to change any of these qualities. We surrendered to reality as it is, ceased to wish it were different, and finished grieving over it. Put in slightly different terms, we forgave ourselves for our character defects. Self-hatred, our most pervasive character defect, evaporated in that moment of self-forgiveness. We had finally let God remove it.[2]

...is Self-Forgiveness

Many of us now became deeply aware that this capacity for self-forgiveness was flowing from a Higher Power. We knew that on our own we didn't have what it takes to accept ourselves unconditionally, for our self-hatred had been too deep and powerful and entrenched in our being. We glimpsed that our Higher Power was infinitely more loving than we had ever suspected. We saw at last that this Power had always accepted us without conditions, exactly as we are, without expectation that we would change, and would continue into eternity to love us in this way. This discovery took our breath away. Somehow it changed everything.

DECISION TO SURRENDER

At peace with ourselves at last, we now looked back at Step Six and were astonished by the sixth and seventh words in it: "God remove." The hope we had first experienced in Step Two was rekindled. Yes, we are powerless, but God is not! We can't change ourselves, nor will we ever be able to change ourselves, but a Higher Power can. Now the word "ready" made sense. Beyond our conscious awareness, in the dark and silent labyrinth of our being, the process of Step Six had been preparing us to make a decision similar to the one we faced in Step Three. All that agonizing depression had done its work: We were ready to surrender and fall on our knees before our Higher Power. We were ready to let God take over.

STEP SEVEN:

Humbly asked God to remove our shortcomings.

HUMILITY: THE GIFT AND THE KEY

Having fully let go of the delusion that we have the power to change our own defects of character and having forgiven ourselves for being as we are, we now approached Step Seven. Its opening word is critically important and, if we have completed Step Six to the necessary depth, we know what it means. "Humble" is defined as "not proud or haughty; not pretentious…."* It entails deeply accepting the reality of who and what we are, without judgment and without comparing ourselves to others. It involves being in right relationship with ourselves and our Higher Power. It means knowing that we lack all power to change ourselves, and that our Higher Power does not. The gift of Step Six has been humility.

THE FRUITS OF HUMILITY: CONNECTION WITH A HIGHER POWER

With humility we know who we are in relation to who God is. We know that we are the creature and the Higher Power is like the pure air we breathe. It surrounds us, envelops us, permeates us, becomes and remains part of us, sustains our very being from the moment we are born until the day we exhale our final breath. We see that we have been as oblivious to this Power's presence as an infant is to air. We have taken it for granted, failed to notice it, until the time when the pollution of our disease contaminated it. As the toxin levels mounted, every level of our being was poisoned by the noxious fumes. We became physically ill, we choked and gasped with mounting desperation, we were very nearly asphyxiated.

Higher Power Dwells Within

Then we got sober and began our recovery journey. As we took the first six Steps the poison gas progressively receded, and the pure life-giving air of our Higher Power flooded our being once more. In Step

*By permission. From ***Merriam-Webster's Desk Dictionary*** ©1995 by Merriam-Webster, Incorporated, at www.Merriam-Webster.com.

Seven we become fully aware of this precious gift. We first inhaled it in the welcoming rooms where our Fellowship meets, we breathed it in as we worked with our sponsor, and in the final acceptance stage of Step Six we felt it penetrate into our laden hearts to lift the burden of our depression. We know now that we are not the Higher Power and yet this vital Power dwells within us, no further away than our breath.[3] We realize at last how utterly dependent we are upon this Power and how much we can trust it. We also know the depth of misery we have experienced as we tried to do what we are powerless to do, and we are ready to ask God to take over.

Higher Power Has Power!

In Step Seven we call on our Higher Power to do what we cannot. We request that this Power—who knows us more intimately than we know ourselves—enter into our minds and change the circuitry, rewire us so we think differently. We invite this God to make all decisions regarding what needs to be deleted, what needs to be reprogrammed, and what needs to be created anew. With our newfound humility of knowing the limitations of our power and the vastness of God's, we are free of any delusion that we could wisely make such decisions for ourselves. We now truly accept that only a Higher Power knows what is best for us, and we are willing to believe that this Power is benevolent and has our best interests at heart.

FURTHER FORGIVENESS

Dissolution of Guilt

As we take Step Seven, the process of self-forgiveness begun in Step Six penetrates deeper into our being. The tenacious residue of guilt that shrouded us is swept away. Guilt had been our constant companion when we were acting out in anorexia and bulimia, and with sobriety it did not disappear. Sometimes it intensified as we took the Fourth Step, and it usually reached the boiling point when we plunged into the abyss of our depression in Step Six. We simply could not forgive ourselves for being the creatures that we are, with our dishonesty and self-centeredness and other twisted characteristics. As we dissolved in this bubbling cauldron of guilt, we quit struggling and calmly accepted ourselves, and the process of self-forgiveness began. Now in Step Seven this process is complete.

Surrender to Love

In Step Seven we surrender our hearts fully to our Higher Power. We give that Power everything that we are, to do with as it will. As soon as we do that, we experience even more deeply the love this Power has for us. We feel the intensity of this love burning into us, searing away the last possibility of self-blame. If God can love us as we are, shortcomings and all, who are we to withhold love from ourselves?[4] Even the idea of holding a grudge is ridiculous in the face of such love. We know that we have been forgiven, long before we did anything that needed to be forgiven, and that we cannot alter the absolute love that lies behind this forgiveness. We are caught up by this vision of love, our minds reel from it, we cannot comprehend it, and we cower before it. We feel diminutive, yet because this phenomenal love is directed toward us, we know we are magnificent beyond description. Our Higher Power makes us so. We become capable of loving ourselves, because this Power has loved us first.

CHANGED BY LOVE

Mysterious Transformation

With self-acceptance, self-forgiveness, and self-love solidly at work within us, the mysterious power of Step Seven comes to fruition. We go forth as transformed creatures. Self-acceptance overflows on those we meet, for it is no longer possible to refuse to accept them as they are. It is impossible to hold a grudge against others when self-forgiveness is blazing in our hearts.[5] We are more attentive and loving with others, able to put ourselves in their shoes and empathize with them, when we are motivated by deep self-love. We laugh at our old belief that we are the center of the universe, because we know now that we are nothing without a Higher Power. Nor can we imagine that we are invisible, because we have also been shown that the Creator's love makes us of infinite value. We cannot deceive ourselves and others once awakened to the truth of love. We can no longer think negatively with all that is positive suffusing us. We cannot judge another when we no longer judge ourselves. We need not fear anything when we know that a Power of infinite love dwells within us. We can no longer strive for perfection because we know, with our entire capacity to know anything at all, that we are already perfect in God's eyes.

Love: Authentic Power

So the central paradox of Steps Six and Seven is that *when we arrive at the point of accepting ourselves as we are, not in spite of our defects but* with *them, then and only then do we become capable of change.* When we quit trying to change ourselves and focus instead on our Higher Power, coming to a deep experience of that Power's unconditional love for us, then this love can change us. Once we know we are acceptable to the Creator, self-centered as we are, then we no longer need to be self-centered. When we fully grasp that our Higher Power loves us even with our dishonesty, then we no longer need to lie. Once we comprehend the breadth and depth of God's loving presence in our lives, then it is impossible to fear anything and we no longer need to pretend we are in control. We have been privileged to have the Great Mystery whisper its secret in our ears: that the only authentic Power in the universe is the power of love.[6]

Captured By Love

In the course of this transformation we begin to be motivated by a powerful desire for closer connection with the Source of this infinite love, and we long to follow only the path that is ordained for us by such a compassionate Higher Power. We yearn to be of service to this Power and to let it more fully change us, so that we can find the union we crave. We have been captured by Love itself.

Defects Become Assets

To our further amazement, we often discover as we move through Step Seven that our Higher Power works *with* the qualities that are deeply ingrained in our personality.[7] Rarely does the Creator radically excise these characteristics from us, else why would we have been created that way to begin with? A folksy proverb states that "God don't make junk!" Rather, as a potter works with her existing clay, our Higher Power prefers to soften and gentle the innate characteristics that have been twisted by our disease into defects, to make them useful once again. For example, we might have been born persistent individuals, people who endured and kept going until an undertaking was complete. Clearly, this was an admirable part of our makeup. Then, as we acquired our disease, this intrinsic quality was perverted into stubbornness; into uncompromising rigidity of thought and action; into obstinate unwillingness to yield under any circumstances, often to our own detriment and that of others. Our natural persistence had now become an obvious character defect. When we reach Step Seven our Higher Power may return this quality to its former state, and stubbornness becomes steadfast perseverance once again.

The paradox here is that what was a dangerous character defect has become a first-rate character asset! At last the word "restored" in Step Two makes perfect sense. All we need for this remarkable transformation to occur is a Higher Power unleashed within us. All we need is to surrender to the hands of the potter, to a loving God, and miracles result.

CHANGE TAKES TIME!

Patience

To be thoroughly changed by the Twelve-Step Program we must spend adequate time in Steps Six and Seven. Because these Steps seem obscure, because they require being rather than doing, because their process includes a phase of painful depression, and because they are given such cursory treatment in the Big Book, some of us glossed over them. We pushed forward to Step Eight before we had experienced deep self-forgiveness, connection with the Author of love, and transformation of our attitude toward ourselves and others. The result was usually a descent into further mental chaos, further self-abuse, further harmful actions, and sometimes even the highest cost of all: relapse into anorexic or bulimic behavior.

Never Complete

Having said that, we also need to realize that the process of Steps Six and Seven is never perfectly complete. We have all found ourselves returning to them again and again, at every stage of our sobriety, even after we have taken the remaining five Steps. For we are creatures of pitifully short memory, and we all forget periodically that God is everything and that of ourselves we are nothing. So we fall out of balance, lose all humility for a time, try to direct our lives again. Then our character defects rush to the fore. Operating out of our defective thinking once again, we create mayhem in our lives. Sooner or later we wake up and notice what we've done, talk to our sponsor about it, and move on with the process of change.

CHANGE: JUST FOR TODAY

Thorns in the Flesh

In Step Seven we also need to be willing to trust that only a Higher Power knows what defects of character need to be refashioned and which ones we need to retain, relatively intact, *for today*. Every day is different, which is the reason most of us pray the Seventh Step Prayer every morning. For example, our Higher Power may know that we need to remain somewhat arrogant today in order to become aware of this defect and turn to God. Without this residual arrogance, we might think we were doing just fine and didn't need a Higher Power anymore. The continuing presence of at least some degree of arrogant thinking thereby ensures, for today, our total dependence upon our Higher Power. Since remaining dependent upon this Power is the only way to remain sober, our arrogance on this particular day has served a useful purpose. God wants us to stay sober and will at times use unexpected means to help us do so!

What Makes Us Useful?

Or on another day, some residual dishonesty might be useful to our Higher Power. If at first glance this statement appears ludicrous, perhaps a concrete example will clarify it. Imagine that Annie, a long-time A.B.A. member, lies to Betty when she is chatting with her before a meeting. Annie notices her lie and calmly approaches Betty after the meeting to apologize and tell her the truth. The benefit to Annie is the opportunity to learn something about her ongoing capacity for dishonesty and to feel gratitude that she has a Higher Power who loves her enough to wake her up to it. Perhaps Betty, a relative newcomer, had been secretly judging herself as not being good enough to fit in with the group anymore. After hearing Annie's apology she leaves the meeting feeling quite different, saying to herself, "Well, maybe I'm not so bad after all. If even Annie after all those years of recovery still sometimes lies and can then apologize so easily, then maybe there's hope for me! I think I'll continue coming after all. Maybe I'll even ask Annie to sponsor me." Clearly, both Annie and Betty have received great gifts from this incident. Annie's lie was very useful to the Creator, who looks for every opportunity to catalyze our spiritual growth.

Noticing Without Judgment

Observe in this anecdote how Annie is able to respond to her own dishonesty. She has arrived at a deep level of self-acceptance, the fruit of long sobriety. So she doesn't despair, flagellate herself, condemn herself, go out and binge and purge, or run away forever from the group. She quietly notices her mistake, thanks her Higher Power for the gift of awareness, then cleans up her mess. She is able to see what she would once have labeled a "bad" quality in herself as truly an opportunity for her Higher Power to work in her and in others. She leaves the meeting feeling good about herself, lighter and closer to God.

Useful to the Creator: Imperfection

Vitally important to learn here is the fact that our character defects are transformed for one primary purpose: so that we can be useful to the Creator. Our Higher Power's work in us is not in the service of our comfort. Often we are most useful to God when we are uncomfortable. A thorny character defect digging into our flesh keeps us seeking, restlessly moving forward along the path of spiritual growth. It keeps us from becoming complacent. It keeps us praying, going to meetings, working with a sponsor, doing the Steps, reaching out in service to others. In short, it keeps us doing the work of staying sober. It is hard to imagine anything more useful than that. Were we to become elevated to sainthood, pristinely perfect, we would have no need to do these things. We and no one around us would receive the enormous gifts that flow from our ongoing brokenness. Thank goodness we will never be anything but imperfect![8]

We will discuss this issue again in Step Ten, but it is important here at Step Seven to grasp that we will never be totally free of our character defects. We may sometimes perceive ourselves as making no progress at all, but this is an illusion. Slowly, slowly, as we stay sober and continue to walk the Steps one day at a time, this Power of love molds us into what we were created to be: creatures capable of volitional love of astonishing proportions. And that is all we need in order to live happy and purposeful lives free of anorexia and bulimia.

The Next Level of Change— Steps Eight, Nine, and Ten

10

INDIVIDUAL CHANGE: STEPS FOUR THROUGH SEVEN

THE LAST chapter dealt with the four Steps most directly concerned with the process of individual change. We saw how the Higher Power, to whom we decided to surrender our minds and our actions in Step Three, then directed us to explore the twists and turns of our insane thinking processes in Step Four and to share what we had learned with another human being in Step Five. Following that vigorous activity, we were then drawn into the mysterious cocoon of Step Six: a time of waiting in the dark, of being with ourselves and our Higher Power, that led in turn to Step Seven, to a stream of authentic self-love fed by the healing waters of the Higher Power of Love itself. This resulted in a profound alteration in the way we think.

We emerge from Steps Four through Seven considerably altered, able to move forward in our lives as different people. Because our thinking has been transformed by God's love, we show up differently, we act differently, and often others comment on the change in us. Rarely any more do we think about our weight or about our bodies or about food. We have been relieved of the desire to alter our physical beings as we were relieved of the desire to change our mental processes at the end of Step Six. We accept our bodies, and we are happy. We have been restored to sanity. A Higher Power has made all this possible.

STEP EIGHT:

Made a list of all persons we had harmed, and became willing to make amends to them all.

AWAKENED TO THE TRUTH: RELATIONSHIPS

At this point the process of Step Eight immediately comes into play. Completing Step Seven is like waking up after sleepwalking, emerging from a hypnotic trance, being released like Sleeping Beauty from the enchanted spell cast by a malevolent sorcerer. We look back over our lives and shake our heads in disbelief at how sick we have been for so long. We see in a completely new light the mangling of our relationships that resulted from our sick behavior. Our eyes are fully open to the truth about what we did to ourselves and others by following the ruinous script of our anorexia and bulimia. Most of us saw at least some of this damage as we took Step Four, but the difference now is that we have fully forgiven ourselves, so we are no longer tarnished by pathological guilt. Instead we experience profound sadness over what we have done. We are deeply grieved and find ourselves impelled to repair the damage as best we can. The stunning paradox is that *we can only take full responsibility for our past actions after we have quit blaming ourselves for them.*

IMPELLED TO REPAIR THE DAMAGE

Making the List

We move into Step Eight as a natural result of our altered thinking. We do not take Step Eight. Rather, it takes us. It is not possible to be transformed by God's love and yet remain in a space of cavalier disregard for others.[1] We *must* make amends for what we have done. Our inner need to do so is as intense as the greatest thirst we have ever experienced. We pull out pen and paper and begin to set down the list. As we write the names of those we have harmed, more and more names come to mind. Our Higher Power is directing us.

We write the names of those close to us. We see how we hurt them through our anorexia and bulimia. Then it occurs to us that we have continued to hurt them since we sobered up, as we went on acting in deeply self-centered, dishonest, and controlling ways. We realize that the list will be longer than we had at first imagined. On and on we go, including everyone we have lied to, everyone we ignored, everyone we maligned out of jealousy, everyone we stole from, everyone we cheated, everyone we tried to control, everyone whose lives we meddled with, everyone to whom we were disrespectful, everyone we tried to dominate, everyone we burdened with our incessant demands for attention and approval.

Importance of a Sponsor

When the list is complete, we review it and discuss each name with our sponsor. We know by now that we cannot trust our own thinking, that we need always accept spiritual direction from someone who knows us well, who can see places where we may have gone astray. We ponder the character defects behind each harmful thing we did. More and more becomes clear to us. We then look carefully again at the wording of Step Eight.

Amends: Further Change

"Amends" signifies "compensation for injury or loss."* It involves reparation. Contained in this term is the word "amend," meaning "to change for the better; improve…."* And any lawyer will state that in legal terminology the word "amend" refers to only one thing: change. So *it is only possible to make reparation to others after our attitude toward them has changed for the better.* We are not spiritual giants. Although the Higher Power of love and forgiveness has been engraving itself on our hearts, the process is not yet complete. We notice that our thinking is still marred by resentment toward some of the people on our list, that we have not yet forgiven them for something we believe *they* did to us.

Willingness May Come Slowly

Therefore, it takes time to become willing to make amends to them all. This process cannot be evaded or controlled, and it is important to stay with it. Some of us, still burdened with impatience, tried to push through to Step Nine and made amends before we were ready. We acted out of our old insane thinking that told us we could change ourselves by force of will. The result was often unfortunate, resulting in further harm to the person we were approaching and to ourselves. However, we once again received from this experience the opportunity to learn something about ourselves, about our impatience and self-will and powerlessness to change ourselves.

*By permission. From ***Merriam-Webster's Desk Dictionary*** ©1995 by Merriam-Webster, Incorporated, at www.Merriam-Webster.com.

STEP NINE:

Made direct amends to such people wherever possible, except when to do so would injure them or others.

WHERE TO BEGIN

Although there are some people on our list to whom we are not yet ready to make amends, our sponsor usually encourages us to move forward into Step Nine with the folks we are ready to deal with. Indeed, we are often eager to do so, so intense is our yearning to clean up the mess we have made of our relationships.

MOST IMPORTANT CHANGE: INDIRECT AMENDS

As we consider and discuss exactly *how* to take this Step, we discover that since we have sobered up, and especially since we have been walking through Steps Four though Seven, we have already begun making amends. Usually beyond our conscious awareness, we have been acting very differently toward many of the people on our list. We have quit lying to them. We have become considerate of their needs and have been striving to be helpful to them. We have begun to treat them with respect. We have left alone people whom we previously pestered for attention. We have learned to bite our tongues instead of telling people what to do. We have quit trying to manipulate them into doing what we thought they should. We now realize that others have a right to their own ideas and to do what they choose to do. We have developed a real awareness that we do not know what is best for them. We have stopped trying to be the center of attention. We have quit believing that we are invisible and that our actions have no impact on others. Most of all, we have become profoundly cognizant of the fact that others are just as deeply loved by God as we are, that we are all of equal value in the eyes of the Creator, and that we all have a unique place in the universe that only we as individuals can fill. This change in attitude changes the way we relate to others.

Every action results from a thought. As God changed our thinking about ourselves and others through Steps Six and Seven, our actions of necessity changed as well. We now realize that we have been making the most critically important amends possible by living differently. Our sponsor reassures us of this fact as well. Conversely, it does no good whatsoever to toss off a glib apology for what we have done if we are simply going to do it again, if we are not willing to act differently hereafter. Many of us apologized incessantly when we were practicing anorexia and bulimia. People grew tired of hearing us. They only wanted us to change.[2] Many of those folks have become delighted with us since we sobered up and have begun following the Steps, because now we finally do act differently.

DIRECT AMENDS

Straight Talk

Nevertheless, we sense that still more is required to free our hearts. The word "direct" means "stemming immediately from a source;...leading from one point to another in time or space without turn or stop; straight...."* So Step Nine involves going to the people we have harmed and having a straight talk with them about what we have done. We share briefly what we have learned about ourselves, how we feel about the harm we caused them, and what we are now doing differently to repair the damage. In this talk we go straight from one point to the next without turning to peripheral information. In other words, we omit any mention of *why* we did what we did, any attempt at making excuses for ourselves. We state very simply what we did, what defect of character we were exhibiting, and what we are prepared to do about it now.

Some concrete examples may clarify this. We might say to our parents, "I stole food from you when I was bingeing and purging. I reckon that the total cost of what I took is two thousand dollars. I feel really sad about my dishonesty, and I apologize for harming you. I would like to repay this money at the rate of a hundred dollars per month." Or to our friend, "I lied to you many times when you invited me to eat lunch with you in high school. I made excuses to avoid eating. I never considered how my lies affected you, how you felt when I rejected your offers of friendship, and I feel sad about that. Since I'm recovering from anorexia I don't tell those lies anymore. Thank you for not giving up on me." Or to our grown daughter, "During your teens I was frequently unavailable to you because of my bulimia. I was always thinking about food and my weight, and when you came to me for support I wasn't there to listen or understand your problems. Sometimes in the evenings when you tried to talk to me, all I wanted was to be alone so I could go and binge in private. I missed watching

*By permission. From ***Merriam-Webster's Desk Dictionary*** ©1995 by Merriam-Webster, Incorporated, at www.Merriam-Webster.com.

your basketball games because I was home bingeing and purging or at the gym doing a workout. I feel sad about my self-centeredness, my dishonesty, and my failure to meet my responsibilities as a parent. I feel sad about missing all those opportunities to get to know you and to show you how much I love you. I'm living differently now, and I can't make up for all the harm I did to you. I am truly sorry."

No Demands, No Expectations

Notice that in making direct amends we never place demands, even covert ones, on the person we are addressing. We never try to control them. We do not ask them to forgive us for what we have done, nor expect them to think better of us, nor hope they will feel sorry for us. We are dealing with our side of the street only, and we recognize that we are making these amends for ourselves, so that we can hold our head up when we meet this person in the future, liberated from guilt.[3] How they respond is none of our business.

And yet, paradoxically, we also take Step Nine for the benefit of those we are approaching, for in making amends to others we liberate them as well as ourselves. Frequently those closest to us were held hostage by their love, by their unstoppable concern for our welfare as we were gripped by anorexia or bulimia. They had been tortured without mercy as they feared for our lives; as they witnessed our unraveling, physically and mentally; as they discovered their powerlessness over our disease. Now, in Step Nine, we are given the opportunity to break their chains, to release them from their torment.[4]

Pleasantly Surprised: Healing of Relationships

Because of this phenomenon, we have often been astonished and delighted by their response. Frequently the person we are approaching smiles graciously and says, "Don't worry about it. I'm just glad you're getting well." We discover the generosity of which human beings are capable as we listen to such responses. The result is often a further melting in our own hearts, a reawakening or renewed affirmation of our love for the other person. We then glimpse the vast and mysterious power of Step Nine: it channels the healing power of the Program into our relationships as it further restores our capacity to love. The power of the Step is thus not limited to us alone but also extends to the person we are approaching. Sometimes the other person further shocks us by apologizing for what they have done to us. Love begets love. Truth begets truth. Then we experience an even deeper mending of our fractured relationship with this person. We can embrace one another and walk away mutually unburdened and healed.

Unpleasantly Surprised: Tempted to Defend

Of course, such a sequence of events does not always occur. The person we approach may respond by venting their anger at us or may even bring up other things we have done that hurt them, things we have forgotten or to which we were oblivious at the time. It is important in this case to listen quietly, to remember that our Higher Power is with us to provide what we need at this moment, and to ask that Power for guidance. Never do we react by countering what the other person has said, by arguing or debating the matter or defending ourselves. We may need to excuse ourselves and leave, and we do that respectfully. We do not accept verbal abuse from anyone, for that would be damaging to our souls and of no help whatsoever to them.

EXCEPTION TO THE RULE

Injury vs. Discomfort

In pondering how to make amends, it is vital to note the strong caveat in the final phrase of Step Nine. We must never directly approach a person we have harmed if we would injure any human being by doing so. There are even rare situations where we would injure *ourselves* by making a direct amend. Our sponsor is the best guide in making these discernments. She will let us know if we are trying to use this exception as an escape hatch to avoid making an amend that will merely cause us discomfort. There is a world of difference between discomfort and injury. Sometimes even a grievous injury causes no discomfort: Ask a paraplegic with an assailant's knife thrust deep into her thigh how much pain she feels. And sometimes non-injurious and even wondrous events cause the most intense discomfort known to humankind: Ask any woman who has just given birth how she felt twenty minutes ago. Clearly, we do not injure or harm ourselves by making an amend that we are simply embarrassed about. On the contrary, we are doing great good for ourselves and others by assuming the fullest responsibility possible for the harm we have done, difficult as this may be in the short term.

FURTHER CHANGE, FURTHER FORGIVENESS

Intimacy

As we make our amends, one by one, we notice that our hearts are healing. When we refer back to the list of names from Step Eight, we discover that we have let go of further resentment and are now ready to make amends to people whom we never thought we could forgive for what *they* had done to us. Such is the awesome power of Step Nine. It continues what God began doing for us in Steps Six and Seven, by bringing about further change, further restoration to sanity, further clearing away of the perverted thinking that blocked us from intimacy with ourselves and God and others. Steps Six and Seven brought forth the beautiful blossoms of change in our inner beings, and Steps Eight and Nine ripen these blossoms to fruition in our relationships with others.

Awakening to Joy: Gratitude

Long before we have completed Step Nine we undergo another transformation. Uncluttered as we now are, our minds clear and free of the debilitating burden of guilt we carried for so long, we truly awaken to the fullness of life. The colors that we started noticing after taking Step Five deepen. The sky is not merely blue; it is azure and indigo. The roses are not merely red; they are scarlet and fuschia and vermilion. Everywhere we look we recognize the artistry of the Creator. We feel a depth of calmness in ourselves alongside the most exuberant joy we have ever experienced. We become inwardly still and present to the moments of our lives and to the Higher Power who dwells within us. Nothing escapes us now. We notice the nuances in what people say and do around us, we remember what has gone before, we make connections that were previously impossible for us. We begin to discover the limitless possibilities for happiness contained in this marvelous gift of life the Creator gave us. We are filled with humility and gratitude for all we receive. We discover why people with longtime sobriety have claimed to be grateful for their anorexia and bulimia, for we realize that we could never have reached this profound capacity for living without having passed first through the fire of our disease. We find ourselves and God, and we know that all is well.

STEP TEN:

Continued to take personal inventory, and when we were wrong promptly admitted it.

BACK TO EARTH: ONGOING CHANGE

Lest we think that our progress in the Steps to this point qualifies us for canonization, Step Ten calls us firmly back to reality. The process of transformation that God has begun in us will never be complete. Life and recovery never stop, and the essence of both is change. We must continue to grow or else wither and die. There is no middle ground, no point of stasis. Nothing in the universe is static, and we must accept that fact if we are to know true happiness.[5]

THE VALUE OF MISTAKES

Perfectly Imperfect

Step Ten recognizes that as human beings we will always be given opportunities for further growth. It further recognizes that much of this growth will come about through initial failure, through making mistakes. The Creator intended this when our species was placed in the universe, for free will would be an illusion, a cosmic lie, if we do not use it at times to make poor choices.[6] We were created to learn by many avenues, including that of making mistakes. That is why the perfectionism engendered by our disease was so disastrous for us, because it denied our essential humanity and, in doing so, cast us completely out of touch with ourselves. The truth is that to be perfectly human we must be imperfect, we must make mistakes.

Noticing and Cleaning Up…

Whether as anorexics and bulimics we make more mistakes than other folk is completely irrelevant. *The only relevant fact is that in order to grow spiritually we must learn to notice when we are wrong and to clean up the messes we make*. Through the practice of Step Ten our Higher Power teaches us to do that.

…When We Are Wrong: Lapses Into Insanity

The word "wrong" in this Step refers to acting in ways that are false, unjust, mistaken, not fit or suitable, or incorrect. So in taking Step Ten we stay alert to those occasions when we are dishonest, when we act unjustly toward others, when our ideas and beliefs have been erroneous, when we fail to do whatever is suitable in a given situation, and when we have acted incorrectly. We notice, for instance, the times when we think in our old self-centered ways, believing that everyone is watching us when we enter a room. We notice that we have lied to a friend about our feelings. We observe our attempt to control our sponsor's impression of us by struggling to sound clear when we are really hopelessly muddled. We are aware of reacting to a glorious morning with a negative comment about the likelihood of rain later on. We notice our thinking when we sit in a meeting feeling superior to the current speaker. We are attentive to our judgmental thoughts about a stranger on the street. In short, we notice when we have lapsed into insanity.

NOTICING EVOLVES: GRACE AT WORK

From Powerlessness...

The reader may recall that this practice of noticing actually began when we engaged in the process of Step Four and, later on, of Step Six. At that time we couldn't stop seeing our character defects. We were fully awakened to them. At times we felt overwhelmed, bombarded by our own observations. We noticed ourselves being dishonest, self-centered, judgmental, arrogant, and controlling wherever we went.

...To Choice

At some point, often in proximity to Step Seven, we began to experience small periods of time intervening between our awareness of a character defect in our minds and the action we were about to take based on that defect.[7] For example, we saw ourselves *about* to lie to our partner, and we experienced a momentary pause—akin to a freeze-frame in a film—before the lie actually popped out of our mouth. In this temporal space we could actually decide whether to lie or not. Or we were tempted to control our son by telling him to stop crying, and before succumbing to the temptation we felt a brief moment in which we could do otherwise. This ability to make a choice about an imminent action was new for us who are powerless over anorexia and bulimia, and was clearly the result of a Higher Power at work in us. We became conscious of grace operating in us, and we were humbly grateful for it. We came to see that this was one means by which God was going about the business of removing our shortcomings.

Further Choice: Opportunities to Learn

Now in Step Ten this ability to notice our own insanity becomes fully operative. More and more often we experience real choice in what we are about to do. All of us at times still act out in very sick ways and create a little more chaos in our lives by doing so. Then we get the opportunity to learn something more about ourselves and to clean up another mess.

PROMPTLY ADMIT

Note that this Step instructs us to promptly admit when we are wrong. It implies we must admit our lapses into insane thinking as well as into unfit actions. To whom do we admit them? To ourselves and to God and to another human being, of course, following the pattern of Step Five. We generally discuss the matter with our sponsor and almost always, if we have acted out and harmed someone, with the person we have wronged—except when to do so would injure them or others. For instance, if we try to manipulate our partner into doing the laundry by lamenting about our exhausting day at work, we need to go to him and admit what we did as soon as we notice it. This is true whether or not we were aware of our dishonesty and our attempts to control him prior to acting as we did. All of this is essential for our continued growth into the person we were created to be, and into becoming useful to the Creator.

STEP TEN: DAILY GROWTH THROUGH STEPS FOUR TO NINE

It should be obvious that Step Ten incorporates an ongoing movement through Steps Four, Five, Six, Seven, Eight, and Nine. Again and again, continuously throughout our days, we have the responsibility and the privilege of taking these six Steps, thereby ensuring our continued spiritual growth. What a brilliant plan this is! It is so perfectly beautiful that it could have been designed only by a Higher Power who loves us beyond comprehension, who yearns for us to continue to grow in the direction of life, love, freedom, and joy.

Fully Awakened— Steps Eleven and Twelve

11

STEPS ONE THROUGH TEN: BLUEPRINT FOR HEALING

IN OUR discussion of the first ten Steps we have glimpsed a spectacular design for comprehensive healing from anorexia and bulimia. Let's summarize this overall blueprint before moving on.

In the first three Steps we are concerned with finding release, through admitting personal powerlessness and coming to believe in and surrender to a Higher Power, from the deadly compulsions to starve or to binge and purge that still constantly threaten to overcome us. Seen as a whole, Steps One, Two, and Three bring about healing in our relationship with a Higher Power, with the Creator. Through them we come to let God be God: the only One capable of directing the universe.

Steps Four and Five move us beyond our insane *behaviors* into awareness of the twisted *thinking* patterns that fuel them. Steps Six and Seven catapult us into a process of liberation from our pathological thinking, a change that permits us to forgive and to love ourselves. Regarded as a cohesive unit, Steps Four through Seven cultivate healing in our relationship with ourselves, enabling us to find inner peace. Through them we come to let ourselves be ourselves, as we were created to be.

In Steps Eight and Nine we clear away the odious debris from our past and thereby mend our capacity to love others and to enjoy wholesome interactions with them. Step Ten keeps us current in this area of personal relations. Viewed together, Steps Eight through Ten engender healing in our relationships with others, without which our newfound inner peace would be short-lived indeed. Through these Steps we come to let others be themselves, and we find serenity in that.

The big picture reveals Step Ten daily weaving together Steps Four through Nine, on the loom of the first three Steps, into a seamless garment that clothes us in a manner ever more befitting to creatures of divine heritage. As we continually take Step Ten we become wide awake to our own magnificence, to the beauty and power given us by the Creator, and to the privileged position we occupy in the universe. We are humbly grateful for all of this, are aware that the God who gives us sobriety actually dwells within us, and take seriously our responsibility to use our power wisely and to walk gently through our lives on this planet.[1] Knowing our kinship with the Creator, we now long for ever deeper union with this Higher Power.

STEP ELEVEN:

Sought through prayer and meditation to improve our conscious contact with God as we understood God, praying only for knowledge of God's will for us and the power to carry that out.

NEW GOAL: UNION WITH HIGHER POWER

It is now clear to us why this Step is placed so far along the path of our healing journey. For it is only by walking through the first ten Steps that we reach a place of sufficiently deep yearning to know and love God that our only desire is for connection to this awesome Being, to this Power who has first loved us enough to liberate us from our insanity.[2]

STAGES OF PRAYER

Primitive Prayer: Steps One to Three

Granted, we have been using prayer as a recovery tool since we first crawled into the rooms of our Fellowship. Many of us even prayed before we got here, and indeed recognized the Fellowship as God's answer to our pleas for help. In order to sober up and stay sober, we all needed to pray frequently for the grace to surrender, one meal at a time, to the Creator's will about what we should eat. However, these prayers as we sobered up and took the first three Steps were very primitive, like the cries of an infant wailing for its mother's breast. They were more in the nature of pitiful whimpers than anything else. They were, however, all we could produce at the time, and our Higher Power tenderly answered them.

Maturing Prayer: Steps Four Through Seven

As we moved through Steps Four, Five, Six, and Seven, our prayers matured, evolving from desperate requests to be relieved of our insane thinking processes, into prayers of surrender to God's will for the way we needed to show up on any given day, for the way we could be most useful to our Higher Power.

Self-Forgetting: Steps Eight and Nine

Following our first deep experience of forgiveness in Steps Six and Seven, our prayers shifted further as our vision expanded from our desire to be comfortable in our own skin, into a longing for healing in our relationships with other people. Although most of us didn't recognize it at the time, we actually made a quantum leap as we moved through Steps Eight and Nine, because we were now more concerned about others than about ourselves. We had entered the realm of true self-forgetting that all great spiritual leaders have identified as the essence of mature spirituality.[3] (An important aside is to note that self-forgetting is in no way synonymous with self-neglect, because paradoxically it is only through self-forgetting that we can truly care for ourselves emotionally and spiritually. Another paradox is that we can only arrive at this authentic self-forgetting by following a path of intensive self-scrutiny.)

Grown-Up Spirituality: Step Ten and Beyond

Step Ten converts Steps Four through Nine into a daily discipline leading to advanced spiritual maturity, to the humility that thirsts for union with a Higher Power in love and knows this entails being God's servant, one who ardently seeks to do one thing only: the will of her Higher Power. Once Love has claimed our hearts, we can desire nothing less.

Adult Prayer: Step Eleven

Step Eleven embodies this mature spiritual development and lays out a concrete course for its completion. Key words are "prayer" and "meditation." To "pray" signifies "…to ask earnestly for something; to address God…with supplication."* Meditation, on the other hand, involves quiet waiting and contemplation. So Step Eleven directs us to both actively request something and to be still in the presence of our Higher Power while waiting for something.

CONSCIOUS CONTACT IS COMMUNICATION

What is this something that we are to seek? Nothing more complex than "to improve our conscious contact with God." The word "conscious" stands for "aware; …mentally awake or alert; … intentional."* And "contact" is "…relationship; connection; communication…."* Thus Step Eleven is about searching for a better means of intentional communication with our Higher Power, one that allows us to be fully awake and aware of our precious relationship with it. Communication is a two-way street. It involves both parties listening and speaking.

"Conscious" is Not a Feeling!

Notice that the Step says nothing about enjoying warm sensations, feeling close to our Higher Power, or experiencing ecstasy. It says nothing about our feelings. Rather it instructs us in the discipline of communicating with God using the totality of our mental power as human beings. How we feel is irrelevant to the practice of this Step.[4] Our experience has been that on some days we feel happy and joyful during our time of prayer, on others we feel angry and frustrated, and on still others we feel nothing but flatness and boredom. None of that matters. Every intimate relationship is marked by times of closeness and distance, of harmony and conflict, of shared joy and bitter pain.[5] The affiliation will be healthy as long as both parties continue to communicate, to speak honestly and listen to one another. Our relationship with our Higher Power is no different from any other in this regard. As long as we don't abandon it, the connection between us will endure and thrive.

*By permission. From ***Merriam-Webster's Desk Dictionary*** ©1995 by Merriam-Webster, Incorporated, at www.Merriam-Webster.com.

SEEKING GOD'S WILL ALONE

Abandoning Big Daddy

In its final phrase, "praying only for knowledge of God's will for us and the power to carry that out," Step Eleven clearly guides us in the matter of what we are to ask of our Higher Power. We see immediately that the Step assumes a fully mature spirituality, in that it instructs us to pray for *only* two things, both of which revolve around our Higher Power's will rather than our own. In other words, by the time we get to Step Eleven we have long since abandoned the idea that the Higher Power is a sort of big daddy in the sky, someone who is there to grant our every passing whim. The word "only" is a particularly strong word. It implies that we are to pray for *nothing* other than knowledge of God's will and the power to do it. "Knowledge" refers to "...clear perception of truth; something learned and kept in the mind."* So we are to ask our Higher Power to let us know the truth about that Power's desires for every aspect of our daily lives. We are also to ask for the power—the ability, energy, and strength—to carry out those desires.

Still Powerless, Still Needing Power

In these very specific directions, Step Eleven reminds us that we are powerless; that unless a Higher Power gives us the muscle and stamina to carry out God's purpose for us, we will always have no strength of our own. This is truly Step One revisited, on a novel and much deeper plane, yet for the identical purpose to that on our original visit: to engender humility.

GOD'S WILL VS. SELF-WILL

God's Will: The Still, Small Voice Without Urgency

When, newly sober, we first read Step Eleven, many of us wondered how God's will would be revealed. Would a Higher Power place a message in our mailbox each morning to direct our actions for the day? Would we be led to a burning bush? Would we at the very least receive brilliant flashes of insight clearly illuminating our path? When we finally arrived at Step Eleven by painstakingly walking through the previous ten Steps, we smiled at our former naïveté. Then we took Step Eleven, day in and day out, and we slowly learned that God's will for us is almost never revealed in clear unmistakable terms. Rather we are

*By permission. From ***Merriam-Webster's Desk Dictionary*** ©1995 by Merriam-Webster, Incorporated, at www.Merriam-Webster.com.

given tiny intuitions about what to do in a given situation, a quiet hunch deep in our bellies, a persistent feeling impelling us to take a certain action. God's will almost never has urgency attached to it, so if we feel strongly compelled to do something right now, we are usually operating out of self-will. God's will for us will always wait for the time required to make a phone call to our sponsor to check out our thinking. *If it does not occur to us to check in with another person regarding a significant action we are about to take, we are almost certainly in self-will, not in touch with God's will.*

God's Will: No Obsession, No Debate, Always in the Present

God's will is not revealed through obsession, so if we can't stop thinking about something, if we are tormented by an idea, we are usually generating that ourselves out of our old insanity. God's will is revealed with quiet simplicity, with a deep unwavering knowing, so if we notice that we are debating something in our minds or piling up a list of logical reasons for taking some course of action, we are usually engaging our self-will. We have also learned that God's will is always in the present, not in the future or the past. If invited, our Higher Power will always direct us in the here and now, and this guidance usually occurs through prosaic knowledge of "the next right thing": getting dressed for work, eating breakfast, taking a nap, asking a child how was her day at school, buying a gift for a friend, going to the bathroom.

God's Will: Sobriety

Most of us have learned that on a practical basis we know very little about God's will for us other than the unchanging fact that our Higher Power wills for us to be sober, physically and emotionally. *Never does the Creator will us to relapse.* God's will is invariably that we be free of enslavement to anything, including anorexia and bulimia, and that we live at peace with ourselves and others.[6] Such a state is impossible if we are thinking insanely or acting out compulsively with food or exercise. So generally we pray for the specific spiritual power needed to stay sober in each moment of our lives: strength to eat soberly when we'd rather not; courage to face someone and tell them we were wrong; the ability to trust our Higher Power when we are tempted to give up; willingness to go to a meeting; endurance to bear the torture of thinking we are fat; the capacity to be honest with ourselves about our motives; humility to know that we are nothing without a Higher Power; perseverance to stand up again after a fall; wisdom to learn from our mistakes; tolerance to accept other people as they are; patience to listen to someone we'd prefer to ignore; compassion to understand other people's burdens; the generosity to share with others; the ability to forgive someone who has harmed us; the capacity to celebrate someone else's success; the grace to be centered on God rather than on self. And so on.

Ask, and You Will Receive

We discover that *when we humbly ask for the spiritual gifts we need for sobriety at this moment, we receive them*—usually very quickly. We learn that our Higher Power is not only willing to bless us but is also eager to do so. This Power often waits for us to ask for what we need.[7] Yet at times we don't know precisely what we need for our sobriety. We are confused and feel distant from our Higher Power. At such times we simply turn to God and humbly breathe, "Please help me!" We may need to continue saying this prayer for some time before we recognize that whatever help we needed has appeared.

Higher Power Knows Best

As we practice Step Eleven, we become more and more convinced that God knows what is best for us and that we rarely do. That is why as we become more spiritually mature we almost never make specific requests of our Higher Power other than those discussed above. By now we are thoroughly convinced that the only route to true happiness and peace is through surrender to God's will for us. We therefore desire, more ardently than ever, to know what God would have us do and to be capable of carrying that out.

CHANGING CONCEPTIONS OF GOD

Mysterious and Benevolent

As we get to know our Higher Power better through the practice of the first eleven Steps, our ideas about this Power usually change radically. We recall the Higher Power we conceived at Step Two and may be shocked at how differently we conceive God now. This change provides further evidence that there really is a Higher Power at work with us and in us as we recover. We often sense a real individual personality in this Higher Power, someone who wants to be known by us and yet remain a Great Mystery, and certainly someone who wants for us all that is good and whose action in us is invariably directed toward our benefit.[8] We sense by this time a Being who knows us far better than we know ourselves, and always loves us.

Our Primary Relationship

We usually notice by now that our relationship with this Higher Power has become more intimate than any human relationship we have ever known. We experience giving and receiving, a flow of energy in both directions between this Power and ourselves. We also are aware of how important this relationship has become to us. By now we often identify it as the primary relationship in our lives, the one of greatest value, for we know that it makes all other relationships possible.[9]

Great Mystery: Indwelling Yet Transcendent

Furthermore, by the time we get to Step Eleven and practice it daily, we generally know that this Higher Power truly dwells within us, in our physical bodies, in our very cells.[10] This is a real mystery, because although this Power is indwelling, it is also distinct from us. It is not us, and in its essence it is radically unlike us. It infinitely transcends all human capacity for compassion and forgiveness, for ingenuity and imagination, for patience and forbearance. It is inestimably bigger than we are. We are not the Higher Power, and yet this Power is as close to us as our heartbeat, as our breath, as the rumblings of our digestive tract.

Conceiving God as indwelling often shifts us further along the pathway of surrender to God's will, because to not surrender is to fight the very cells of our own bodies. (Of course, that is precisely what we did in our anorexic and bulimic behavior.) Somehow, knowing that a loving Higher Power is within us makes us *want* to care for ourselves physically, to eat enough and sleep enough and play enough, and it also leads to complete acceptance of our bodies exactly as they are. God dwelling within our bodies makes them perfect. We have no reason anymore to judge or reject them, to control or change them, to fight against them. On the contrary, we have every reason to honor our bodies, to love and respect and tenderly nurture them.

It should now be clear to the reader that we anorexics and bulimics arriving at this stage of the Twelve-Step Program have been truly restored to sanity, in the fullest sense of the word.

STEP TWELVE:

Having had a spiritual awakening as the result of these Steps, we tried to carry this message to others suffering from eating disorders, and to practice these principles in all our affairs.

SPIRITUAL AWAKENING: PERSONALITY CHANGE

The first thing we notice about Step Twelve is its division into three interconnected sections. The first phrase declares that by the time we arrive at this point we have already experienced a "spiritual awakening." Our spirit—the inner property that animates us, converting our otherwise dead bodies into living ones—has undergone a shift as radical as that which occurs when one is awakened—roused from the unconscious state that we refer to as sleep. In other words, our inner being has been transported from the sleepwalking state in which we practiced anorexia and bulimia into a fully conscious state wherein our thinking has been restored to sanity. We have been rendered fully aware of the devious and convoluted ways in which our minds operated, and we are conscious that a Higher Power has straightened out these twists and has profoundly altered the way we think.

Change: The Result of Steps One Through Eleven

This awakening, this personality change we have undergone, has been the end result of walking through the previous eleven Steps. "Result" means something that occurs "...as an effect or consequence."* There is no shortcut, no way to bypass the time-consuming, challenging, and sometimes painful process of moving through all the previous Steps, with all the energetic action and patient waiting that they variously require of us.

There is also no possible outcome from the first eleven Steps other than a change in our consciousness as dramatic as being roused from sleep. Step Twelve reads "*the* result," not "*a* result." With this one small word, the Step specifies what will result from working the first eleven Steps, whether we intended it or not when we began. *There is no way to journey through the Steps without undergoing a radical personality change*, and this change allows us to be released from the thrall of anorexia and bulimia.[11]

*By permission. From ***Merriam-Webster's Desk Dictionary*** ©1995 by Merriam-Webster, Incorporated, at www.Merriam-Webster.com.

CARRYING THE MESSAGE

Impelled by Joy

Secondly, Step Twelve states clearly what we do after we have been spiritually awakened: We "carry the message to others suffering from eating disorders." We who have recovered from anorexia and bulimia, who have been awakened from the enchanted sleep of our disease, know that this desire to pass on to others what we have received springs unbidden from the depths of our inner being the moment we are restored to sanity. The unmitigated joy we experience at our blessed release is always permeated with an intense need to share itself with others. We cannot keep our jubilation to ourselves. It will not be contained. It is impossible to truly experience full liberation from our disease without wanting to shout about it from the rooftops. We passionately long to have others experience the same miracle so we can celebrate it together. This joy is infused with humility: We absolutely know that a Higher Power has brought about the change in us, and our gratitude knows no bounds. This outreach to others who are still suffering is the hallmark of an authentic spiritual awakening. One who claims to be spiritually awakened and yet remains silently self-serving is a liar or, at best, is sorely deceived.[12]

Spiritual Awakening: Healing is Contagious!

Now we see fully the elegant design of the Twelve-Step Program: It is self-propagating, because once an anorexic or bulimic has been healed through the Power behind the Steps, she cannot keep the information to herself. She absolutely *must* tell others about her experience, not out of the drudgery of duty but out of the impulsion of true spiritual awakening. The dissemination of the Program and of the healing Power behind it is thereby guaranteed. Our need to tell others the wonderful news ensures that others will hear it. Only a Power greater than human could have had the wisdom to conceive such a brilliantly simple plan. At Step Twelve we stand in utter awe of this Power.

Embryonic Sobriety Breeds Misguided Evangelism

Many of us experienced glimpses of this irrepressible joy when we were at a much earlier stage of recovery, possibly when we had just grasped our powerlessness and surrendered to belief in the Higher Power that could sober us up. Overwhelmed by the impulse to spread our good news, we rushed about frantically trying to convince other anorexics and bulimics to join us on the highway to freedom. Some of us did a lot of damage in this way; the unfortunate recipients of our feverish evangelism were often repelled by it and bolted in the opposite direction. That is why the Program specifically instructs us to save our proclamation of the news of our healing until we have reached the very last Step. For it is only by passing through all the previous eleven Steps that we can possibly arrive at the spiritual maturity required to effectively carry the message without driving others away.

Service With "Selfish" Motives: Highly Recommended

On the other hand, we also need to remember that giving away what we have received is the surest way to keep it, no matter what stage of recovery we have reached. The Big Book of Alcoholics Anonymous states that repeatedly.[13] So generally our sponsor will encourage us in early recovery to serve other anorexics and bulimics with the sole intention of remaining sober ourselves. This will be discussed more fully in Chapter 13. Suffice it to say here that we are advised to follow the direction of a sponsor in this regard.

What Message?

We should not delude ourselves into believing that we are taking Step Twelve when we do such early service work, for this Step expressly states that we cannot carry "this message" until we have first experienced the spiritual awakening that can result solely from taking the previous eleven Steps. "This" refers to "…the one…just mentioned,…"* while "message" is "a communication sent by one person to another."* Step Twelve thereby implies that *what* we communicate is the wonderful news about how our full awakening from the anorexic and bulimic mindset resulted from walking the journey of the Steps. Obviously, unless we have taken all the preceding Steps and thereby *been* spiritually awakened, we have no personal experience of this phenomenon that we can share.

PRACTICE THESE PRINCIPLES IN ALL OUR AFFAIRS

Spiritual Awakening Changes Everything

The third and closing phrase of Step Twelve instructs us in the final stage of the recovery journey. Now that we are spiritually awakened we

*By permission. From ***Merriam-Webster's Desk Dictionary*** ©1995 by Merriam-Webster, Incorporated, at www.Merriam-Webster.com.

try "to practice these principles in all our affairs." To paraphrase this, the final leg of the recovery path involves an attempt to display our new way of thinking and acting in every aspect of our lives: every arena we enter, everything in which we participate, everything we do, everything that concerns us. We must allow the transformation that our Higher Power has wrought in our personalities to shine through us wherever we go and whatever we do and to whomever we meet. To accomplish that requires our conscientious effort, for it means walking the Twelve-Step journey continuously every day of our lives.

Steps One Through Twelve: Onerous Task…

We have already seen that arriving at Step Twelve demands a painstaking movement through each one of the previous Steps, in the order they are laid out. On the basic framework of Steps One through Three we exercise the discipline of Steps Four through Nine by taking Step Ten every day. To do this effectively necessitates the continuous application of Step Eleven to clear the channel of communication between us and the Higher Power who directs us on a moment-by-moment basis. And taking all eleven Steps results in a climactic spiritual awakening that impels us to carry the message to others and to live, ever more fully, one day at a time, out of the new values and beliefs we have acquired.

…and Worth the Effort!

What a superlative design for sober living is this! We discover that operating in accordance with the Twelve-Step Program necessarily results in our becoming useful to the Creator, for we will show up quite differently now than we did when we were starving or bingeing and purging. We will be beacons of hope for others with eating disorders. We will be walking testaments to the Power who can restore to sanity anyone who is willing to do the work of recovery. With our roots sunk deep in the stream of a loving Higher Power, we will be present to all whom we encounter, becoming living fountains of compassion. We will be "God-in-skin" for others. Now awake to God's presence in us, we will recognize our Higher Power everywhere—in every stone, every blade of grass, every living creature. We will discover that our only desire is to return this Power's love, so grateful are we for it. We will constantly search for ways to love God back, and we will find that our relationships with others are the most fertile ground for doing that.

Is Usefulness God's Hidden Purpose?

Indeed, many of us believe that this conversion into beings who are useful to the Creator is our Higher Power's underlying purpose in restoring us to sanity. That is a matter about which we can only speculate, for which of us limited human beings can know the mind of God? Obviously, no one. Nevertheless, we are capable of examining the evidence, and what we have observed is that as recovered anorexics and bulimics we lead lives of immeasurably greater value than ever before. Instead of spending every waking moment, and many sleeping ones, consumed by thinking about what our bodies weigh and by planning which lavatory to purge in, we now use our time seeking to better love our spouses and to be productive workers and to be agents of change in a society riddled with insanity. We are useful whether we are called to a modest life mending our children's shirts and reading Lewis Carroll to them at bedtime, or to a dazzling scientific career that brings restoration to the ozone layer and splashes our photograph across the daily papers.

We have also noticed that serving the Creator is the surest route to genuine happiness, real joy, and bona fide freedom; to all that eluded us when we lived under the sway of our subversive disease. And we have come to believe that such happiness, joy, and freedom are God's will for us.

The most awesome aspect of our rebirth into lives of peaceful sobriety and usefulness is that such restoration came about through encountering a Higher Power who regarded us as valuable before we ever sobered up, a Power who loved us from the beginning and sought us out, sick and broken as we were, to convince us that we were not merely accepted but passionately and ardently desired. Our Higher Power didn't wait for us to change before accepting us. This God placed no ultimatum, no deadline, no agenda for change on us, but rather gathered us up as a mother's arms enfold her nursing infant, demanding nothing in return. The result in us has been an inner transformation that seeks to give back everything.

The Fellowship of A.B.A. 12

THE TWELVE Steps, taken together, have proven to be a perfect pathway to deep healing for us who have recovered from anorexia and bulimia. The preceding four chapters have explored in meticulous detail precisely how the Steps transform us from beings who were hopelessly lost in a labyrinth of insane obsessions about our bodies and enslaving compulsions to destroy ourselves with bizarre eating behaviors, into whole persons at peace with ourselves and capable of full participation in our lives. The two chapters before that dealt with the importance of physical sobriety as the indispensable foundation we must pour prior to taking the Steps that connect us with a Higher Power who does the tough work of restoring us to sanity. In this chapter we will look at the *Fellowship* of Anorexics and Bulimics Anonymous—an entity quite distinct from the Twelve-Step *Program* of Anorexics and Bulimics Anonymous.

THE POWER OF THE FELLOWSHIP

The Newcomer's Experience

The best way to understand the Fellowship we share is to experience it. Walk as a newcomer into any meeting of A.B.A. and you will see our Fellowship in the intimate circle where we sit and in the welcoming gazes which greet you. You will hear our Fellowship as the speaker to the newcomer tells her story, admitting without shame or melodrama to past behaviors similar to your own, behaviors that you would until now have chosen to conceal at any cost rather than to disclose to another human being. You will sense our Fellowship in the rapt attention you are given as you are invited to share, in the compassionate silence that receives your halting attempts to speak of your pain and holds you while you do so. You will touch our Fellowship in the hands that clasp your own during the closing prayer, in the warm embraces you are offered before you leave the room.

Belonging Generates Hope

There is enormous power in our Fellowship. None of us could have sobered up without it; without seeing walking, breathing miracles around us at meetings; without hearing their lurid stories from the past and their jubilant accounts of the present; without feeling the safety of our gatherings and sensing that we belonged somewhere at last. Before reaching A.B.A., we all walked as strangers in a strange land, irretrievably lost, alienated from everyone and everything by the guilty secrets we harbored. Now, finally, we were home. We could relax and sink into the safe haven of our Fellowship, knowing that we were not alone anymore, that we needn't explain anything, that others understood us before we spoke, that we were accepted simply because we were the forlorn and fragmented creatures that we were.

Indeed, we all needed the support of this Fellowship in order to get sober. We needed to hear the message from others who had gone before us, to dare to hope that we too could follow in their footsteps and recover as they had. We needed to listen to their encouragement when we were struggling, to learn that it was all right to fail and to start again. We needed to glean insight as we listened to them share experiences similar to our own. We needed to feel the surge of strength that washed over us as we experienced our sponsor's loving acceptance and heard her helpful suggestions. We needed to discover that together we could all do what none of us could do alone—let go of our insane eating and exercise practices and begin life anew.

The Fellowship Can Sober Us Up

Many of us stayed sober for long periods of time on the power of our Fellowship alone. We attended scores of meetings, drank gallons of coffee after them, phoned other members daily, enlisted sponsors and poured out our hearts to them. As a result of these actions we gained sufficient strength to enable us to surrender our eating and exercise practices to a Higher Power. Usually, whether we were conscious of this or not, we were using the Fellowship itself as our Higher Power.

THE FELLOWSHIP IS NOT THE PROGRAM

Unfortunately, some of us stopped there, content with sobriety alone. We felt better physically and mentally than we had in years. It was a relief to be able to eat a meal with our family again and to be unchained from the toilets where we purged. We felt released from our private hell, and that was enough. When others shared in meetings about how demanding Step Four was or how challenging Step Nine was, we decided right then that we would not venture into them. These Steps people talked about seemed altogether too burdensome for our liking. Besides that, they sounded pretty obscure. We couldn't understand their fancy wording, and we weren't about to admit *that* to anyone. No, we were doing just fine, thank you very much.

Sobriety Alone is Not Enough

After a time in this space, we gradually sensed that something was wrong. We became bored with sobriety because we felt no excitement anymore. We missed the drama and fireworks of our former lives. Eating all those normal meals had acquired the monotony of routine, and using the tools of recovery was even worse. We were in a rut. We were tired of those stupid meetings, where people mouthed clichés and droned on and on about the same old things. Our sponsor sounded like a broken record, nattering away about the importance of the Steps. We had better things to do than service work or reading Twelve-Step literature every day. Besides, what good was recovery anyway? Although sober, we still thought that we were fat and that losing a few pounds would make us feel better. Or perhaps we still thought about food all the time and reflected wistfully on the good old days of bingeing and purging. It hadn't been so bad after all, and sobriety certainly wasn't the blissful state others alleged it to be.

Without a Higher Power: Relapse

Most of us relapsed quickly once we reached this sorry frame of mind, otherwise known as a "dry drunk."[1] (This term humorously describes the mental state of an addict without her drug and without a Higher Power to restore her to sanity. Most of us have ventured into a dry drunk at some point in our recovery and often label it "hell on earth.") Those of us who did not immediately relapse hung around meetings whining about our ill-fated lives and envying others who seemed happy in their sobriety. Then we too relapsed, needing to suffer ever deeper levels of pain and despair before we crawled back to the group, willing now to go to any lengths for spiritual and emotional healing. Some of our members died in their relapse, never making it back to our Fellowship. We grieve their loss, and we thank them for what they taught the rest of us about the fatal nature of this disease we all share.

The Program and the Fellowship: Recipe For Freedom

The simple truth is that the power of the Fellowship alone will not change the way we think as anorexics and bulimics, no matter how long we stay sober. We will continue to operate out of self-hatred, self-centeredness, fear, dishonesty, our illusion of control, judgmentalism, perfectionism, self-pity, and other character defects, until we commit to the Twelve-Step Program. As we saw in previous chapters, *only through taking the Twelve Steps do we allow a Higher Power to release us from our insane thinking.* And yet, paradoxically, we need the Fellowship of Anorexics and Bulimics Anonymous to support us in maintaining sobriety while we journey through the Steps. It is the cradle that rocks us, the arms that embrace us, the air that sustains us while we take the Steps. In other words, the Fellowship channels the precious gift of sobriety to us, without which we cannot do the Twelve Steps and thereby be freed from our deranged thinking.

FORMAT FOR MEETINGS

We meet together frequently to support one another in recovery. Our meetings are generally ninety minutes in length and are chaired by our members in rotation. What follows is a suggested meeting format we have found useful for our gatherings. This Preamble comprises a summary of essential information covered in this book, and we recommend reading it in full at the beginning of every meeting. We all learn slowly, and we need to hear this material again and again before we can even begin to absorb it into our minds and hearts.

Notwithstanding the copyright laws that apply to everything in this textbook, the authors and publisher hereby grant blanket permission to any A.B.A. member or group to copy the next seven pages containing the Preamble for Meetings, *as long as it is reproduced in its entirety and is not otherwise altered.* Any two or more anorexics or bulimics meeting together for purposes of recovery may call themselves an A.B.A. group, provided that, as a group, they have no other affiliation or purpose and provided that they adhere to the principles outlined in this textbook. We would be interested to hear from those who obtain favorable results from the use of the A.B.A. approach to recovery, and we invite such people to contact us, using the address located on the final page of the Preamble for Meetings.

ANOREXICS AND BULIMICS ANONYMOUS™ PREAMBLE FOR MEETINGS

Welcome to Anorexics and Bulimics Anonymous. My name is ——— and I'm in recovery from ———. Please join me in a moment of silence to reflect on why we are here, followed by the Serenity Prayer.

God, grant me the serenity to accept the things I cannot change, courage to change the things I can, and wisdom to know the difference.

OPEN MEETING / CLOSED MEETING INTRODUCTORY STATEMENT

This is an open meeting *of Anorexics and Bulimics Anonymous. We welcome all of you, and particularly any newcomers. In keeping with our primary purpose and our Third Tradition, which states that "the only requirement for A.B.A. membership is a desire to stop unhealthy eating practices," we request all who participate to limit their sharing to problems related to their eating disorder.*

OR: ***This is a closed meeting*** *of Anorexics and Bulimics Anonymous. In keeping with A.B.A.'s primary purpose, attendance at closed meetings is restricted to those who have a desire to stop unhealthy eating practices. If you think you have a problem with unhealthy eating, you are welcome to participate in this meeting. When speaking about our problems, we request all who share to limit themselves to difficulties related to their eating disorder.*

Anorexics and Bulimics Anonymous is a Fellowship of individuals whose primary purpose is to find and maintain sobriety in our eating practices, and to help others gain sobriety. **A.B.A. is not allied or affiliated with any other 12-Step Fellowship or outside organization.** There are no dues or fees for A.B.A. membership; we are self-supporting through our own contributions. The only requirement for membership is a desire to stop unhealthy eating practices that we have come to realize are progressively destroying our lives, physically, mentally, and spiritually.

In this group we discover that our insane eating, starving, exercise, and purging behaviors are addictive in nature—that is, out of our own control—and that we actually *use* these behaviors, and the inner physical changes resulting from them, to numb our emotions and escape from ourselves. In doing so, we also fall out of touch with others and out of step with the universe of which we are a part, and we deprive ourselves of the opportunity to be fully alive in our present time and space.

Furthermore, we learn that we are carrying out these insane eating, starving, exercise, and purging practices in obedience to a deceptive, immensely powerful voice within our own minds. This is the voice of a *disease* that is chronic, progressive, and potentially fatal. The first action of this cunning and baffling disease is to cast us into a state of unawareness, in which we fail to recognize that we are in mortal danger when we carry out its insane commands.

We learn that the payoff we receive from this disease for our obedience to its demands is nothing more than a mirage: an *illusion of control* over our lives and our future. We learn that the disease's principal weapon is overwhelming and paralyzing fear, and that it holds us in its lethal grip by inducing profound guilt and shame within us. The disease lies to us at every turn. It even convinces us that we are *to blame* for our own sick condition, that we freely choose to do the insane things we do, and that we are unlovable.

In this circle of healing we learn, one step and one moment at a time, to awaken to the truth about our disease, to recognize its lies, to see how it entraps us, to trust in a Higher Power who loves us unconditionally, and to turn our will and our lives over to this loving Power.

As we recover, we come to experience this Higher Power—the Spirit of life itself—at work within us, empowering us to live without *any* illusion of control. We also learn to truly *own* our lives and to take charge of ourselves in a way that had not been possible before.

Our program is deeply spiritual, but not allied with any religion. We have found it applicable to our healing journey regardless of our religious beliefs, for we know that our eating disorders are *primarily* mental or spiritual diseases, although they also comprise a physical component. More specifically, we have a mental obsession that compels us to restrict our food and/or to binge and purge, coupled with a physical "allergy" in our bodies that ensures we will continue restricting or bingeing and purging, once we have begun.

In our healing process we use the Twelve Steps, adapted from Alcoholics Anonymous, as the foundation of our spiritual journey. Here are the Steps we take: ***(Ask the group or an individual to read them aloud.)***

THE TWELVE STEPS OF ANOREXICS AND BULIMICS ANONYMOUS

STEP 1: We admitted we were powerless over our insane eating practices—that our lives had become unmanageable.

STEP 2: Came to believe that a Power greater than ourselves could restore us to sanity.

STEP 3: Made a decision to turn our will and our lives over to the care of God, *as we understood God.*

STEP 4: Made a searching and fearless moral inventory of ourselves.

STEP 5: Admitted to God, to ourselves, and to another human being the exact nature of our wrongs.

STEP 6: Were entirely ready to have God remove all these defects of character.

STEP 7: Humbly asked God to remove our shortcomings.

STEP 8: Made a list of all persons we had harmed, and became willing to make amends to them all.

STEP 9: Made direct amends to such people wherever possible, except when to do so would injure them or others.

STEP 10: Continued to take personal inventory, and when we were wrong promptly admitted it.

STEP 11: Sought through prayer and meditation to improve our conscious contact with God *as we understood God*, praying only for knowledge of God's will for us and the power to carry that out.

STEP 12: Having had a spiritual awakening as the result of these steps, we tried to carry this message to others suffering from eating disorders, and to practice these principles in all our affairs.

We also adhere to our adaptation of the Twelve Traditions developed by Alcoholics Anonymous. I've asked ——— to read the Traditions today.

THE TWELVE TRADITIONS OF ANOREXICS AND BULIMICS ANONYMOUS

1. Our common welfare should come first; personal recovery depends upon A.B.A. unity.

2. For our group purpose there is but one ultimate authority—a loving God as expressed in our group conscience. Our leaders are but trusted servants; they do not govern.

3. The only requirement for A.B.A. membership is a desire to stop unhealthy eating practices.

4. Each group should be autonomous, except in matters affecting other groups or A.B.A. as a whole.

5. Each group has but one primary purpose—to carry its message to the anorexic or bulimic who still suffers.

6. An A.B.A. group ought never endorse, finance, or lend the A.B.A. name to any related facility or outside enterprise, lest problems of money, property, and prestige divert us from our primary purpose.

7. Every A.B.A. group ought to be fully self-supporting, declining outside contributions.

8. Anorexics and Bulimics Anonymous should remain forever nonprofessional, but our service centers may employ special workers.

9. A.B.A., as such, ought never be organized; but we may create service boards or committees directly responsible to those they serve.

10. Anorexics and Bulimics Anonymous has no opinion on outside issues; hence the A.B.A. name ought never be drawn into public controversy.

11. Our public relations policy is based on attraction rather than promotion; we need always maintain personal anonymity at the level of press, radio, TV, and films.

12. Anonymity is the spiritual foundation of all our traditions, ever reminding us to place principles before personalities.

(Reprinted and adapted with permission of Alcoholics Anonymous World Services, Inc.®)

We learned that it was impossible to work the Twelve Steps until we were "sober" in our eating practices. Without physical sobriety it is impossible to recover from any addiction, including anorexia and bulimia.

Many of us puzzled over precisely what "sobriety" means. We tried various ways of changing our eating practices. We tried modifying our exercise patterns. We tried cutting down on our binges or refraining from purging afterwards. We tried eliminating the binge/purge cycle, while simultaneously falling into the trap of anorexic restriction of our food intake. We tried allowing ourselves to eat, while continuing to exercise to compensate for the food we ingested. We tried many other half-measures, while still clinging to little vestiges of control to avoid that most fearsome state: getting fat! Or, if we were already overweight, we clung to these control measures to lose weight. Some of us appeared unconcerned about our weight and instead engaged in controlling behaviors to avoid feeling our feelings.

We learned through all this experience that the intoxicating "drug" to which we are addicted is not the act of starvation or exercise or the binge/purge cycle itself. Rather, the "drug" of anorexia and bulimia is ***the feeling of being in control of our food and body weight and shape***. This sense of control is generated in us through restrictive eating practices, or through purging after we binge, or through exercise. Many of us learned that to become fully sober we needed to let go absolutely and ***surrender all control of our food, exercise, and body weight and shape to a Higher Power***. In early recovery this Power worked through other human beings. Later, as we are restored to sanity by following the Twelve Steps, we come to connect with this Power alive within ourselves.

SOBRIETY IS SURRENDER. And it is not a passive state of submission but rather a highly active, entirely voluntary letting go that requires intensive work on a daily basis. We learned that sobriety is experienced only one day at a time (or one meal at a time!), and that we cannot be sober through willpower. We learned that sobriety is a gift from our Higher Power and that we can ask for this gift on a day-by-day or meal-by-meal basis. We learned that when we honestly asked for the grace to surrender *for this meal*, we received it. We learned what tools of recovery worked for us in the difficult process of getting sober and staying sober. Here are some of the tools many of us have found useful:

THE TOOLS OF ANOREXICS AND BULIMICS ANONYMOUS

1. **Prayer:** asking a Higher Power daily for the means and strength to stay sober…even though we may not yet truly believe in such a Power.

2. **Quiet Time:** in which we center ourselves and clearly focus our energy on receiving the gift of sobriety.

3. **Reaching Out:** telephone contact with another recovering person before and/or after meals.

4. **Meetings:** both A.B.A. and other Twelve-Step meetings are critically important in maintaining sobriety. Many of us in early recovery attend ninety meetings in ninety days.

5. **Reading:** the textbook of our Fellowship and the "Big Book" of Alcoholics Anonymous are especially useful.

6. **Sponsor:** we ask someone in the Fellowship with more sobriety than we have to sponsor us. This person is essential to guide us through the Twelve Steps and is often available to assist us in maintaining sobriety.

7. **Journaling:** periodically recording in written form what we are feeling and learning on our journey through recovery.

8. **Service Work:** our most powerful tool. Even when all else fails, working with another anorexic or bulimic will save the day and allow a Higher Power to keep us sober!

Is anyone here for their first time? (***If so, ask a sober member to speak to the newcomer, outlining "what it used to be like, what happened, and what it's like now" as a result of joining this Fellowship and working the Twelve Steps.***) Is anyone coming back who would care to identify themselves?

Does anyone have a topic to put forward for today? ***(If there are newcomers, the topic of the first three Steps is strongly suggested.)***

The meeting is now open for sharing, either on this topic or any other that you need to speak about, related to your eating disorder. I'd like to remind everyone that, out of courtesy, we refrain from interrupting others as they speak. We are not here to counsel or practice therapy on anyone, but to share our personal experience, strength, and hope. Please identify yourself each time you begin to speak. ***(If the group is large, add: "Since our group is large today, please be aware of the time so that everyone will have an opportunity to share.")***

(Five minutes before closing time, resume leadership as follows.)

We are nearly out of time. Does anyone else wish to speak?

Our Seventh Tradition states that we are fully self-supporting, declining outside contributions. At this time we pass around a basket and invite A.B.A. members only to contribute toward our expenses.

In closing, let's remember that we are an anonymous group meeting in deep trust of one another. Whom you see here and what you hear here, let it remain here.

I've asked ——— to read the Ninth-Step Promises today from the Big Book *(found on pages 83-84)*.

Are there any announcements for the good of A.B.A.?

Are there any sobriety milestones? 30 Days? 60 Days? 90 Days? Four months or more? ***(Give a token to anyone celebrating these milestones.)*** This group celebrates yearly birthdays at the last meeting of the month.

Can I please have a couple volunteers to clean up after the meeting?

Would all who care to, please join me in closing the meeting with a prayer. ***(The Serenity Prayer, Lord's Prayer, or Third Step Prayer.)***

Revised 02/2007

CONTACT INFORMATION:

ANOREXICS AND BULIMICS ANONYMOUS™

MAIN P.O. BOX 125

EDMONTON, AB T5J 2G9

CANADA

www.anorexicsandbulimicsanonymousaba.com

Tools of Recovery 13

CONTAINED WITHIN our Preamble for Meetings is a list of tools we have found useful in maintaining sobriety. All of us in recovery from anorexia and bulimia use these tools on a daily basis, for together with the Twelve-Step Program they comprise the "footwork" of recovery that God will not do for us. *It is our responsibility to do this simple footwork, thereby opening up the door of our being to allow God's grace to do for us what we cannot do for ourselves: keep us sober.* A statement often heard in recovery circles is: "We can't think our way to healthy actions; we must act our way to healthy thinking!" Using the tools is how we take action.

TOOL 1: PRAYER

We have learned it is critically important to pray if we are to have any hope of staying sober. Most of us pray formally at least five times each day: in the morning, before every meal, and at bedtime.

In the Morning

Our morning prayer usually consists of a simple request for help throughout the day ahead, the help that will keep us sober. We often pray on our knees at this time, because this posture allows us to experience powerlessness at a cellular level in our bodies and is thereby conducive to humility—a deep sense of our nothingness without our Higher Power. Merely formulating our prayer mentally is very helpful indeed, and most of us have discovered the additional benefit of praying out loud. We are not purely spirit, and our bodies are an important aspect of who we are. So we pray out loud to engage our entire being in prayer, to feel our prayer rising out of our chest and taking shape on our tongue and lips, to hear the words with our own ears. We urge anyone who has never done this to try it.

Before Meals

Before meals we ask our Higher Power for the grace to eat according to the Creator's will for us at this meal, and we give thanks for sobriety and for the food itself. If we are to select and prepare our own food we generally pray before beginning this task, asking our Higher Power to guide our thinking and our hands. If another person is preparing or serving our meal, we ask for the grace to trust that God is working through that person's hands. Some of us pray on our knees before meals, especially if we're experiencing tormenting thoughts about the size or shape of our bodies. If we are not in the privacy of our own homes, we can almost always find a restroom or other private space where we can go to pray before we eat. Eventually we learn that, wherever we are, our Higher Power is present and invariably listening; we simply become inwardly still and breathe a silent prayer.

At Bedtime

At bedtime we thank the Creator, usually again on our knees and out loud, for everything we have experienced this day. We like to name the blessings we are grateful for: the gift of sobriety; the bounty of our Fellowship and the beautiful people who support us in recovery; the gift of life itself and of healthy bodies—or of sick ones; the joys and the sorrows we felt today; the capacity to feel anything at all; the success we enjoyed at our place of work, and the mistakes we made that provide us with opportunities for further growth; the gift of faith that allows us to come before the Creator as we are; the fun we had today; the laughter that sprang out of our bellies; the tears we were able to shed. Everything is a gift, and gratitude is the discipline of knowing that, rather than the warm and mellow feeling that may or may not accompany our knowing.

The Purpose of Prayer

The Danish philosopher Kierkegaard once stated that the purpose of prayer is not to influence God, but to change the nature of the one who prays.[1] We all need to pray at every stage of recovery. Those of us who are atheists or agnostics often had difficulty with prayer in early recovery, because we felt foolish or hypocritical addressing a Higher Power in whom we did not yet believe. However, we were so desperate that we were willing to follow any suggestion, so we tried it. To our amazement, it worked. The fact that we did not believe in prayer was irrelevant to its efficacy. The fact that we did not believe in God was irrelevant to God's love for us and desire to bless us with sobriety. *All that was relevant was our willingness to take action, whether we believed that it would help us or not.*

This is in fact true of every recovery tool we can name, not just of prayer. If we are willing to use the tools, sobriety will eventually find us, even if we have no real faith in this phenomenon. This is another mysterious aspect of the recovery process, and we can't explain it. However, many of us have come to regard this mystery as convincing proof that a Higher Power exists and that God indeed has the power we lack. Most importantly, we see it as evidence of the nature of this Higher Power: one who loves us beyond reason or comprehension, passionately and extravagantly and unalterably. We have a God who waits for us to eternity and infinity, and there is nothing we can do to change that fact. When we know this, we know everything that matters.

TOOL 2: QUIET TIME

Forms of Meditation

We use the term "quiet time" rather than the more formal "meditation," because some people are frightened by the latter word. Some of us do practice specific meditation techniques, many of them based on Eastern philosophies or religions.[2] Others get nowhere with these methods or are reluctant even to try them. For these folks, quiet time may work best when it is combined with a simple activity like ironing laundry or scrubbing a floor, some task that demands little mental attention and thus frees up our consciousness to be occupied by our Higher Power.[3] Many of us prefer to spend quiet time outdoors with the wind and the trees, or in our garden in contact with soil and earthworms and plants.

However we practice it, all of us need time alone, being quiet and still, and most of us take it on a daily basis.[4] There is no other way to become conscious of God's intimate presence within us, nor to connect deeply with the Power that keeps us sober. In early recovery our attempts to be quiet may seem fruitless, so dominated are we by our unrelenting obsessions about food and body weight and shape. Once again, that doesn't matter. All that matters is our willingness to take the action of creating quiet time. A Power greater than ourselves accepts our attempts, however primitive and stumbling they may be, and graciously keeps us sober.

Roadblocks

Some of us are afraid of silence in early recovery because we dread the derogatory mental voices with which we derided and vilified ourselves as our disease progressed. After we sober up, these voices do not immediately disappear. In fact often they intensify, and we need the reassurance of our sponsor that they are merely the cries of a disease fighting for its life. Sobriety threatens to demolish our disease, and it does not die quietly. It will do anything to lure us back to its fickle embrace, and tormenting obsession is one of its chief weapons.

If we are afraid to engage in quiet time, we need to pray for the courage to do it anyway. Our request will be granted, and as we practice this discipline it gets easier and eventually bears the fruit of occasional intense feelings of connection with our Higher Power. These moving experiences spur us on to continue this spiritual practice.

TOOL 3: REACHING OUT

Participation With Others

The first two tools can be used when we are alone, in the solitude of our home or workplace. Reaching out is the first tool that requires us to show up and interact with other human beings. No one stays sober in isolation. We all need the support of others walking the same path.

Channel of Grace

Telephone contact with others in recovery is an invaluable method of opening the floodgates to God's grace. In early recovery many of us need to make a call before we eat each meal, or afterward, or both—a practice commonly referred to as "bookending." With the strident chant of obsession reverberating in our minds, there is often no other way to deal with the practical necessity of eating, no other way to get in touch with reality. The voice of another anorexic or bulimic reassuring us that we truly need to eat can have a great calming effect. Listening to this support brings us in contact with the Power that enables us to proceed with our meal and refrain from purging afterwards.

Taking the Action

The telephone can be useful anytime and we must learn to use it liberally. Even if no one is home at the other end of the line, the action of picking up the phone helps us to get centered at difficult moments. The simple act of leaving a message on someone's answering machine allows us to hear our own voice and can serve as a conduit of grace to keep us sober.

Reluctant to Call?

In early recovery most of us are reluctant to reach out to others for help, believing that we are imposing on their time or bothering them. We think they would be too polite to tell us this, so we take care of them by not placing them in this awkward position to begin with. We leave our "five-hundred-pound phone" on the hook. Only when we are feeling completely desperate, out of other options, and close to relapse do we finally pick up the phone and cry for help. By then it may be too late; our insane thinking may have progressed too far to avert relapse.

It takes most of us a long time to trust that the person we are calling is capable of deciding whether or not she is available at that moment to receive our call, and longer still to see that attempting to second-guess her is profoundly disrespectful. We begin to grasp that our belief that we know what another person needs is blatant evidence of our own arrogance, of our disease.[5] Furthermore, by trying to make her decisions for her we deprive her of the opportunity to learn to take care of herself. We rob her of a chance to further her spiritual growth!

The Paradox of Giving and Receiving

Much later in recovery, when fellow members begin reaching out to us for help, we discover the true joy engendered by being useful to another person in her time of need. We learn that by making ourselves available when she calls for help, we have received a far greater gift than we could possibly have bestowed on her. We grasp the meaning of the admonition, "Give the gift of receiving; receive the gift of giving!"[6] There is nothing more catalytic to sobriety, to spiritual growth, than performing an act of loving-kindness toward a fellow human being. We will discuss this further when we look at the tool of service work.

At any stage of recovery, therefore, reaching out and asking for help from another person contributes to her sobriety as well as our own. The Higher Power works in such paradoxical ways!

TOOL 4: TWELVE-STEP MEETINGS

Recovery Visible Before Us

We alluded earlier in this chapter to the power that is audible and visible and tangible when we walk into meetings of our Fellowship, and all of us have experienced this power. It is the Higher Power alive and working among us who share this disease and the solution we have found. In the previous chapter we saw how spiritual transformation resulting from walking the Twelve-Step Program cannot be contained. It takes over our physical beings and spills out in every direction to touch those around us. The light in our eyes when we have recovered from anorexia and bulimia; the softness in our voices as we give credit to the Power to whom it is due; the spring in our step when we are unburdened of all that kept us sick; the easy stance of our bodies that results from true self-love; the laughter that bubbles out of us as we see through new eyes the humor in our crazy thinking and behavior; the warmth in our properly nourished bodies when we hug one another—these things cannot be hidden and serve as powerful testimony to others that authentic recovery is indeed possible. Instead of vibrating masses of human cells, we are now still and comfortable in our own skin, and others notice.

Generating Hope

And all of us, not just newcomers, need again and again to see with our own eyes and hear with our own ears the compelling message of hope that is available to us at meetings. For we have short memories. Left to our own devices and in the solitude of our homes, we quickly lose our spiritual focus and dive into the daily grind, forgetting the fact that as anorexics and bulimics we are utterly dependent upon a Higher Power for our sobriety. As soon as we forget about God, our disease gets its toe back in the door of our minds. Then, before we know it, we start thinking in old self-centered ways, contemplating what lies we need to tell, and scheming about how to control some person or situation. In other words, we relapse spiritually and emotionally, and we have seen how that will lead eventually to physical relapse.

Sick? Find a Meeting!

So we keep going to meetings to remind ourselves of how sick we still are![7] Our Fifth Tradition implies that the principal reason we meet is to allow suffering anorexics and bulimics to find the Fellowship and hear the message that those of us who have recovered carry to them. And yet, paradoxically, we need to be there for ourselves, to maintain our own sobriety. Sitting in a meeting, especially if there are newcomers present, we remember that we have this disease and that it is only by the grace of God that we are not dying from it today. We come away with renewed humility and gratitude, prepared to embrace another twenty-four hours of this gift of sober life we have been given.

Supporting One Another

In the city where A.B.A. originated we meet frequently to support one another in sobriety. There are scattered meetings of our Fellowship in other cities and towns, most of them initiated by people who have found sobriety in our midst and have moved to other places. At this writing, we maintain telephone contact with sober people on two continents, so we invite anyone interested to write to us for further information about Anorexics and Bulimics Anonymous in your area. Contact information is located at the end of Chapter 12.

The Gift of Other Fellowships

Most of us, and certainly anyone living in an isolated community, have found support by attending meetings of other Twelve-Step Fellowships as well. Many of us are also alcoholics or drug addicts and need to participate in Alcoholics Anonymous or Narcotics Anonymous in addition to our Fellowship. Those of us without chemical addictions often attend *open* meetings of these two Fellowships, simply because they are available, long-established, and their members are often rich storehouses of wisdom about living sober and incorporating the Twelve Steps into daily life.

In attending other Fellowships we are respectful of their Third Tradition and are careful never to mention anorexia or bulimia during the meeting. If invited to share, we identify ourselves as "addicts" and speak only in general terms about our insanity and about recovery today. When we act with respect and humble gratitude, our universal experience has been that we are welcomed with open arms by the members of other Fellowships. Without their support, we could not have maintained our sobriety simply by attending our own infant Fellowship.

TOOL 5: READING

Using the A.A. Big Book

We encourage all our members to read, study, and reflect on Twelve-Step literature on a regular basis. All of us anorexics and bulimics who recovered prior to the publication of this volume used the Big Book of Alcoholics Anonymous as our principal text. We believe it to be an inspired work written by the Power who called the first hundred hopeless drunks to recovery between 1934 and 1939. One of the co-founders of that Fellowship, Bill W., held the pencil that wrote the words, but it is clear to us reading the book today that he could not possibly have formulated the concepts contained therein. The wisdom in that text is light-years beyond a mind that had been sober for less than five years. There is only one possible source: a Higher Power working through him.

"Translating" Other Literature

When reading the literature of other Fellowships, we make a simple translation of the other addiction, wherever it is specifically named, into the language that fits for anorexia and bulimia. For example, in the Big Book we strike out the word "drinking" and insert "restricting our food" or "bingeing and purging" or "exercising," as appropriate to the sentence and to our idiosyncratic behavior. Later in recovery many of us find this practice unnecessary, for as we become accustomed to distilling the principles that apply universally to all addicts, we barely notice the references to specific addictions. We know by now they are all merely different tips of the same iceberg. By this point we have left the tip and are dealing with the iceberg's submerged bottom, with the insane thinking processes common to all addicts.

Why Read?

We need the literature of other Fellowships simply because it is there, and it has worked to teach the Twelve-Step Program of recovery to addicts of all sorts for decades. Why reinvent the wheel? There is no way to improve upon what is already found in the Big Book and other texts, and we have no desire to write it down again in our literature.

We all need to learn to pick up Twelve-Step literature throughout the day, especially at difficult moments when our obsession is raging. Once again, the action of opening the book, even if we do not retain or even comprehend what we read, opens the door to our Higher Power.

By taking action, we give God an open invitation to bless us with the gift of sobriety. In our experience, God never misses an opportunity to do precisely that.

TOOL 6: SPONSORSHIP

Unbroken Lineage

Beginning in 1934, the gestational period of Alcoholics Anonymous, the practice of one addict sponsoring another has been a continuous tradition in Twelve-Step recovery. This practice is vitally important to the healing process of all of us, for a number of reasons.

Reasons for Sponsorship: Too Sick to See

The first and most important reason for sponsorship is contained in the dictum, "You can't heal a sick mind with a sick mind." In other words, all of us coming into recovery are desperately ill, although we usually don't know it yet. True, we know we are defeated and despondent, but we really haven't the faintest clue about the breadth and depth of our insanity. We are unaware of how our addictive disease has permeated every level of our thinking, every fiber of our being, every attitude and value we hold, every premise out of which we operate. If we do have some budding consciousness of the scope of our insane thinking, we often label it as moral degeneration or, worse still, as an inevitable aspect of the normal human condition. "Everybody is self-centered," we may proclaim. "It's a dog-eat-dog world out there. Why should I try to change that? I won't survive in the real world if I quit thinking about myself first!" Or we may assert that everyone cultivates dishonesty in our world, that it's quite a useful practice, and that we see no reason to change. Or that our society is based on competition and control, and that our workplaces and homes compel us to strive to control others before they control us.

All these statements, and many others we utter and think in early recovery, are undisguised evidence of how sick we are. We have completely lost touch with the pristine blessedness of our original condition as the Creator intended us to be. We were not created to operate out of self-centeredness, but out of a river of spiritual and physical connectedness with the Creator. Never were we intended to be liars and cheats and thieves, but to dwell always in the shimmering glow of honesty. The Creator never willed us to dominate and control others, nor to manipulate or be subservient, but to take our place as adult humans fully responsible for ourselves and deeply respectful of the right of others to their own feelings and thoughts and decisions. We were created to walk without violence in the universe, to be keenly aware of our interrelationship with everyone and everything about us, to be open channels of love for one another, to place our spirituality ahead of everything else.

In early recovery we are oblivious to how far we have strayed from this state of original blessing.[8] We have no way to grasp the truth that anorexia and bulimia have blinded and deafened and crippled us, have wrapped us in a concrete casing of self-deception. So we need the help of others to crack open this shell and let the Great Reality in, to allow the healing of our minds to begin. A sponsor is one who is key in this process. She has gone before us into the light of sanity, so she sees what we cannot: how very sick we are. Having been where we are, she comprehends the totality of our blindness and has compassion for us. Because her healing process is further advanced than our own, she has a deep commitment to the truth as it has thus far been revealed to her, so she can see where our thinking is flawed and twisted, and she is willing to risk being honest with us. Above all, because her loving Higher Power is sculpting her as she heals, she is able to love us in our woundedness and thus become our first real experience of our Higher Power's love. She is "God-in-skin" for us.

Reasons for Sponsorship: Guidance Through the Steps

The second and associated reason for sponsorship is for guidance through the Steps. The Twelve-Step Program is uncharted territory for all of us entering recovery. Even if we were to read everything ever written about them, only a sponsor can direct us in actually taking the Steps. She can shepherd us, point out pitfalls, share her experience of a particular Step, illuminate it for us. She also appears mysteriously endowed with an intuitive sense of timing. She seems to know when we are ready to take each of the Steps in turn, when to slow us down and when to nudge us forward. *No one can take the Steps with any deep level of effectiveness unless she has a sponsor.* Alone, we are still burdened by our self-deception and by our pervasive self-loathing, and we will almost invariably go astray.

Reasons for Sponsorship: Maintaining Sobriety

The third purpose in sponsorship is for support in maintaining sobriety. No matter how long we have been sober, all of us remain anorexics and bulimics for the remainder of our lives. All of us are utterly dependent on a Higher Power for every moment of our sobriety. Without this Power we are doomed to relapse into insane thinking, for our disease patiently lies in wait to detect the first moment when we disconnect from the Power that keeps us sober. As soon as we do that, it pounces and begins to direct our thinking from the toehold it has gained. It then mushrooms as it feeds on itself, gaining an iron grip on our minds before we even notice it, and by then it may be too late to avert physical relapse. Only the grace of God can interrupt this inevitable progression, and a sponsor is frequently the first conduit of this saving grace. She usually notices our lapse into insanity before we do, and she loves us enough to be frank with us. We then have the opportunity to listen, to talk further about what is going on in our minds, and to return to our Higher Power before it is too late.

Reasons for Sponsorship: Getting Honest

The fourth purpose in having a sponsor is to practice being open and honest with another human being. We are responsible for doing this, for no one can force us to be truthful. All of us as sick anorexics and bulimics are experts at concealing our thoughts and feelings and even our actions. Letting go of this *modus operandi* is a lengthy and arduous process for most of us. We generally strive to be candid in our sharing at meetings, but after a while we discover that it is possible to hide behind our words in that setting. When we work one-on-one with a sponsor it is more difficult to lie, to "forget" to mention some crucial piece of information, to camouflage our twisted thinking. The safety of the sponsor-sponsee relationship often enables us to risk stripping away our defenses, to be vulnerable with someone we have come to trust. It is in this context that many of us first experience authentic intimacy with another human being.

Procrastination

Many of us procrastinate before asking someone to sponsor us. Still burdened by our pathological thinking, we deem ourselves unworthy to take up someone else's time, or we are afraid to be seen or fearful of committing ourselves to the recovery process lest we fail. Or, out of our inflated sense of our own influence, we think that we might drag a sponsor back into her disease, that she will be unable to take care of herself if our neediness overwhelms her. (As discussed earlier in the section on reaching out, we have no idea how disrespectful is this thinking.) Or perhaps we look around at meetings and judge no one to be healthy enough or smart enough or loving enough or wise enough that she will be capable of understanding and assisting us, complex and unique creatures that we believe ourselves to be.

Such delay in obtaining a sponsor is almost invariably a mistake, and many of us learn costly lessons in this way. Without a sponsor, we sit in meetings with insanity rampant in our minds, and the longer we stay there the sicker we get, until we finally relapse into anorexic and bulimic behavior. It is only by taking the risk of opening up to a sponsor and hearing her responses that we can begin to think differently.

Choosing a Sponsor

In choosing a sponsor, we do well to select someone of the same gender as we are, someone who is herself working the Steps under the direction of a sponsor, someone who has a quality of sobriety that we respect and wish to emulate. We generally opt for someone whom we can talk to with ease, but it is not essential that we feel a close kinship with her. A sponsor is not a bosom buddy, nor a mother or sister, nor a nursemaid or hand-holder. Rather she is a mentor, a pilot, one who is willing to listen and to be honest with us, no matter how much risk that entails for both of us.

Waiting for the Perfect Sponsor?

There is no perfect sponsor, no one who can be consistently available, always honest and loving, invariably insightful and accurate, never operating out of her own diseased thinking. We are all anorexics and bulimics when we enter the Fellowship, and we all remain so, no matter what stage of recovery we have reached. It is vital to remember that it is God who heals us all, and a sponsor is simply someone through whom our Higher Power works. This Power can employ any one of us, no matter how frail or blind or broken we still are, to reach another anorexic or bulimic. We have found that God is the Great Improvisor,[9] so in the final analysis it matters little whom we ask to sponsor us, because our Higher Power will work through whomever we ask, will use that person as a channel of abundant grace. All that matters is our willingness to find a sponsor and to work with her to the best of our ability. We signal to our Higher Power that we are willing to be healed when we obtain and utilize a sponsor. God will do the rest.

Sponsoring Others

Once we have been sober and working the Steps for a time, newcomers begin asking us to sponsor them. This is a great gift and a sacred responsibility, one that furthers our own recovery in unexpected ways. We learn how to sponsor others by doing so, and at first most of us feel unequal to the task. We do well to remember at this point what we already know from our experience with our own sponsor, that a Higher Power is in charge of the process and that we are but instruments in that Power's hands. So we pray for guidance, check in with ourselves and with our sponsor about the matter, and reach the best decision we can. The most important consideration in undertaking to sponsor someone is the matter of honesty. Can we be frank with this person? Are we operating out of some hidden agenda, perhaps a belief that we can save her if we manage well? Are we lying to ourselves about our availability, about the amount of time and energy we can give her? Do we feel repelled by this person, or powerfully attracted to her? If so, we usually have some inner business to attend to before we decide about sponsoring her, for our strong reaction is evidence that some wounded area of our being has been triggered and needs to be dealt with.[10]

In working with a sponsee, we remember that we can pass on only what we ourselves have first received. A slogan in recovery is: "You can't give what you haven't got!" In general, we sponsor others in the same way that we have been sponsored, because that is all we know and all we can offer. As we work with others, we soon discover we are receiving great gifts that further our own growth: opportunities to practice being honest, being God-centered, being free of our illusions about control. We get to practice listening deeply to another; being attuned to our inner feelings about what we hear; reflecting in silence before we speak; being patient with a human being who is just as splintered as we are; sharing our own deepest secrets; forgiving ourselves and the other when we make mistakes. We are given the incomparable privilege of admission into the soul of another human being and of watching her change. Sponsorship allows us to witness a Higher Power at work before our eyes, transforming both of us into more loving and whole persons. There is no greater gift.

TOOL 7: JOURNALING

What To Do With Feelings

Many of us find journaling a useful aid in maintaining sobriety. In early recovery we often feel bombarded by our feelings: overwhelmed by blazing anger, wrenching sadness, agonizing depression, trembling fear, wondrous contentment, ecstatic joy. We are apt to label some of these feelings as "negative" and some as "positive." We require considerable spiritual maturation to recognize that all feelings are simply feelings,[11] that none of them have intrinsic power to harm us, that they are part of the human condition, and that they are gifts from the Creator aroused in us at a particular moment for a purpose frequently beyond our knowing. We all need to embrace the entire range of our feelings, and journaling is one outlet that supports us to do so.

What Feelings?

Especially in early recovery, most of us have great difficulty identifying our feelings, so accustomed are we to running from them through our addictive behaviors. Sometimes we don't even know when we are experiencing a feeling, let alone are we capable of labeling it.[12] We simply seem restless and can't sit still, or experience a pressure in our chest or our belly, or find tears welling up in our eyes for no apparent reason, or start trembling uncontrollably.

Our Bodies Never Lie

Although we may label them through our thinking, feelings are primarily *visceral* phenomena, an important aspect of our physical nature as humans. We believe that feelings will never mislead us or lie to us, whereas our thinking lies to us frequently. So we need to learn to trust our feelings and question our thinking.[13] This may be the direct opposite of what we were taught as children.

Responses to Feelings

We can respond to our feelings in any number of ways. There is always the possibility of avoiding them through relapse into anorexia or bulimia, or through turning to an alternate addiction by lighting up a cigarette or taking a pill or a drink. (Fortunately, as time goes by and we begin to love ourselves and appreciate sobriety, these escape hatches hold less and less appeal for us.) We can flee to our rational brain and try to analyze and explain what is going on within us. We can use a recovery tool by calling our sponsor or going to a meeting. And sometimes we are courageous enough to surrender, to *stay with* our feeling and process it, trusting that our Higher Power is always with us and will allow no harm to befall us. Perhaps we curl up on our bed under a blanket and imagine we are in God's arms, or we sit and weep freely, or we pound on a pillow and curse until we're hoarse.

Whenever we accept the grace to stay sober at such times, we have the opportunity to go *through* our feelings and come out the other side.[14] Many of us are amazed the first time we do this to discover that we are still alive afterward, that we haven't dissolved or become unhinged. We discover that we feel calm and at peace with ourselves, that we have quit trembling and the pressure in our belly has vanished and our eyes are now dry. We often feel an intense connection with ourselves and our Higher Power, deeper than anything in our previous experience. Sometimes an ancient wound mends, allowing us to see the past in a new light. In this way we learn to trust our feelings and become convinced that they are a gift from God. Each time we do this and work through our feelings, we become more willing to do it again and less willing to abort our feelings the next time they come up.

Keeping a Record

We often need to record what we experienced as we stayed with our feelings. Journaling is one method of doing this. As we write, words often appear unexpectedly on the paper. Re-reading what we have written, we may be amazed at what is before us. In other words, a Higher Power guides us to further learnings even as we write.

Hate Writing? Other Outlets

Some of us dislike writing and choose to "journal" through other creative outlets such as painting or drawing or sculpting or photography or music, according to our various gifts. When we become whole through the miracle of recovery, we discover that all humans are true artists, and we delight in learning to express ourselves.[15] When we were still sick in our anorexia and bulimia, all our creative juices had dried up because we had disconnected from the Creator, from the flowing Source of all original expression.

Whatever method of journaling we select, this practice is a useful tool in maintaining sobriety, for through it we enter the mysterious inner landscape where God dwells.

TOOL 8: SERVICE WORK

We have come to believe this to be our most powerful tool, one that will suffice to keep us sober when everything else fails, so we encourage all our members to employ it freely.[16]

But I've Served All My Life!

Many of us balk at the idea of service, for we equate it with what we were taught as children, that our job in life was to make others comfortable and happy and to deny—or at least subjugate—our own needs in the process. In recovery we are starting to recognize that practicing this dictum was part of what originally led us to anorexia and bulimia.[17] Now here is our sponsor, suggesting that we look for ways to be helpful to others. We want no part of that!

Serving Out of Self-Interest

Our rebellion results from our failure to understand the purpose in service work. When we calm down enough to listen, we hear the whole of our sponsor's instructions. "I suggest you *do service work with other anorexics and bulimics in order to stay sober. If you don't do so, you will almost certainly relapse.*" In other words, we are to find ways to serve others for the sole purpose of our own sobriety, purely out of self-interest. Now *that* is a novel concept, one that liberates us from our old ideas about service. Intrigued, we give it a try. We arrange the chairs at meetings or put them away afterward; we make coffee or offer to refill someone's cup; we greet a newcomer or converse with her after the meeting; we phone a fellow member to ask how she is doing or share where we're at; we go out for coffee with someone who is struggling; we agree to be someone's sponsor; we help someone move to a new apartment; we accept a call from someone in distress; we attend a new meeting, or a long-established one, to ensure that sober members are present when the newcomer walks through the door.

Discovering the Benefits

As we experiment with these and many other methods of service, we discover that we are indeed staying sober and that it is growing easier to do so. Not only that, we are starting to *want* to do service because we feel truly happy afterward. Furthermore, we find ourselves beginning to deeply care about others in the Fellowship and to search for ways to be helpful to them. As we recover still more, we notice that our caring is no longer restricted to members of our Fellowship but has broadened to include people everywhere we go. No longer do we give up our seat on a bus because our parents taught us to do so, but because we have compassion for the tired-looking stranger carrying her packages. No longer do we offer a foot massage to our spouse out of a sense of duty, but because we deeply desire to give him pleasure. No longer do we take our children to the park because good mothers do that, but because we delight in their company and in their laughter.

In short, by taking actions initially based on pure self-interest, we are transformed into loving human beings capable of true self-forgetting.[18] Who could have foreseen such a paradoxical change as we made our first halting attempt at service work when we were two days or two weeks sober? Only a Higher Power, obviously. What a masterful design for spiritual re-creation!

But Isn't Service Twelfth-Step Work? I'm Not There Yet!

In our discussion of Step Twelve in the previous chapter, we drew a distinction between service work and the work of "carrying the message to others suffering from eating disorders." We believe that, although formal Twelfth-Step work is one form of service work, not all service work is Twelfth-Step work. This Step tells us that "carrying the message" is possible only *after* we have experienced the "spiritual awakening" or personality change that results from taking all the Steps, because it is only then that we have a message worth hearing. We encourage all our members at every stage of recovery to use the tool of working with others to further our own sobriety; and we urge everyone to avoid confusing this with "carrying the message," something that can only be done as we are spiritually awakened. Nevertheless, our very presence in the Fellowship—especially as we are transformed into loving people through service work as described above—becomes a powerful communication of hope to the newcomer, more powerful than any explicit message we could utter.

Why The Traditions? 14

WE HAVE alluded at several points in this textbook to one or more of the Twelve Traditions, a set of principles developed by Alcoholics Anonymous and used today by almost every Twelve-Step Fellowship in the world. They are policies of group governance that were hammered out on the anvil of sometimes bitter experience by Alcoholics Anonymous during the first fifteen years of its life, and formally adopted in 1950 at its first International Conference.

Unless it adheres to the Twelve Traditions, it is unlikely that a Twelve-Step group will survive. Therefore, it behooves our members to familiarize themselves with all the Traditions and with the rationale behind them. They are superbly discussed in A.A.'s book, *Twelve Steps and Twelve Traditions*, so in this chapter we wish simply to add a few further reflections on each of the Traditions to supplement what is contained in that excellent text.

TRADITION ONE:
Our common welfare should come first; personal recovery depends upon A.B.A unity.

We have come to believe that the most critically important word in the Twelve-Step Program and in our textbooks of recovery is the word "we." It is the first word of the First Step, the first word of the Preface in this book, and the first word of the Foreword to the first edition of the Big Book. Its pre-eminent place serves as a constant reminder that no one suffering from any addiction ever recovers alone.[1] In isolation we die, yet together all of us can do what none of us can do alone: get sober and stay sober; and find happiness, joy, and authentic freedom from our lethal disease. This is so because the healing Higher Power upon whom we all depend works most lavishly through our collective presence.

As recovering anorexics and bulimics, we have all been touched frequently by our Higher Power in a variety of ways, sometimes when we were alone. Yet these occasions are vastly outnumbered by the times when God reached us profoundly through the words or actions of others in recovery, whether inside or outside a meeting.

This being so, we have a momentous responsibility to stay together in an effective manner. Our very lives depend upon the ongoing viability of our Fellowship. Each one of us has the duty to always place the common welfare of the group at the top of our list of priorities, and this sometimes demands sacrifice of our individual desires. For a group of anorexics and bulimics, who in our disease are thoroughly self-centered, to achieve unity of purpose requires an act of Providence. Fortunately we have a Higher Power, one who changes our hearts if we humbly ask.

Sometimes it is *through* our working toward unity in our Fellowship that the Creator brings about a change in our self-centeredness. This is at times a painful process, as many of us can attest following a lively business meeting of our group. We may leave with bruised feelings or even bitter resentment; yet if we work these through, keeping the common good of the group at the forefront of our minds, we eventually notice we have begun to think of ourselves less and of the welfare of others more.

TRADITION TWO:

For our group purpose there is but one ultimate authority— a loving God as expressed in our group conscience. Our leaders are but trusted servants; they do not govern.

This Tradition embodies the wondrous equality that characterizes every Twelve-Step Fellowship, including our own. The practice of true equality is a shockingly unorthodox experience for most of us when we first encounter it in our gatherings.

The concept of equality itself is revolutionary for virtually all anorexics and bulimics, who in our diseased thinking had always considered ourselves either superior to everyone else, inferior to everyone else or, more often, superior and inferior simultaneously. We saw in an earlier chapter of this book how such self-centered and judgmental thinking had dominated most of us from our early lives, long before we became anorexic and bulimic. Rarely had we ever experienced ourselves viscerally as the equal of another human being.[2] Even our closest friends became the target of our comparisons as we incubated this toxic way of thinking.

In Anorexics and Bulimics Anonymous we encounter a parity that fractures our disease to its core. Everyone in the group, even if she is brand new and still fainting from starvation or trembling from her last binge and purge, has an equivalent place in the meeting; an equal opportunity to speak and to be heard; an equal voice in every decision; an equal right to influence the direction in which the group will go. Such staggering egalitarianism is at first too much for us to bear. It is so foreign that it sets us reeling. We may sit dumbfounded, unable for a time to take our place or find our voice, unable to assume the awesome responsibility inherent in such privileged equality. We always found it easy to delude ourselves, playing Queen Bee one moment and Lowly Worm the next. To grasp that we are simply ourselves, neither more or less important than the person seated next to us, takes most of us considerable time and healing.

As we continue to show up and participate in this mutuality, the Higher Power who pervades the Fellowship breeds true humility within us. We begin to assimilate our equality and demonstrate it in our actions. We lose our fear of speaking up and of remaining silent. We become better able to listen and truly hear the ideas of others as we are released from the constant judgmental chatter within our own minds.

We grow calm in the face of group conflict, more trusting of the group process and of the Power who directs it. We become deeply aware of the only Power greater than us all; and we take our place before the Creator, with deep respect for the person who stands to our right and to our left. We know now that we are all on the same plane and that God speaks through us all.

TRADITION THREE:
The only requirement for A.B.A. membership is a desire to stop unhealthy eating practices.

Exclusivity is anathema to Twelve-Step recovery. The doors of Anorexics and Bulimics Anonymous must always remain open to everyone who wishes to be there, regardless of race, gender, age, personality, occupation, financial status, physical appearance, garb, odor, linguistic capabilities, political leanings, religious persuasion, coexisting addictions, and so on. We regard all these external characteristics as the Creator does, as inconsequential. All are welcome who stride, slither, or stumble into the room, simply by virtue of the fact that they are there.

Many of us initially exclude *ourselves* because we cannot get past our externals, in particular our self-perceived size and shape. Almost every newcomer has been absolutely convinced that she is too fat to attend a meeting of Anorexics and Bulimics Anonymous. In fact, it is a miracle that anyone makes it through the doors at all. In the beginning most of us try to conceal our bodies behind voluminous clothing, parcels, backpacks, handbags, hats, shaded glasses, veils of hair, and other such interesting disguises, hoping to make ourselves invisible. So certain are we that everyone in the room is scrutinizing our bodies and taking notes that we usually hear nothing at our first meeting except the startling statement, "You as a newcomer are the most important person in this room," and the admonition to "Keep coming back."

Those of us who are desperate do return, and gradually the sound of others speaking penetrates our muffling cloak of self-consciousness. Later still, we make out the words they are saying and begin to connect them into meaningful phrases and even sentences. Then we perk up our ears, because we hear others telling *our* story and our secrets! Who let them into our minds and into our kitchens? Were they hiding in the closet last night observing what we did with food? How can they possibly know in such excruciating detail what we were thinking an hour ago? Horror of horrors, can they read our minds? The hair on the back of our neck stands up as we listen, so eerie is this phenomenon.

Gradually the blessed truth dawns upon us that they are speaking from their own experience, telling *their* story, and that it is identical in its essence to our own. Suddenly we know to our core that we are not alone anymore. After years of hiding our thoughts and behaviors from others, we no longer need to do that. The riveting and yet palliative effect of identifying with others is indescribable. Waves of consolation and relief wash over us and sometimes spill out of our eyes, so intense is this feeling of belonging somewhere at last, of homecoming.

Some of us needed more time than others to identify that we belong here. This was particularly true if our frankly anorexic or bulimic behavior was part of our cobwebbed past and we currently used compulsive eating practices as our drug of choice. In this case, we were certain that the gatekeeper of Anorexics and Bulimics Anonymous would take one look at our ample bodies and slam the door in our face. We were stunned to discover that there was no gatekeeper and no door to slam, that no one gave us so much as a second glance when we took our place at the meeting. On the contrary, everyone except us seemed to assume we belonged there, and greeted us with warmth and courtesy. Such a welcome allowed us to continue attending long enough to hear fragments of our story coming out of the mouths of others. Then we too knew we were in the right place and started to hope that the solution they had found could work for us.

The phenomenal equality embodied in Tradition Two blossoms in our Third Tradition. We all have an equal right to attend our Fellowship and to decide for ourselves whether or not we belong.

TRADITION FOUR:

Each group should be autonomous, except in matters affecting other groups or A.B.A. as a whole.

Although Anorexics and Bulimics Anonymous is a united and cohesive whole, every one of our groups has its individual flavor. This is only as it should be, for the Creator's gift to all creation is diversity.

As practicing anorexics and bulimics we exhibited little variance. Our behavior was characterized by a tedious repetitiveness, day in and day out. As discussed in Tradition Three, listening to the stories of other members permits us to discover this identity. We see that our most shameful behavior is similar to everyone else's. As newcomers we remain vigilant, watching closely for others to display shock or disgust as we tentatively share the horrifying and embarrassing details of what we did to our bodies with food, purging, and exercise. What we observe instead are nods and other expressions of compassionate understanding. Through these experiences we slowly learn that we are not unique, that the most bizarre behaviors of which we had been capable—behaviors that we thought irrevocably separated us from the rest of the human race—have all been done before. This identification with others constitutes the groundwork of our healing process as we abandon the illusion of separateness. The self-imposed mark of Cain begins to fade from our foreheads.

In our early days at A.B.A. we even resemble one another physically much of the time, especially those of us who have lost a significant amount of weight through acting out in our disease.[3] Many of us arrive at our Fellowship gaunt and emaciated and bundled up in bulky clothing. Yet we are so shrouded in the mists of self-deception, so convinced of our singularity, that we generally fail to recognize the startling resemblance we bear to others in the room.

But with sobriety our real differences emerge. As we sober up and do the Twelve Steps, we become ourselves. By admitting our identity with other anorexics and bulimics, we come to know our authentic differences and to honor them. Then we discover how truly unique we are, like multicolored stones in a gem case, each one possessing its own special fire and cut, each one of equivalent value to the jewel collector.[4]

It is only fitting that, in our glorious God-given variety, the groups in which we participate will similarly develop their own distinctive personalities. Our Fellowship not only recognizes but also celebrates this heterogeneity by enshrining it in our Fourth Tradition. Through its principle we are called to fully explore our fabulous multiplicity, and at the same time to assume the enormous responsibility of placing the welfare of the united whole first. We must learn through our group conscience to tune in to the care of the Creator for our entire Fellowship, while at the same time pursuing the individual course of our group.

Every group is needed. Each one has its place. Each one is responsible for becoming what God intends it to be: a warm haven for another lost soul who will feel at home there, who could find no kinship anywhere else.

TRADITION FIVE:
Each group has but one primary purpose— to carry its message to the anorexic or bulimic who still suffers.

The principle behind this tradition embodies the awesome trust that the Creator places in us who were once so dreadfully unworthy of anyone's trust. God hands us the sacred responsibility of passing on the miracle wrought in us to others who need it. As a group we must not only practice the Twelfth Step, we must see it as our *only* priority. This Tradition charges each of our groups with the daunting task of ministering to anorexics and bulimics who are still suffering, of communicating to them the glad tidings that recovery is possible through the Twelve-Step spiritual path that snatched us from the jaws of destruction.

We do not meet for our own comfort, nor because we are bored on a Tuesday evening and have nothing better to do than drink a cup of coffee with our chums, nor because we desire a sounding-board off which to bounce a lament about our sad lot in life. We gather together for one purpose only: to provide a wellspring of hope for the hopeless. This includes not only the newcomer and those of our members who are struggling to find sobriety, but also long-time members experiencing the blows of outrageous fortune.

In order for the group to effectively carry its message to those still suffering from anorexia and bulimia, it must adhere to the principle of Step Twelve. In other words, the group itself must have "had a spiritual awakening as the result of these Steps." Otherwise it has no message worth hearing. For a group to experience spiritual awakening it must undergo a corporate personality change sufficient to bring about relief from its self-centeredness, its dishonesty, and its illusion of control. Clearly, this cannot occur unless a solid core of its individual members are assiduously working the Twelve-Step Program in its entirety, so that a Higher Power is able to guide the group's actions.

The longer we have been participating in the Fellowship of A.B.A., the more responsibility we bear to ensure that our groups adhere to Tradition Five, and indeed to all the Traditions. Those of us who have been given the gift of long-term sobriety must take the lead in this. We cannot afford to sit back passively and hope for the best if we see the group losing its singleness of purpose, for the cost in human lives may be incalculable. If suffering anorexics and bulimics do not consistently hear the essential message of hope at every one of our gatherings, we will have failed in the mission entrusted us by the Creator. If we fail too often, we will eventually pay the price ourselves by relapsing.

We must not be negligent in this matter. When we participate in meetings, whether there is a newcomer present or not, we do well to stop and pray before we speak, asking our Higher Power to guide our minds and hearts. We remember that we are not there to engage in idle ramblings about the fun we had over the weekend, nor in woeful reflections on the current health-care system or the reigning political party, nor in windy philosophical discourse on the evils of materialism in modern society. Words have great power. It is important to choose with care what and how we share during a meeting.

In sharing we ask God to keep us focused on the task at hand—that of carrying the message of Anorexics and Bulimics Anonymous to anyone in the room who is still suffering. The only message worth hearing is our personal knowledge that recovery is possible through working the Twelve Steps. We speak about the purpose of the Steps: to connect us with a Higher Power who solves our problem of powerlessness. This Power has gifted us with sobriety today so we can joyfully proclaim our personal experience of this good news. If we neglect to do so, we will lose the gift.[5]

TRADITION SIX:

An A.B.A. group ought never endorse, finance, or lend the A.B.A. name to any related facility or outside enterprise, lest problems of money, property, and prestige divert us from our primary purpose.

Our Fellowship is often invited to bring its message to outside organizations, including schools, colleges, community health venues, drug and alcohol treatment centers, and prisons. Bewildered staff in these settings have often been floundering for years, desperate for guidance from anyone who will shed light on the raging epidemic of anorexia and bulimia in their midst.

We respond generously to all such invitations, knowing they are really issued by the Creator. We send volunteer speakers to assist with in-service staff training and to carry the message directly to students, clients, and inmates in these various settings. Sometimes we establish regular A.B.A. meetings in these institutions, especially those whose sole purpose is the treatment of eating disorders.

When carrying out this activity, we take great care to let our audience know that we are not affiliated with the institution wherein we speak, nor with any other established enterprise, that we are but an itinerant band independent of all allegiances other than to the Power who has healed us. Our Fellowship's sacred purpose of carrying the message to those suffering from our disease would be greatly hampered were our name associated with that of any other organization. Practicing anorexics and bulimics are burdened by prejudice and resentment, and we have no desire to arouse emotions that might close the mind of anyone who needs to hear the message we bear.

TRADITION SEVEN:
Every A.B.A. group ought to be fully self-supporting, declining outside contributions.

This principle of financial independence follows naturally from the Sixth Tradition. We are economically beholden to no one, and we refuse all offers of financial compensation from outside sources. Money always has visible or invisible strings attached to it. Were we to accept funds from anyone other than our own members, we would place ourselves at risk of outside domination.

We believe that the Creator alone provides for all our needs, including the small amounts of money we require to stay afloat. God works through human beings. As each of us recovers in our Fellowship, we feel the stirrings of deep gratitude within us, a gratitude that seeks to return to the Creator whatever poor gift we can find to repay our impossible debt. We have received the gift of restoration of our minds and our lives. Digging into our pockets at meetings to pay for literature, room rental, and coffee is the very least we can offer as tangible proof of our grateful hearts.

We contribute what we have to offer, whether money or time or talent, to support the operation of our Fellowship. All gifts are needed, not just hard cash. Just as important is the work of stacking chairs and answering mail and creating the literature that carries our message. We pour out our energy in these pursuits, still hoping to repay our Higher Power for at least a fraction of what we have received. The only problem is that the more we give, the more we receive from a Higher Power who seems unacquainted with the concept of fair exchange. When we move a finger for ten seconds in support of our group, we receive an avalanche of grace. Thus our indebtedness grows exponentially. We would do better to cease trying to repay such a God, but our awakened hearts will not allow us to do so. Love has transformed us, carved its initials on our being, made us alive to its Presence within us. We cannot stop loving, we cannot stop giving.

Clever God! Who else but a Higher Power could have masterminded this superb design—the same one we saw operating in Step Twelve—that ensures the viability of our Fellowship. As long as there are recovered anorexics and bulimics drawing breath on this planet, we are assured of all the support we need to continue spreading the healing influence of the Creator.

TRADITION EIGHT:

Anorexics and Bulimics Anonymous should remain forever nonprofessional, but our service centers may employ special workers.

The principle of nonprofessionalism in the work of our Fellowship is fundamental to its survival, and therefore to the very lives of us, its members. The concept of service freely rendered was planted in us as individuals by the Seventh Tradition, and it blooms in the Eighth into a guiding principle for our operation as a group. Never can we accept material return for the service work we do in carrying the message to others, for we have already received the highest payment of all: the free gift from the Creator of sobriety itself.

If we lose this spirit of free service, we forget how utterly dependent we are on God for our sobriety. We saw earlier in this book how dangerous is such forgetting. It is the breeding ground of relapse. For loss of humility maims our spirits, and spiritual malaise naturally generates mental and physical sickness. Our twisted thinking returns as we begin to operate once more out of self-centeredness and dishonesty, and it is only a matter of time before we begin to perceive ourselves as fat and are compelled to do something about that.

The surest means of avoiding this malignant progression is to pray always for the gift of humility and to nurture this humility by giving freely of ourselves to others. Doing so keeps the channel within us open to the grace of God, and our experience has been that a Higher Power fills every available space to the bursting point. This Power needs no second invitation. The Creator is no miser, is never stingy or mean with us creatures. Ask, and you will receive.

Some of our members are situated in paid employment that brings us into contact with anorexics and bulimics seeking a solution for their illness. For us, it is vital to keep the Eighth Tradition ever in mind. As social workers, nurses, physicians, counselors, we might be tempted to regard our jobs as a form of service work. They are not. We are being paid to perform a specific task with those who come into our care, and we are responsible to our employer for the completion of this assignment. Even though at times we may speak to anorexic and bulimic clients about A.B.A. and encourage them to attend meetings, we must never view this as Twelfth-Step work. Otherwise, we might decide that, since we had already done our duty as faithful members of A.B.A., we could afford to go home and put our feet up instead of going to a meeting that night. Or instead of responding to a phone message from a bereft fellow member in the throes of a crisis threatening her sobriety. Or going out for coffee with her after the meeting. Or visiting a member who is ill and housebound or hospitalized. Or volunteering an hour at our central office to answer the phone or package literature for distribution.

To neglect the performance of such free service is to invite disaster into our lives as recovering people. Some of us have bitter experiences with relapse that have proven this fact more than once.

Our Fellowship can, of course, employ people—whether members of our Fellowship or not—to perform the jobs that keep our service centers going. For example, we may need a secretary to type letters or a receptionist to field telephone inquiries. Such employees are not being paid to do service work, but to allow our Fellowship to stay in operation so that we can be available to anyone reaching out for help. This practice, as advocated by Tradition Eight, is important to the outreach activities of A.B.A. as a whole.

TRADITION NINE:
A.B.A., as such, ought never be organized; but we may create service boards or committees directly responsible to those they serve.

This Tradition brings the concept of free service to fruition by giving formal structure to those members who are called to a particular form of service work. The best way to understand this principle is by looking at a concrete example.

When this textbook was first envisioned more than two years ago, our Fellowship called forth people to do the practical work of creating it. We needed writers to put into words the concepts under which we operated. We required editors to revise the manuscript, bringing it fully into line with what we know to be true about recovery. Copy editors were needed to correct the grammar, spelling, and punctuation. We needed experts who knew how to format the text on a computer screen to prepare it to become a printed page. We required others who knew about the business of publishing. Clearly, we required a host of members working together if our imagined textbook was to become a reality.

So we gathered together a cadre of people deeply interested in the project. We gave this Book Committee freedom to organize themselves as they saw fit, to meet whenever and however they decided was necessary, to execute their mandate in whatever way worked best for them. As they labored in love together, the manuscript took shape. But long before it went to the printer for mass production, we wanted to see what they had written and have a close look at the budget they expected our members to cover through group funds.

All of us in the Fellowship had the opportunity to be involved at this point. We entered into lively debate and critiqued the text itself. We questioned every proposed expenditure and set a sales price for the book that would cover its cost and allow for further outreach. Our Book Committee had been formed to serve us all, so we had the final say about what our textbook would contain, what its final form would be, and at what price it would be sold. We could all be the boss, so to speak, because we had full confidence that our real Employer speaks through our group conscience. We knew that the Creator was the true Author of the book, that it could never have been written without the creative inspiration of our committee members, and that such inspiration came from a Higher Power alone.

Our Ninth Tradition embodies the principle of *ad hoc* organization. We needed a structured Book Committee to execute a particular mission, and when this had been accomplished the group disintegrated. Its members resumed their places among our general membership, this task behind them, and turned their attention to whatever the Creator would call them to do next—perhaps sweeping the floor or brewing the coffee for the next meeting, or driving a stranded fellow member to her home on a cold winter night.

Our Fellowship has no formal organization under normal circumstances, because it needs none. When we recover through the

Twelve-Step Program we are transformed into beings capable of humble service wherever it is needed, beings so committed to loving ourselves and one another that we need no director to keep us in check. Love alone does that.

TRADITION TEN:

Anorexics and Bulimics Anonymous has no opinion on outside issues; hence the A.B.A. name ought never be drawn into public controversy.

The principle contained in this Tradition is known in ordinary parlance as "minding our own business" or, as others have phrased it, "staying on our own side of the street."[6] This concept is of critical importance, not only to our sober living as individuals, but also to the continued survival of our Fellowship and the effectiveness with which we carry the message to others.

The sole concern of Anorexics and Bulimics Anonymous is to tell others suffering from our disease about the Twelve-Step spiritual solution we have found, to carry to them the joyful message of the victory that comes only through admitting total defeat, to proclaim the good news of the liberation that results from surrender to a Higher Power of our own individual understanding. The moment we lose our focus on this mighty purpose is the moment we cease to be God's instrument in this healing work.

This may best be understood through some concrete examples. We do not, for instance, hold any corporate opinion regarding other solutions to the diseases of anorexia and bulimia. How the multitude of physicians and other therapists working in this field carry out their mission is none of our concern. These dedicated people are of service to many, including our own members, and we heartily applaud their efforts. We are happy for those anorexics and bulimics who have been guided to recovery by such professionals. Knowing that the field of eating disorders is broad and long, with plenty of space for everyone called to serve, we hold no delusion that we have found the only answer, nor even one that could suit everyone afflicted with our disease.

Nor do we hold any opinion on the way in which the concept of a Higher Power must be conceived.[7] We do not tell our members anything at all about religion nor advise them regarding which formal religious beliefs they should hold. In meetings we do share freely about our personal route to connection with a Higher Power; yet even in this intimate setting we shy away from using sectarian terms, so as not to inflict our particular beliefs on others. We strive always to be sensitive to those who so kindly listen to our babbling—and in particular the newcomer. Were we to hold forth using the language of a television evangelist, for example, we might drive away a fragile newcomer who happens to be agnostic or atheist. If she dies from her disease without ever returning to our circle, we will have a good deal to answer for. And at the public level our Fellowship maintains utter silence in the area of religion, for what others believe about the God-concept and how they live their beliefs is absolutely none of our business. The subject of which sect is killing off another in the name of its particular deity is not our concern, even if it fills the morning papers. Nor do we comment on the wonderful work being done by some religious organization in Papua-New Guinea, even if the town is abuzz with the news. We recognize that religious fashions come and go. We must adhere to what endures: the singular mission entrusted to us by the Power who called us to recovery.

Similarly, Anorexics and Bulimics Anonymous holds no opinion in the arena of business and economics. The marketplace is none of our affair, even if it be flooded with entrepreneurs from the fitness and weight-loss industry peddling their wares. Their legitimacy or lack thereof is not ours to judge, and we studiously avoid comment at a public level on this issue. On the other hand, when speaking among ourselves with the question of sobriety hanging in the balance, we have the grave responsibility of sharing our ideas about weight-control products with others who wish to recover from our disease. The topic is not an outside issue at this level, for an anorexic or bulimic will generally not get sober if she buys skim milk or diet soda or the latest exercise equipment to use in her basement. And if she does not get sober, she may die. This information we are solemnly bound to share with one another.

Were the name of Anorexics and Bulimics Anonymous to be drawn into public controversy, we might fail to fulfill the mission entrusted us by the Creator, that of carrying our spiritual message to other anorexics and bulimics who wish to hear it. Our sacred responsibility is to guard our integrity at all times, that we may remain an effective instrument in God's hands.

TRADITION ELEVEN:
Our public relations policy is based on attraction rather than promotion; we need always maintain personal anonymity at the level of press, radio, TV, and films.

This Tradition and the one following are concerned with the quintessentially important concept of anonymity. It is fitting that these Traditions are the last word in the principles that govern us, for on anonymity our very life as a Fellowship depends. The previous ten Traditions lead us to this climactic conclusion, to the anonymity that ensures our survival.

Anonymity is about humility. When we were new to the Fellowship we had no inkling of this fact, and we were simply relieved that we could remain anonymous in the midst of all these strangers. We were embarrassed enough to admit that we were anorexic or bulimic, let alone that we were a person of stature in the world beyond the meeting. No one asked to see our credentials or proof of identity when we came through the door. We were not required to admit we were lawyers or politicians or nuns. Our anxiety was also alleviated when we learned that no one in the room would betray us to the outside world by sharing our dark secrets with those from whom we hid. No one, for example, would phone our employer and inform him of our bingeing and purging on his time; nor would anyone call up our spouse and tell him we had lost five pounds in the past week and advise him to get us to a doctor, and quickly.

Later in recovery as God relieves us of our self-centeredness, our desire to hide, and our need to control what others think, our ideas change radically. We lose all fear of being seen and being known, exactly as we are, and at times in our exuberant release we swing to extremes of self-disclosure. We seek out opportunities to proclaim to all who will listen that we were the craziest priest who ever donned a cassock, the sickest ballerina who ever did a triple pirouette, the weirdest physician who ever took the Hippocratic Oath. No longer do we need to conceal ourselves, for once we have discovered that God is everything, we have nothing more to gain and nothing more to lose.

Later still, when we fortunately arrive at an even more mature stage of the healing process, we grasp yet another level of truth. We see our excessive self-disclosure as evidence of subtle arrogance and grandiosity, as merely another manifestation of self-centeredness. Drawing attention to ourselves is just as pathological as hiding under a rock, for both are based on a degree of self-absorption that defies description. As we develop a deeper connection with the Power who sustains everything, we long to efface ourselves, to become so transparent that this Power alone will radiate through when others look at us.[8] When we arrive at this place, we understand at last the profound wisdom of Tradition Eleven.

Anonymity, which is our corporate form of humility, is about giving the glory to God alone, and in the public realm that requires a sacrifice of our persona for the greater good. Flaunting our individuality detracts from the pristine beauty of the message we carry; and once we become aware of the destructiveness of such pretentious posturing, we are obligated to refrain from indulging in it. As we efface ourselves that the Creator may shine, we become even more intimately connected with the Power who heals us.

TRADITION TWELVE:

Anonymity is the spiritual foundation of all our traditions, ever reminding us to place principles before personalities.

Seen in the light of what we have just explored in the Eleventh Tradition, the Twelfth makes impeccable sense. The literature of Alcoholics Anonymous teaches us that humility is the spiritual foundation of every one of the Twelve Steps, and just so is anonymity—corporate humility—the basis of all the Traditions.

The Twelve Steps are a lifelong itinerary for individual spiritual growth. We are impregnated with the essence of humility when we admit personal powerlessness, become willing to believe in a Being who possesses the power we lack, and decide to subjugate our thinking and our actions to that greater Power. Taking a searching inventory of our warped minds and confessing the whole of this to another can do nothing but nurture humility as we become deeply aware of our alienation when we walked separate from the Creator. Preparing to let God change us according to divine purpose, and asking God to do that, is the ultimate dance of humility in the most intimate recesses of our being. Repairing the damage we have done to other people in our blind march to death engenders further humility as we see with our own eyes an awesome healing Power at work in our relationships. Taking ongoing inventory of ourselves and admitting our daily failures is no tedious mechanical chore, but a daily renewal of humility. To seek prayerful conscious contact with a Power for whom we now ache with love, and to ardently desire only to act in accordance with divine will, is to imbibe and ingest and inhale humility. And arrival at the zenith of a spiritual transformation that cannot contain itself, that must overflow into every area of our lives, is the perfection of humility wherein the creature, now fully effaced, fuses with the Creator.

In the Twelve Traditions we see this breathtaking design for spiritual growth repeated at a group level. When we place our common welfare ahead of any member's personal whims, we are initiated into humility. To bow to the conscience of the group because we recognize it as the voice of a Higher Power is to surrender our self-will in favor of divine will—the very heart of humility. When we accept everyone who wishes to be in our midst, letting go of all control measures and membership criteria, as a group we are demonstrating a degree of humble trust in God that is the stuff of saints. To allow each group full autonomy over its own affairs, absolute right to its own unique flavor, is to humbly recognize and celebrate the diversity ordained by the Creator. Clearly stating that our ministry to the still-suffering anorexic or bulimic is the primary purpose for our group's existence is tantamount to sacrificing our egocentric desires for the good of another human being—an action that incites the angels to sing. When our group renounces all affiliations other than to the Power who has healed us, we stand stripped of all idols before the Creator, cloaked in humility. In embracing voluntary poverty the group casts itself on the mercy of God alone, and God's response is to give us more gifts than we can use in our humble service of the Creator. To eschew professionalism in our work as servants of a Higher Power is to humbly testify to the world that the sobriety we have been freely given is as much wealth as we can bear. In remaining fundamentally unorganized we consent to engage in life as a process, with fluidity, pledging ourselves to ongoing evolution and to the unseen orchestration of the Creator. When in humble silence we abstain from all corporate opinion on outside issues, we avoid being drawn into controversy that could irreparably damage our effectiveness in completing the assignment handed us by our Higher Power. To focus on living sober, trusting that our visible behavior is the only advertisement our group needs, and to remain faceless and nameless in the public eye, is to practice the highest level of humility. And when we place the principles by which we recover ahead of every other consideration in the affairs of our group, we aspire to be so God-centered that we become one with the Creator—the epitome of anonymity.

The reader will have observed through the course of this discussion that the Twelve Traditions flow one into the next in an orderly progression that is nothing short of magnificent. Together they form a cohesive luminescent whole, a radiant protective aura within which our Fellowship and its individual groups live and thrive. When the group adheres to the Traditions, it ensures its own vitality and viability. If it deviates from them, it signs its own death warrant. We have seen this demonstrated many times. The truth of this releases Anorexics and Bulimics Anonymous as a whole from any need to censure or discipline an individual group for violating the Traditions, for it will inevitably self-destruct. The Creator is in charge.

To The Family 15

WARNING: The content of this chapter is intended for use only by families of anorexics and bulimics who have attained the age of majority. Parents of minor children with eating disorders are reminded of their legal responsibility to ensure that their children receive appropriate medical care whenever they are ill, and are strongly advised to consult qualified and knowledgeable health professionals.

EATING DISORDERS ARE FAMILY DISEASES

Effects on the Family

LIKE ALCOHOLISM, eating disorders are family diseases.[1] As one member becomes ill with anorexia or bulimia, the entire family is affected and itself becomes ill. Everyone is baffled by the bizarre changes in the sick member. Tempers inevitably flare. Fear pervades the family home, choking out trust and planting seeds of suspicion. Communication breaks down. Silence and pretense dominate the scene, interspersed with heart-wrenching times of noisy recriminations and bitter tears. Easy laughter and shared affection become distant memories. Everyone's love is sorely challenged as the family home is converted to a land laid waste by an unseen enemy.

The Sick One Notices, Too

By the time we reached Anorexics and Bulimics Anonymous, most of us were acutely aware of how our insane behavior with food was affecting those we loved the most. We had seen their tears and their silent suffering, heard their urgent pleas for us to quit doing what we did with food, felt the wall of their anger, sensed the desperate pain in which they lived every day. We longed to be able to reach them, to make them understand what was going on with us, to help them grasp that we couldn't stop doing what we were doing even when we wanted to. We wanted them to know we were not anorexic and bulimic out of spite, out of a desire to hurt them. We yearned to tell them they were not the cause of our eating disorder, and we tried to do so, but either we could not find our voice or they could not hear us. We saw their bewilderment, and we knew it well because deep within we were just as mystified and confused by our behavior as they were. How could we help them when we couldn't help ourselves? How could we make them comprehend what was incomprehensible to us?

As we progressed in our disease and our pain increased, we often felt like small children encountering a gargantuan horror. It was too big for us to deal with and we longed for a rescuer. We wanted our loved ones to save us from the anguish in which we lived from day to day and yet we knew they could not. We began to see how much we needed help and we knew that our families couldn't help us, for we were painfully aware of how deeply conflicted we were in our relationship with them. We loved them intensely and at the same time experienced an unrelenting need to fight them, to assert ourselves around food and exercise, to lash out in anger or to retreat in sullen silence when they or anyone else tried to control us.

What a terrible dilemma for everyone concerned!

AB-ANON SPEAKS

Knowing the difficulties faced by our loved ones, we wish to include a chapter addressed specifically to them. In preparing this section of our book, we consulted a sister Fellowship that was founded in our city of origin a number of years ago. They call themselves "Ab-Anon" and their purpose is to help and support families and friends of people with eating disorders, using the same Twelve Steps as do we in Anorexics and Bulimics Anonymous. They in turn model themselves after a similar Fellowship that supports families and friends of alcoholics.[2]

We approached our Ab-Anon friends and asked them to write down everything they wish to tell the readers of this book, everything important they have learned through living with the diseases of anorexia and bulimia in their loved ones. We are deeply touched by their overwhelmingly generous response and wish to express our gratitude to them for sharing their experience, strength, and hope with us in such graphic and evocative detail. What follows is a compilation of their words and writings. They have lived on the front line as parents, siblings, spouses, and friends of anorexics and bulimics, and they know of what they speak.

EARLY STAGES

The Bliss of Unawareness

They shared first how they emerged from not knowing that their loved one was sick, into the light of naming the disease.[3] "For many years I was unaware that she had an eating disorder," says one mother. "Whether this can be attributed to my lack of knowledge about eating disorders, my denial, or her immense secrecy, I am unsure, but probably all played a part." In the early stages of the disease almost all family members were oblivious to the problem. "She had been a swimmer since she was six, so I thought nothing of the fact that she exercised at night," says another parent.

"At age fourteen she became a vegetarian," recalls one mother. "I felt proud that she would go and dig her own vegetables from the garden and cook them. That was something her sisters would never do!" Others also recall initially feeling delight in their loved one's new behavior, seeing what they were doing as an achievement. "At first I was proud that my daughter showed such discipline to control her eating."

The Dawn of Suspicion

At some point every one of these family members began to suspect the truth, but often it took a long time for the nagging suspicion in their gut to become certainty. "When my daughter came home from her summer job that year, I was concerned because she had lost weight and because she was behaving very differently about food. She would not eat with me, she would not sit at the table to eat, she did not join us when there were guests for a meal. This was very troubling, for she had always enjoyed having company for dinner.... The spark that had always been part of her had dimmed."

Many other families also noticed subtle or more blatant changes in their loved one. Says one mother, "She was driven…." And another, "We were no longer eating dinner together as a family. She always had some plausible story why she couldn't join us. What used to be a time of wonderful discussion and relating was now overshadowed with a sadness brought on by the vacant chair." One parent observes, "It was very stressful. Gradually she started looking vacant and gaunt. Eyes that once danced with excitement were now dull and lifeless. Sharp bones were sticking out of her sweaters." And another, "She went into a kind of frenzy. She gave away her ski jacket in the middle of winter. She went on walks for the sole purpose of picking up garbage." And yet another, "While she was complaining about her 'fat thighs,' I was looking at her fingers. Even they had become skin and bone."

Some families tried to confront the problem head on. "Several times I asked her if she was all right," says one mother. "She assured me that she was not anorexic, because anorexia is a psychiatric disease and she did not have a psychiatric disease." And another, "We tried to encourage her to see our family physician, but to no avail."

There's Something Wrong Here!

Often these parents could find no one to share their concern. "The situation was aggravated by the people who were telling her how good she looked since she had lost weight. Every time I heard this, I screamed inside." Says another mother, "She had lost fifteen pounds. I felt that she was too thin, but many people told me she was just lean and I was overreacting." Even professionals sometimes failed to validate parental concern in the early stages: "I had spoken in confidence with the dietitian before my daughter saw her, but she said she had looked specifically [for signs of anorexia] and no red flags came up in their discussion."

The Shocking Truth

Other families were catapulted out of their denial in a shocking and sometimes dramatic manner. "My husband noticed a green garbage bag in the garage," says one mother, "sitting right by the door in full view. After it had been there for days, he opened it and saw many bags of vomit. I approached my daughter and she admitted she had been doing this for six years." Another parent recalls, "One day we found her collapsed on the bathroom floor at home. She was rushed to the hospital.... We knew we were in very serious trouble." Another parent, although aware of the diagnosis in her anorexic daughter, was similarly shaken by the staggering physical progression of her disease. She relates, "I was reading the paper at the table when I heard a noise and turned to see her slumped on the counter. I rushed over and caught her before she hit the floor. I could not at first feel a pulse and immediately thought, 'My God, she's dead.'... The next day she asked me why I was so upset."

FULL-BLOWN FAMILY DISEASE

Living With Her: Unceasing Pain

The Ab-Anon members shared their universal experience of pain as they tried to cope with their loved one once the diagnosis had been made clear. "Watching my sister not eat or eat and purge was very painful. I spent many nights sobbing as I didn't know what to do." One parent says, "The tension and anxiety we both felt over meal times was awful." And another, tellingly, "Her problem seemed to take over the entire family." Says a mother, "I became preoccupied with thoughts of her, terrified that she might die." And another, "I found it hard to relate to her on any level other than her eating disorder. Indeed, in my eyes she *was* her eating disorder."

Grief, Loss, Isolation, Anger

All families experienced grief and loss and often feelings of isolation, of being alone with this problem in their loved one and not knowing what to do. "We had lost the bright, bubbly, beautiful girl we knew as our daughter," laments one mother. "She had been at the top of her class every year, and here she was considering not finishing high school!" Says another, simply, "I wanted my healthy daughter back." And yet another, "I felt a tremendous sense of loss. Here was our intelligent, articulate, and talented daughter who, instead of being able to pursue her education and have a normal social life, was having to deal with this tremendous, life-threatening illness. It wasn't fair to her or to us. My husband and I felt very isolated. We didn't know anyone else who had this problem, and I felt a certain sense of envy toward other families whose children were not experiencing problems. Why our daughter? Why us?"

How To Be?

Everyone had difficulty knowing how to be with their sick family member at this stage. Says one mother, "She behaved in ways that made our interactions unpredictable. 'Walking on eggshells' became my way of life." Another parent's experience was similar, "While at times she was very open to talking, at other times she put up an impenetrable wall around herself."

Attempts to Control

All families attempted to control the eating disorder in their loved one. One father admits, "I tried to take over my daughter's life. I know it doesn't work, it never has, but desperate times call for desperate measures. My attempted control distanced me from my daughter at a time when we both needed to be close. It was pure hell hearing her run the microwave on an eating binge after we had gone to bed or hearing her vomit in the bathroom as she purged. Nothing I said or did seemed to work, and my daughter mirrored my defeat." And a mother says, "I found myself frequently trying to monitor what she ate and scrutinizing her appearance to see if she was losing more weight. My attention was totally focused on her at the expense of both my husband and my other daughter. Conversations with my husband centered on her and her problems." Recalls another mother, "Whenever she did join us for meals it was a battle of wills. She wouldn't eat, and we were trying to encourage her to eat."

Who is to Blame?

Another universal theme is the guilt that families, especially parents, felt as they tried to make sense of their loved one's plight. One mother says, "I experienced an overwhelming sense of guilt. What had we done wrong? We had been dedicated to being the perfect parents, spending enormous amounts of time with our children." And one parent, "I suffered feelings of embarrassment and shame. What would I tell our family and our friends?" Often their guilt mutated into anger. "I was angry and blaming. How could she do this to herself and to us? Surely she knew that in order to live she had to eat." Another mother agrees, "I watched her shrinking and felt helpless and angry that this was happening to such a wonderful young woman." And a sibling from yet another family, "Blaming began within our family as we tried to figure out who was to blame for her eating disorder. My divorced parents blamed each other and my mother blamed me. To say the least, our family grew further apart."

SHE'S IN TREATMENT NOW

Relief, Hope, Fear...and More Pain

Ab-Anon members had a variety of experiences once their loved one reached out for treatment for her eating disorder. One parent recalls, "I felt a great sense of relief when our daughter was hospitalized as I felt she was safely in the hands of a medical team who would monitor her vital signs." Another mother felt differently: "She would spend the next seven months in this ward where she was confined to forced feeding and locked bathrooms. From freedom to a life where every move was controlled. It was the hardest thing I had to do as a mother, to watch my daughter be in an environment I would not have survived myself." And one parent says, "Fear enveloped me again when I heard she was being discharged." Another adds, "The first while I was nervously watching what she was eating again. One day I looked in her closet and was horrified to find every shelf crammed with every kind of junk food!"

Who Can Help Us?

Many family members spoke about their long search for help for both themselves and their loved one. A sibling says, "No help was available to my sister in the city we lived in. No one knew how to deal with eating disorders." Says a mother, "I had been concerned that she had not continued in any sort of treatment for anorexia because she did not feel comfortable with any of the approaches." And a father in another family, "This was a problem I did not understand. I made the error of assuming the professionals did understand and thus was reassured when she told me she was going for counseling.... Two visits to the Emergency Room reminded me of the horrible truth of this illness." And yet another parent, "After her discharge from hospital we went on a ten-day holiday. Her eating habits were bizarre. I could see that she was losing weight again. My greatest fears were returning. What was going to happen now?"

Attempting Meal-Support

Some family members tried to support their loved one in sobering up once they came to Anorexics and Bulimics Anonymous. They learned the importance of surrender of all control of food to a Higher

Power and they offered to be the meal-support helper in this process. Nevertheless, despite unwavering love and a level of commitment that can only be described as heroic, their attempts were almost always futile. One mother vividly describes her experience. "In order for my daughter to start eating in a healthy manner, she asked me to serve her meals. We saw a dietitian together who worked out a meal plan. My daughter knew she needed to trust that her Higher Power would work through my hands to give her what she needed to eat. We both agreed to try this, because there seemed to be no other solution.

"The months that followed were extremely difficult. There were many bitter discussions about what I served, the portion sizes, the combinations I put together. She threw food and dishes. She stood over me as I filled her plate. Her sponsor told her to stay out of the kitchen completely until the meal was served. The tension and anxiety we both felt over meal times was awful. After six months of this she said she couldn't stand the arrangement anymore. She was starting to hate me and she didn't want to do that. For my part, I still could see no option other than to keep going. It seemed to me that my choice was between a live daughter who hated me and a dead one who loved me."

This particular mother's efforts did keep her daughter alive for a time, and this important phase of her recovery taught both of them invaluable lessons about powerlessness. Both mother and daughter learned that love is insufficient to dispel the deadly obsession from the anorexic mind, no matter how deep and unconditional the love and how compelling the necessity. This young woman needed to be honest with herself and her sponsor and admit that she was not sober in this arrangement with her mother, because she couldn't stop using many devious tactics to control what her mother served. She was then able to move to another setting to get sober and has now been fully relieved of her anorexic obsession. Almost two years sober, she looks back on her mother's contribution to her recovery with gratitude.

Love is Not Enough

The important point here is that it is seldom possible for a family member to provide meal-support for their anorexic or bulimic in early sobriety. There seems to be too much enmeshment between them, too much blurring of their boundaries, too much emotional investment in the process. This is true even when the anorexic or bulimic is highly motivated for recovery and her family is deeply loving and caring. The disease is simply too powerful. It can find many ways to insinuate itself into the family dynamics and abort the sick one's sobering-up process. The disease has more power than that of the whole family together. A rule of thumb seems to be, "If you share DNA with an anorexic or bulimic, you will probably not be the channel through which her Higher Power works!"[4]

SUPPORT FOR THE FAMILY

Not Alone Anymore

Our Ab-Anon friends shared a great deal about how their lives began changing after they were led to the rooms of their Fellowship. States one father, "I was apprehensive and skeptical. I received a warm welcome and I could say as much or as little as I wanted. I felt understood, cared for, and welcome. I still do." And a mother from another family, "The sharing and the knowledge that I am not alone has meant a tremendous amount." And yet another, "Through sharing our experiences and feelings, I realized that I was not alone and others were going through the same pain.[5] It was a release to be able to let go of some feelings and to gain insight through our discussions. I always felt more centered after going to a meeting."

Powerlessness

Many members emphasized the important lessons they are learning, lessons they would pass on to others whose loved ones are suffering from an eating disorder. In the eloquent words of one mother: "At the first meeting I felt that I was home. I was told that I would need to learn to make it whether our daughter did or not. I heard people talk about The Three Cs: 'You didn't Cause it, you can't Control it, and you'll never Cure it.'[6]

"Accepting my powerlessness over her disease was difficult.[7] After all, I am her parent and should be able to make things better for her, to fix things for her as I had done so many times when she was a little girl. But this was not a skinned knee or a broken toy, and I could not fix it. The idea of 'letting go and letting God' was very frightening for me at first.[8] After all, if I turned things over to God, maybe they wouldn't turn out as I wanted them to. But I knew I had not been successful in dealing with my daughter's disease and the effects it was having on me. So at first I tried to solve problems on my own, and only when I was at the end of my rope would I finally turn things over to my

Higher Power. Then, time and time again I saw things work out in ways I could never have imagined. What a sense of freedom I experienced when I finally became willing to turn things over to my Higher Power!

Detachment

"I heard people talking about detachment.[9] Initially that seemed to be a cold and unloving thing to do. Then I heard about 'detaching with love' and I came to learn that detachment doesn't mean not caring. Rather it means owning what is mine and allowing my daughter the right to own what is hers. It means getting out of my daughter's way and allowing her to make her own decisions and to experience the consequences of her actions.[10] It was a great comfort to realize that our daughter has her own Higher Power and together they will create her future."

Others also shared about the importance of detachment. Says one father, "On a good day, when I work the Twelve-Step Program, I no longer try to control my daughter and I have something to talk to my wife about other than our daughter's disease. I have come to understand that she has a real 'disease,' not a 'problem,' and that understanding has improved our relationship. I remember a watershed event that proved the Program was working for me. My daughter had made some demand on me, threatening to binge and purge if I didn't comply. With a great deal of fear and a small amount of faith in what I had learned, I told her it was her problem and her decision how she responded. Later on she told me that was a most helpful response, and she knew I finally 'got' it."

Twelve Steps to Freedom

Detaching from their loved one's disease often brought about other unexpected benefits. One mother says, "I now have more energy and can be more positive. By allowing her to take on her own problem, I was able to be more supportive when she wanted help. Tension in the family was reduced and relationships were better because I was not focusing on her. I learned it was a waste of energy to be constantly thinking and worrying about her, especially since this did not make any difference in her behavior! Then, when she had crash times I was able to be there to listen and to hold her through her tears.

"I have learned the value of taking time daily to pray and to develop an inner core of peace. I have learned that I have to carry on with my life and that she has to live her own life and take responsibility for her own actions.[11]... The only person I can change is myself and, through allowing God to guide me and to be my source of help and hope, I gain the priceless gift of serenity."[12]

Another mother writes, "My relationships with other members of my immediate family have improved. As I became open to sharing my experiences with others I grew closer to extended family, friends, colleagues, and people who before were merely acquaintances. As I work the Twelve-Step Program, I continue to gain tools helpful to me in many aspects of my life. I have learned the importance of gratitude and continually thank God for the many blessings of healing that we have all received."

One Day at a Time

A critically important lesson for anyone who loves an anorexic or bulimic is to stay in the present. Says one parent, "I learned it is not people that let us down, but our expectations of them.[13] As I began to examine my expectations against the expectations of others for their children, I understood what this meant. I now attempt to stay in the moment and to avoid imagining what our daughter might do or be in the future. Living one day at a time takes practice, and serenity can only be achieved when we are able to do this."[14]

What if She's Young?

The Ab-Anon Fellowship is comprised of families and friends of anorexics and bulimics who have attained the age of majority. The problems faced by the parents of a minor child who is ill are somewhat different. Anorexia and bulimia often begin in this age group, and parents obviously have a clear moral and legal responsibility to ensure that their child receives life-saving therapy. This obligation is no different from that borne by parents of a child with cancer. We urge such parents to seek the advice of knowledgeable physicians and explore all available treatment options.

AB-ANON SUGGESTS

Our Ab-Anon friends have compiled a list of suggestions for those whose loved one has an eating disorder. Here they are, in their own words:

- Make your spiritual growth paramount in your life.
- Don't minimize the effect this disease has had on your life and the life of your loved one.
- Join a Twelve-Step Fellowship where you may find acceptance and support from others who are dealing with the effects of addictions on their lives.
- Strive to turn your will and your life over to the care of a Higher Power of your understanding.
- Detach from her disease. Stop attempting to control what lies beyond your power: your loved one and her disease. Don't monitor her eating behavior, persuade, or threaten her.
- Have compassion for her and her struggle. Cultivate patience and a non-judgmental attitude.
- Be patient with yourself. Mistakes are part of the process of growth.
- Be honest with yourself about your availability when she asks for support. Give her what you can.
- Remember that your loved one has her own Higher Power, and you're not it!
- Take care of yourself and your own needs. Remember you have a life to lead apart from her.[15]
- Don't attribute every problem in your family to her eating disorder.
- Never lose hope. Take time to pray, for yourself and your loved one.
- Remember that your loved one may gain wisdom and strength through her struggle, as well as tools to live fully. What her life looks like is none of your business!

We would like to invite any reader who has been affected by someone else's eating disorder and who needs support, to contact Ab-Anon for further information about their recovery program. They can be reached by writing c/o Anorexics and Bulimics Anonymous (address at the end of Chapter 12) or through A.B.A.'s website at www.anorexicsandbulimicsanonymousaba.com.

PART II

Here Are Our Stories

Introduction

THIS SECTION of our text comprises selected autobiographical accounts written by some of our sober members. Each of them contains a striking description of what our lives used to be like, what happened, and what they are like now. Our purpose in including these highly revealing narratives is to reach other anorexics and bulimics who will read this book, transmitting our experience, strength, and hope to those who are suffering.

It is said that a picture is worth a thousand words, and we believe that a story is worth a thousand essays. Each one of us has our story, and our tales need to be told. Our collective experience is buried treasure, a gold mine of wisdom that we need to bring into the light of today, to share freely with others who may benefit from it. We hope that any anorexics and bulimics reading these histories will be able to find themselves within the pages. If you can identify with us through our accounts of our lives, then you too can find the solution that we have found for our deadly disease.

Just as "Joan's Story," written by one of our three founding members, is located near the beginning of Part I, so this section of our text opens with a personal chronicle by another of our co-founders. Her writing includes a poignant history of the neonatal period of our beloved Fellowship and hauntingly reveals how a Higher Power was guiding our early pioneers.

In compiling Part II, we have been cautious to select only those accounts submitted by sober A.B.A. members, people who at the time of this publication are maintaining continuous sobriety. The reader can therefore rely absolutely on what they say about themselves, with the assurance that these are accurate reports rendered by anorexics and bulimics who have successfully used the Twelve-Step Program of Anorexics and Bulimics Anonymous as a route to recovery.

Some of the people in the following pages have long-term sobriety; others are relative newcomers. Regardless of length of recovery, the key to our healing has been the development of a relationship with a Higher Power, and each of our members has her own unique experience of that process. We offer our portrayal of that adventure as our gift to you. May you be blessed in the reading of these tales.

Some of us have chosen pen names for ourselves, and wherever other people are mentioned by name a pseudonym has invariably been selected. We do this both to safeguard the privacy of our loved ones and to remain anonymous, that the Power who heals us may be the only voice you hear in what follows.

Mary Beth's Story: From an 'I' to a 'We'... 1

THE OPPORTUNITY to share my story as a recovering bulimic held a few surprises for me. Of course, I know that the quality of life in recovery that I am graced with today is the result of a long journey of different-sized steps. I know that only by sharing my experience, strength, and hope will I continue to be well in body, mind, and spirit. And yet, despite what I know, I have come to see once more how cunning and slippery my disease can be when I am invited to go within, to tell the truth without shame. To remember what it was like and what happened has been an occasion to see even more clearly how this disease bound and gagged and blindfolded me.

Recovering from my eating disorder has been a difficult journey, notwithstanding all the medical intervention and psychological probing I received. Out of all the pathways to healing that I walked, the Twelve-Step Program has been the most fruitful. And so, because I am forever grateful for the unfolding events that led to the founding of Anorexics and Bulimics Anonymous, I offer the reader these pieces of my journey.

I see today that around my eating disorder I was engaged for more than four decades in the deadly twosome of denial and lying. No matter how badly this duet faltered, I persisted in picking it up again and again, making it work to keep the secret. Coming to discover that I exhibited the characteristics of an adult child of an alcoholic, and then admitting that I *am* an alcoholic and addict, was quite enough truth-telling for this forty-six-year-old woman! The Twelve-Step Program of A.A. opened a door to a way of life based on honesty with self and others, a relationship with a Higher Power, and a one-day-at-a-time means of staying clean and sober. I went to meetings, read the Big Book, worked with a sponsor.

Around this time I became more obsessed than ever with thinness at any cost. I regarded this as a gift of sobriety: My thinking was now clear enough that I could work seriously at getting thin for life...again. Even the idea that I might be powerless over anything else was simply not up for discussion. I was finally approaching an acceptable body size. I was obsessed with being thin, with beating my body into submission. Never mind that at 112 pounds I still felt like two hundred. I had no joy, only fear. I could not stop what I was doing. I possessed an illusion of control that was a bulwark against any interference.

The truth is that I had seen my body size as unacceptable from the age of eight. My mother had taken me shopping for a dress. When we discovered in the dressing room that the selected item did not fit, my frustrated mother punched me in the stomach and said, "When are you going to lose that weight!" The shame I felt engulfed me. From that moment I was certain there was something wrong with my body. I was forced to wear clothing designed for "chubby" children. My mother never could abide fat; she ate little and threw up all the time. Whenever they saw us together, people would say, "Oh, Helen, this couldn't be your daughter!" My shame about my body intensified as I grew older, and my pursuit of thinness began. By age thirteen I was seeking the magic fix that was surely just around the next corner. Diet pills, diet aids, crash diets, anything that would quickly shrink my body and generate an illusion of thinness became my consuming passion. I alternated between starving and bingeing, and my weight fluctuated greatly over short periods of time. Meanwhile my guilt and remorse grew and grew. When I reached my thirties, alcohol began providing an increasingly effective escape from my relentless preoccupation with my body.

Now at last, in my mid-forties and sober in A.A., I felt in control of my food, my weight. I discovered compulsive walking as a means of dealing with any ingestion of food. I had learned about nutrition when I was in a treatment center for my chemical addictions. I could never bring myself to purge by vomiting, after watching my mother vomit every night when I was a child, so now the abuse of laxatives and diuretics became my preferred rituals. I found ways to get hold of diuretics, some of which I stole from seniors at my place of residence. I used sauna sweats and laxatives to keep the scale registering weight loss, week after week. I wondered why my legs felt rubbery for days at a time. Over time, I experienced electrolyte imbalance and protein deficiency. I attended Twelve-Step meetings for compulsive eaters, which fueled my fanatical resolve to stay thin at any cost and taught me a few new tricks to lose weight.

The big lie I told myself and others was that my weight loss was occurring spontaneously, with no nudge from me. I believed that no one my age could be anorexic. That was a disease of teenagers. I was merely gaining control of myself, of my weight, at last. My lifelong dream of attaining the perfect body size was finally being realized.

Then the consequences from my unnamed disease began to accumulate. I became more interiorly isolated, even though I participated in A.A. for years, prayed, attended to spiritual practices, and worked professionally in a religious ministry of pastoral care. My spiritual life felt dry and automated; all passion was diverted into my infatuation with weight and body size. My disease progressed and led to my arrest for theft when I was caught stealing laxatives from a pharmacy. Even then I could not stop my sick behaviors and the obsession that fueled them.

My turning point came before my fiftieth birthday, when I experienced loss of control of my bowels at night. I had no sensation of this happening, but would awaken feeling as if I had wet the bed. I was frightened and ashamed and knew I could not keep doing what I was doing. I needed help. Life was clearly unmanageable. My thinking was sick. I had been suicidal earlier in my life, but somehow at this time I did not want to die. And yet I did not see how I could let go of my rituals.

It was then that God did for me what I could not do for myself. I began telling the truth to my physician about what I was doing to my body. In my arrogance and illusion of control, I actually thought she would be surprised! I had forgotten the number of times I evaded her questions or flatly lied. Because she herself was recovering from anorexia, she had known for a long time that I was sick. She had simply been waiting for me to open up. Now, at this very low point in my life, I did. I trusted her with what was going on inside my head. I told her that what I was doing to my body had a lot to do with wanting to be cleaned out. I tapped into a large pool of inner pain, pain that I thought I had dealt with. The floodgate opened and early memories of abuse, of extreme self-loathing, came gushing out. Out of the darkness and into the light is a journey of becoming honest with self, with God, with others. For me that day was the beginning of a journey with another and others. Recovery is a lifelong process toward wellness, balance, and freedom that is new every day.

Three women began meeting in my living room on a weekly basis: Joan J., myself, and a young anorexic and bulimic woman. The nucleus of Anorexics and Bulimics Anonymous was formed. In an atmosphere of trust, honesty, and caring, I began to admit my powerlessness over the way I thought about my body and weight and over the obsession to be thin. Life had become unmanageable and complicated. A niggle in my gut during A.A. meetings led to my admission that I was not sober in my eating.

Little by little, one day at a time, I began to see that food was not the enemy, nor was my body an object to be despised and feared. I let go of laxatives and slowly began to feed myself in a nurturing way. I came to see that my disease was lodged in my thought processes; I had to unlearn before re-learning; I had to become and remain teachable. I had to do for my bulimia what I was doing to remain clean and sober from mood-altering substances: I had to learn to trust in a power outside myself, to make the decision to turn my life and will over to the care of the God of my understanding, one meal at a time.

In our tiny group a new God-revelation began to emerge. Together, the three of us were seeing with new eyes. We had a disease, and we were not our disease. My "I" was finding new life because of the "we" that was growing. Soon other anorexic and bulimic women joined us, and we needed a larger meeting space.

I moved three times during the first five years of our life as a Fellowship, and my various homes continued to accommodate our weekly gatherings. We then moved to the meeting room of a nearby church. The following year saw the opening of a treatment center that used our approach to recovery, and its administrators invited us to expand our Twelfth-Step outreach in that facility. Adhering to the Sixth Tradition, we maintained our separateness and independence, and yet we were eager to cooperate with them. Two new weekly meetings sprang up there, and within a few months there was standing room only.

In our infant days, I was the oldest member of the group, and yet I was no different from the others. We all had similar stories, similar thoughts and feelings, and had sought similar remedies. I felt right at home with them all. Other mid-lifers came as well, and we were all one.

At times other members would stay with me for days or weeks if they needed a safe place to be, a safe place to eat. We supported one another to eat soberly. Other members sometimes provided similar housing. To this day I can see many faces of women from those early days, and I thank God for the gift they were to my recovery. Eventually men began to attend our meetings too, and in the safe haven of our circle they poured out the shame they had hidden from the world.

It was a sacred time. The Twelve Steps, the beliefs, thoughts, attitudes, and spiritual practices that had allowed millions of people to get sober and stay sober all over the world were at work in the midst of us with eating disorders. The principles of rigorous honesty, acceptance, surrender, gratitude, humility, forgiveness, and tolerance were working for and among us. Practicing the Twelve-Step Program, humbly meeting and sharing our experience with others, daily asking the help of a Power greater than ourselves—all this was leading us toward healthy living and real relationships and teaching us what it means to love and be compassionate in our daily lives. All of us had relapses into our disease, especially in early sobriety, and we also acquired the tools to get back on track. Recovery—staying well physically, emotionally, mentally, and spiritually—will always be a becoming. Becoming more aware, more authentic, more courageous.

I am reminded often of what the founders of A.A. said about the Program. "Think it, feel it, live it, and act it…Keep it simple…Ask for help, don't drink today, be grateful for everything, and help another alcoholic." This advice has been a door to recovery for members of A.B.A. over the past ten years. Many lives have been transformed. It is not the last word or the only word. What I share here is my experience only, and I do so out of gratitude and respect for the way recovery found me. I simply pass it on for whatever purpose it may have in this time.

The promises of the Twelve-Step Program do come true, both quickly and slowly. Through the spirit of A.B.A. and A.A. I have found a new freedom and happiness, an acceptance and surrender that ten years ago I could never have understood, new lenses with which to view life within and around me. The truth will always free!

Mary's Story: The Healing of a Family

2

MIRACLES STILL happen today. I should know that, because I am living proof of how coming to know the truth can set you free. For many years I was blind to myself and to everything around me. Although my family was falling apart because of my sickness, I couldn't see it until it was almost too late.

A mere four years ago, my husband of almost twenty years was a workaholic who escaped reality in the solace and privacy of his computer world. Our marriage was one in name only, with the two of us rarely speaking a civil word to each other. Mallory, my fifteen-year-old daughter, had just spent six months on the specialized eating-disorder unit of a local hospital because of life-threatening anorexia. Fourteen-year-old Candace was medicated and convalescing at home following a trip to the Emergency Room after her fourth suicide attempt in less than a year. At twelve, my only son was a rageaholic who suffered severe night terrors. My baby was only three, but she was already refusing to eat when she was hungry to avoid "getting a big tummy."

For many years I had been up early every morning to exercise before going to work. At work I did push-ups during coffee breaks and spent my lunch hour outside walking. I lived on rice cakes and diet soda. At home I rarely ate, although I had a vast collection of recipe books and served my family large gourmet meals. After dinner I insisted that my family accompany me through exercise videos so they wouldn't become couch potatoes and get fat. Afterward I worked out on the treadmill for whatever period of time was necessary to burn off any remaining calories. I did crunchies until my stomach caved in, and I prided myself on being stronger than others for not giving in to my weak human nature when it cried out for food.

I was utterly blind to my disease and to the effect it exerted on those around me, until that Friday when Mallory confronted me with the shocking statement that everything she did she had learned from me. I was stunned when she asked me how I could see the disease in her, but not in myself. I had insisted on her hospitalization against her will, yet I did not recognize any of the same symptoms in myself.

It was for me a moment of grace as I saw the truth. My life had become utterly unmanageable. My family was severely troubled. I was no longer in control, and all my illusions of control were stripped away. I had reached the bottom of the pit, and in my despair cried out to a Power I didn't really know, begging for help. I was willing to do whatever was necessary to change. The remarkable series of events that followed this awakening might be called coincidences, but I prefer to call them "God-incidences" for they are nothing short of miraculous.

Sleep was no longer a possibility, although it was still very early on Saturday morning. I crept into Mallory's room seeking the phone number of a physician she had recently consulted, intending to leave a message on her voice mail stating that I needed help. A smiling God, however, had other plans and I inadvertently dialed the doctor's home phone number. Moments later I was talking to the doctor herself, apologizing profusely for the early hour and pouring out my whole sordid story. She was gentle and kind and dismissed my apologies with the surprising statement that most of God's healing does not occur during business hours. I felt hopeful and reassured when she agreed to see me.

On Monday I called her office before I could talk myself out of it. Not surprisingly there was a long waiting list for an appointment, to which I resigned myself. But God intervened again, and I was called in within a week when another patient canceled.

It was a painful interview as I shared my life story: from an abused childhood in an alcoholic family, through a series of unhealthy relationships, into a marriage riddled with spousal abuse from which I bore the scars of guilt and inadequacy. The good doctor listened patiently before putting her pencil down and briefly sharing her own experience as an anorexic. She then diagnosed me as indeed anorexic—although I couldn't believe that I was thin enough for that label—as well as severely depressed. She said there was little hope that I could ever recover on my own. She prescribed some medication, but added that by itself it probably would not help me. Then came the message of hope: There was a group of people who shared this disease and followed a Twelve-Step Program in loving fellowship with complete reliance on a Higher Power. The key was complete surrender.

I didn't want to be this sick on my own. I wanted to be whole and have an experience of life that I had never had, so that very evening I drove through my tears to my first meeting of Anorexics and Bulimics Anonymous. From the moment I walked through the door, I knew in my heart that I was home. No one condemned me or judged me. I was welcomed warmly, and people openly shared their stories and struggles with me. The words of the Preamble seemed written by me and for me. I was no longer alone. Perhaps for the first time in my life I truly felt that I belonged.

In the weeks following, I attended at least one or two meetings every week. In the acceptance and intimacy of the group I felt safe enough to admit that my eating disorder had at one time taken the form of bulimia. I really heard that, although others could support me, the work of recovery was my responsibility. I eagerly devoured all the literature I could find, obtained a sponsor, and immediately began to apply the Twelve-Step principles to my daily life. The changes were, in my case, swift and dramatic. God entirely removed my obsessions with food, weight, and exercise, so at the good doctor's suggestion I was able to completely surrender to being fed by my family. I let go of all exercise and ate three meals and snacks prepared by the loving hands of my husband and children, all the while experiencing almost no fear of getting fat. I even ate cinnamon toast prepared by my son with extra butter and double the sugar!

At my next appointment I shared with the doctor what had transpired in my life. I told her that I had felt completely different beginning the morning after my first visit with her, and that my husband had observed the change and expressed the wish that I had started taking this magic medication years ago. The doctor chuckled and assured me that this drug does not take effect for many weeks, that the immediate change I had experienced was nothing short of a gift from my Higher Power. I was astonished and even more grateful when the doctor's tests revealed no permanent damage to my body from the abuse I had heaped on it for so many years. God did everything for me that I could not do for myself.

A new peace filled the void that my disease had occupied within me. Both of my daughters soon decided to attend A.B.A. meetings with me. As I worked the Twelve Steps, healing began to spread even beyond my immediate family. My mother, a frail elderly widow, traveled more than a thousand miles to visit me, and accompanied me to meetings while she was here. What she heard touched her heart and allowed her to weep for the mistakes she had unwittingly made in her own life that affected the lives of others. At one meeting she crossed the room to embrace a young woman with the comfort and strength she had never been able to give me as a child. Before she departed for home, my mother held me in her arms and apologized for a lifetime of mistakes. The God of forgiveness filled us both.

As I continued to stay sober and focus on working the Twelve Steps, God's amazing healing power touched hearts where other means had failed. I had been estranged from my adopted sister for many years, and I knew that my recovery depended upon making amends to her. I opened myself up in a letter to her, admitting my mistakes and prayerfully asking for a chance to start anew. Upon receiving the letter, my sister phoned me to say she had been waiting for years to hear those words and accepted my offer to begin a new relationship. Once again, God accomplished through me what I could never have achieved on my own.

After four months I went with my son to spend the summer at the lake. I was hesitant to leave behind the security of my A.B.A. family, but they promised to support me with their prayers. The first two weeks were a nightmare as my son alternated between venting his habitual rage at me and sulking in silence for long periods. Since he and I were alone together, I prayed a lot and trusted in God. Just when I thought I could stand it no longer, the miraculous breakthrough occurred. My son was able to tell me that his fury was for all the years of hell I had put him through with my sick obsessions with food and exercise. The bitter and pathetic memories he shared moved me to tears as I listened in shocked silence, seeing once again how drastically my behavior had influenced others. All I could do was hear his pain and apologize, vowing that with the help of God I would never do such things again.

It is nearly four years since that first brutal day when Mallory confronted me with the truth. Like a domino, the transformation of one person has impacted on an entire family. Today my son is filled with serenity and peace as he cheerfully helps with household chores and relates to all of us in a friendly and positive manner. Candace, the child who nearly ended her life, is discovering herself through drama, music, and writing. She recently participated in a local theatrical production of the gospel message, where her beliefs came alive in the presence of thousands of people. Her poetry, drawn from the well of her pain, has been accepted for publication. Instead of hurting herself, she now finds release in the sweet sound of music with her flute.

Mallory, the one who had the courage to start this ball rolling, has also found within herself the will to live. Her weight is now normal, although she still struggles with her obsessions. She has found a new purpose and meaning in what she endured by valiantly sharing her story with others, especially young girls. In her high school she helped organize an eating disorder awareness program. Through the use of guest speakers and through sharing her own experience, she hopes to help others avoid what she suffered.

My youngest daughter is now seven and has benefited from the recovery of those around her. She no longer worries about her tummy and is able to eat whenever she is hungry. Perhaps I will be blessed to have one child grow up unscarred by an eating disorder, surrounded by a healthy family.

My husband has witnessed miraculous changes in the rest of us and longs to have for himself what he sees in us. He has bravely taken the first tentative steps toward his own recovery, and in doing so has opened the door to a new level of communication in our marriage. Like the rest of us, he is now quick to admit when he is wrong and to apologize for hurtful behavior.

I continue to grow, sometimes with one step forward and two steps back. I see how far I have yet to go, yet I celebrate with gratitude how far I have already come. Knowing that life is a journey and not a destination gives me faith and hope to go on. Every day I remember that miracles still happen today, for I am living witness to one.

Gwen's Story: Willpower Was Not Enough

3

WRITING MY story has been a difficult and painful process. I tell it for three main reasons. First and foremost, I want others who suffer from an eating disorder to benefit from hearing about my experience so they might avoid some of the pain and the shame that was a hidden part of my life. I wish for them the joy and freedom that comes with recovery. Second, I view the process of writing and sharing my story as a valuable experience in my healing journey. I need to look honestly and openly at my disease and myself. Third, I want others who do not have an eating disorder to gain insight into what it is like to have the disease. Hopefully they will find understanding and compassion for those of us who suffer, and they will glean information about how to relate more effectively with a loved one.

The disease of bulimia has been with me for most of my life, for a span of over thirty years. It was my dark secret. Like a devil on my back, it was an awful habit that, no matter how hard I tried, I could not shake. I could only pretend everything was fine and try to accomplish superhuman things to prove to myself and others that I was a capable and worthwhile human being. Family members knew there was something wrong, but it must have been difficult for them to understand when I was unable to talk about it or understand it myself. I am sure they were frustrated with my behavior.

My story begins when I was a small child. Looking back, I recognize circumstances and patterns that may have predisposed me to my disease long before it became active. The middle child of a family of six, I often found that my mother was too occupied with endless household demands to give me the attention I wanted. I learned to soothe my emotions by sucking my thumb and rocking myself to sleep. Despite great efforts of will, I was unable to break the habit of thumb-sucking until I was twelve years old. Meanwhile I found solace in food. My family ate dessert after two meals each day, and breakfast was often pancakes with generous helpings of homemade syrup or jam. We were encouraged to eat heartily and praised for eating everything on our plates. My favorite bedtime activity was a lengthy period of reading, always with an ample supply of cake or other rich food at hand. I savored the sense of warmth and comfort it gave me. At this time in my life, I was also experiencing difficulty in settling disagreements with my brothers and sisters. The solution I most often chose was to withdraw and spend time alone.

As I entered puberty, I became concerned about my body shape and size. I was always short for my age and I knew I was getting plump. I could not find a comfortable bra. Jeans and shirts did not fit well. I felt awkward about my appearance. My best friend was tall and thin, and she seemed to be able to eat whatever she wanted. I failed to observe that she ate a more balanced diet and never filled up on sweets and desserts as I did. I also knew an older girl who was rumored to be bulimic. I thought she was beautiful.

In my fifteenth year my first brief relationship with a boy ended painfully, and I decided something had to be done about my weight. I recall looking into a mirror and promising myself I was going to lose weight even if it killed me. I would use every ounce of willpower to make it happen. I believed if I could be slim and pretty I would be happier with myself and people would like me more. My lengthy battle with bulimia began that day.

It took a long time to lose the first six pounds. It was hard work. I ate little during the day and by evening I was always ravenous. More and more frequently my appetite won out, and as a result I ended up eating much more than my appropriate share. Purging through self-induced vomiting brought relief. During my college years I lived on my own in a large city where I knew very few people. I maintained a pattern of eating scantily on fruit and protein-rich food during the day. In the evenings, hungry and alone, I was unable to resist the urge to find comfort in food. Bingeing and purging began to take up more and more of my time. It took me away from outside activities and potential friends. After each purging episode I promised myself it would not happen again, but I could not summon enough willpower to resist. I was caught up in a vicious cycle from which I could not break free.

I managed to graduate from college with reasonably good grades and began my professional career in critical-care nursing. My fiancé was aware that my eating habits were abnormal, but he accepted me as I was. We were soon married and I was trying hard to control my obsession with food. Throughout pregnancy and the early years of raising our children, I practiced my bulimia whenever I could find the privacy to binge and purge, still promising myself, each time, that it would be the last. I felt like two people. One side of me was a hardworking responsible woman, and the other part was a sneaking person who hid behind closed doors. My husband showed concern about what I did with food, but his interest was focused on his sports and activities with his male friends. We found little time for companionship. He found excitement elsewhere and I found comfort in food. It was a painful existence, but my wonderful children brought brightness to my life. I would move mountains for them.

It took many years for me to realize I might be passing unhealthy attitudes and behaviors to my children. As my daughter entered puberty, I noticed she was exhibiting attitudes toward food that were similar to mine. I became concerned as I realized that my children and future generations could be affected by the behaviors I had tried to keep hidden for so many years.

Despite the consuming nature of my disease with its powerful demands on time and energy, I led a busy life. Over the years I actively pursued many activities. I became accomplished on the piano, played in a musical band, rode horses capably, participated in dog obedience training, became a qualified swim instructor, and coached as a volunteer for several years. Involvement in church included singing in the choir, teaching Sunday school, participating on the board, and working with various committees. My children's lives took high priority as I volunteered in school and coordinated extracurricular activities. I tried to be a perfect mother and I looked for high achievement in my children. They became frustrated trying to live up to my expectations. I did not see that I was a demanding perfectionist and that I was trying to prove my self-worth through my children's achievements as well as my own.

Unhappy in my marriage, I went back to college and started a new career with regular working hours so I could be available to my children and still earn a decent wage. For the next six years my bulimia receded. I was highly motivated and finding little time for distraction of any kind. I managed to stay sober in bulimia for one full year and truly believed my battle with it was over, even though I still thought I had to restrict my food in order to control my weight.

My world began to fall apart when tragedy struck our family. My daughter's fiancé of three years was killed in an awful accident. My granddaughter was born six months later, and shortly after was diagnosed with a profound hearing loss. My life spun out of control as I ran even faster, trying to fix everything, especially for my daughter and her child. I was stressed out, worn out, and becoming very ill. When I abandoned my career to provide my granddaughter with the intervention she needed, I was filled with mixed emotions. Feelings of frustration, anger, and hopelessness were prevalent. I turned to food for solace, and my bulimia moved back into my life with a vengeance. I felt like I was on a merry-go-round that was going faster and faster. All I wanted to do was to stop the music and get off. My headaches were unbearable and I frequently felt too ill to function effectively. I believed I was going to self-destruct.

I knew about a Twelve-Step group for people who ate too much and I had saved the phone number. Thinking I was too busy and, with my small figure, would not fit in, I had never called. Now, as I reached a point of desperation, I heard about a group called Anorexics and Bulimics Anonymous. I began attending meetings and immediately knew I belonged. At meetings and under consultation with a wonderful doctor who understood my disease, I learned that my eating disorder is a form of addiction. It has been a great relief to hear that I did not cause my bulimia and that neither I nor my family is to blame. I now know I have an illness that is chronic, progressive, and incurable. I know I must eat three meals a day and must never binge and purge again, because one slip will plunge me into a full-blown active phase of my illness. I have learned that sobriety is not about willpower and control, but about surrender and acceptance. For me this means surrendering all control of my life and the lives of others to my Higher Power. I must regularly attend meetings and work the Twelve Steps faithfully so I can continue to grow spiritually.

By the time I began attending meetings I had, once again, managed to remain sober for one full month. I knew my challenge lay in staying sober for the long term, and I was willing to do whatever it would take to attain that goal. Although I had serious doubt that God existed, I accepted there must be some source of power that could help me. I surrendered to the support of my group and followed my physician's instructions. On advice, I began to pray, saying simply that my faith was weak, that I was angry because of the tragic events in my life, and that I needed help to survive. I also had to accept that I must give up my will; I must stop trying to take control of everything in my life, including my weight. It was difficult for me to surrender to eating breakfast every day because I had an unreasonable fear my weight would balloon out of control. I needed several weeks to discover that, on an intake of three daily meals, my hunger cravings disappeared and were easily satisfied with a small snack. I felt much calmer and more in tune with an inner voice that told me when I was hungry and when I was unhappy or upset. The next major revelation came as I discovered I was filled with destructive emotions that were harming me. Feelings like disappointment, frustration, and resentment served as strong triggers; I experienced a powerful urge to comfort myself with food when I felt ill at ease. As I worked the Twelve Steps, I became more able to accept my emotions and release them in healthy ways, instead of allowing them to build up inside me. I was learning that issues concerning food presented as the symptom of my illness, but issues of spirit and soul lay hidden at a deeper level.

Today, I am thankful for the fact that I reached my bottom and I knew I could not go on living as I was. I am thankful that my obsession was lifted and I no longer have the urge to binge and purge. I no longer eat to relieve loneliness or frustration or boredom, and I am finding much healthier ways to satisfy those needs. I am growing in my ability to recognize situations that make me uncomfortable, and I am able to deal with challenging situations more effectively. I have been continuously sober for almost two years. My connection to my Higher Power has come through prayer, meditation, and the support of my group. I know God exists within me as well as in the universe and, just like the smooth running of the universe, my body has been designed to give me what I need.

I give thanks for my sobriety. Although the process of healing involves hard work and is not fast or easy, it is a most rewarding journey. I am starting to model a healthier lifestyle for my family and I have faith in the future. I am thankful to be alive and healthy. I celebrate life and I give thanks to God for the gift of each new day.

Emma's Story: In God's Hands

4

THE IMAGE of hands holds an important meaning for me in my recovery journey. Every day I need to place myself into the faithful hands of my Higher Power. Every day, I need to open my own hands. I receive what I need when I stop clenching them tightly into fists. I receive what I need when I open my hands to allow the unexpected.

I cannot pinpoint the moment when I developed anorexia. I do recall restricting my food as early as the seventh grade. I also recognize at that time the beginning of a strong need to be a "good" person, perhaps my way of making myself special. I grew up as a high achiever, excelling in many things. Somehow, I developed a need to hold onto the affirmation of others by trying to earn it.

Eighth grade was a time of spiritual wellness for me as I encountered God in a new and powerful way through summer camp and retreats. During this time, my eating practices were normal again, and food was simply another part of life. I see now the connection between having God at the center of my life and being able to eat normally.

The seed of anorexia was still planted within me, however, and I unconsciously nourished it by my growing need to be a good girl. I was a perfectionist who pressured myself to achieve high ideals, whether by following all the rules at school or by doing kind deeds for others. When it came to my attitude toward myself, although I was learning about a God who is Love, I struggled continuously with feelings of shame for not doing things well enough. "Should," "enough," "right"—these are all words used by my disease.

As I approached my mid-teens, our family went through a difficult period. One of my grandfathers sustained a serious head injury, robbing him of the capacity for independent living. My other grandfather was diagnosed with acute leukemia. That same year a beloved uncle suffered a ruptured brain aneurysm and died within a few days. My parents, who had always kept me safe and secure, were unable to prevent these tragedies and the resulting pain we all experienced. Looking back, I now wonder if this first real encounter with powerlessness pushed me to take control, to do whatever I could to avoid such pain in the future.

Following these events, my eating practices gradually went downhill. More and more, I needed to do things "right." I needed to feel safe from the pain of failure and rejection. Surrounded by so many societal messages about the importance of eating well and exercising, I easily justified my food restrictions. In fact, I deeply believed that I was doing what I "should" do. Food was something I believed I *could* manage. Instead of facing squarely the uncertain nature of life, I dealt with it indirectly through trying to control my food and my body. With my perceptions skewed, I became convinced that food and exercise *were* the issues to which I must attend, unaware that the real issues were buried much deeper inside.

This striving for the magical "enough" affected many other areas of my life. Our A.B.A. Preamble states that "the disease's principal weapon is overwhelming and paralyzing fear" and that "it holds us in its lethal grip by inducing profound guilt and shame within us." How well I recall the guilt and fear that soon became the driving forces of my life, that demanded uncompromising obedience from me. They hid a deep pain, a deep cry for worth, a deep hole that I sought to fill by being perfect. Perfectly good. Perfectly living the Gospel. Alone in my sickness, I didn't have a balanced perspective of what that meant, and I felt that I failed to measure up. I was not "enough." So I kept trying. I restricted my food. I denied myself and deprived myself, desperately giving away time, energy, and possessions. Whether or not others needed or wanted these things, I needed a reprieve from my feelings of shame.

As time went by, I felt even greater pain as I saw how much my behavior hurt those who are dearest to me. This intensified my guilt, and the only solution I could think of was to try even harder to make things perfect. The restrictions to which I turned to ease my pain made the hurts even worse.

Over the next three years I made some responses to my parents' growing concern. I consulted dietitians, visited a doctor, met once with a psychologist, and even attended a few A.B.A. meetings. But I wasn't ready to let go. No matter how much I tried on my own to follow the advice given me, my confused perspective and powerful fear won out over my best efforts.

My bottom came two months after I left home to attend Bible college at the age of eighteen. The time I spent there was so valuable! God's Spirit touched me, held me, loved me, opened me up in spite of myself. I experienced the healing that comes through real belonging. Still, I continued restricting my food intake and exercising compulsively; these behaviors and anorexic state of mind were so much a part of me. I lost even more weight. I remember my intense fear that I wasn't exercising and eating "right," dragging myself out of bed to go for early-morning walks in full winter gear. I knew that I needed to let go, but I could not trust that I would get what I needed if I did so. Then, I got sick with the flu.

I stayed overnight in the hospital. While I was there, the attending physician expressed concern about my extremely low weight and recommended that I look into a treatment program for eating disorders at a well-known hospital. I was finally ready to receive that information; my Higher Power had slowly been preparing my heart. I felt safe and warm, as if held in the hands of One who would take good care of me. In that space I was able to face the truth about how very sick I was with anorexia. I decided to return home, intending to recover quickly so that I could get back to the college and complete my year of studies.

What an unanticipated detour I was to take! Back home, the first important decision I faced was about the route I needed to take to recover. I could see only two options at that time: admission to the hospital program or working the A.B.A program. I am very grateful that my parents allowed me to make this decision for myself, even though they must have felt hopeless when I rejected hospitalization. I believed that no matter how much my body healed, the real healing I needed was much deeper. I chose Anorexics and Bulimics Anonymous. As I took the leap of faith into recovery, I was amazed to recognize God's generous provision for my needs.

Most certainly, the crucial concern of early recovery is physical health. I was emaciated and physically weak, and my mind was in no condition to feed my body, no matter how desperate the necessity. In order to get sober, to surrender all control of my food and my weight, it was essential for someone else to serve my food. I couldn't do that for myself, especially at first when I needed to eat extra to regain the weight I had lost. There I was, the "giver," in a position of admitting total need of another human being!

At that point an extraordinary door opened for me. A dear friend, a nun whom I had known for many years, lived in a small religious community near my parents' home. I talked with her about what I needed and, before I could ask, she offered to approach the other sisters to see if they would be able to support me. Within two weeks of leaving the college, I moved again, this time into the sisters' convent. I lived with them for four months, and miracles happened there.

Three incredible sources of strength kept me going. The greatest of these was my Higher Power. I received such grace, the first being a heart open to recovery. I shared prayer time and daily Mass with the sisters. This contact with God became my lifeline. I prayed hard for the grace to eat what was set before me, no matter how scared I felt. And, one meal at a time, I received that grace. It wasn't always easy. Before each meal I prayed that God would work through the hands of the friend who served me, and that helped me to trust. As my body replenished itself and my weight returned to normal, I was given the grace to continue trusting.

A second source of strength was Anorexics and Bulimics Anonymous. Regular meetings were the medicine I needed to take and offered a constant reminder of the journey I was on. Through listening, I could often recognize my own thoughts and anxieties in others' words. Through speaking, I could give voice to my own insanity and struggles and be understood. Again, I experienced the healing of belonging. I put out my brokenness for others to see, and was still accepted and loved. Plunging into the Twelve-Step way of thinking frightened me, but other members encouraged me to "take what I need, and leave the rest." As long as I desired to get well and was willing to keep an open mind, I didn't have to embrace everything I heard at meetings. I could gently sift through it and retain what fit for me. The other members were always willing to help me. For the first couple months I called my sponsor every day and often called others as well.

Thirdly, other people sustained me. Before coming into recovery I felt irritated and uncomfortable when others showed concern about my health and tried to help me. But once I was ready to get well, I welcomed others' concern—I needed it. I was constantly amazed by the amount of love and support I received. There was the doctor who understood my disease and the recovery path I had chosen, and who regularly monitored my condition. There was the dietitian who got to know me, reassured me, and met with the community of sisters to give them specific instructions about my nutritional requirements. There were the sisters themselves, who prepared and served my meals and welcomed a confused and frightened girl into their home. There were special friends who stuck by me and visited me. And there were my parents, who loved and encouraged me through it all. I know I could never have begun the recovery journey on my own, without all these people who accepted me as I was and gave so abundantly of themselves. At every stage of the process, I needed to express my fears, my emotions, and my frustrations…to give voice to what was going on within. Many ears were willing to listen.

I am still on this recovery journey and continue to travel with A.B.A. Recovery doesn't look like I first imagined it would, and its meaning constantly changes as I change. I am more than ever aware of the beauty of living one day at a time; each day is different and works itself out differently. I need to pray every morning, asking for help, asking my Higher Power to show me how to take care of myself throughout the day ahead. When I am afraid or uncertain about how things will work out, I need to remember that God always desires my greater good and well-being, and that my task is to let go in trust.

I am learning to trust that God works through my own body, directing me through my hunger and fullness, through my energy and need for rest. I continue to experience times when I once again worry about food or exercise. I am an anorexic, and that means this obsession is part of me. Sometimes it is there to help me grow spiritually. I am grateful for God, for Anorexics and Bulimics Anonymous, and for the support of caring people, all of whom help me to live through my obsession, not in it.

A friend reminded me recently that my life is a miracle. Every moment that I am truly alive and participating is a gift from God. Although I never did return to the Bible college, I returned to life. Today, as I move into the third year of recovery, I am engaged in my second year of university, and I smile as I think of all that I have experienced: new classes, new relationships, exams, a lot of growing up. Dealing with the stuff of life. I am grateful for where I am today. I know that I do not walk alone. I am held in the palm of God's hands.

Gwyneth's Story: Saving Grace

5

MY BATTLE with bulimia began many years ago, earlier than I ever realized. Looking back now at my younger years, I see a very frightened child who used food as a trusted companion and nurturer. I cannot remember ever having a healthy relationship with food. Rather, it was the only thing that comforted me and allowed me to run away from unwanted feelings, feelings that I am learning to face head-on today in my recovery, almost forty years later.

My early life history provides some clues to the direction I went in my life. Belonging to a large family of seven children, with an alcoholic father and domineering mother, I experienced some terrifying situations that contributed to my already low self-esteem. I tried desperately to fix everything for everyone at home and, when I couldn't, felt like a dismal failure and even more insecure. I spent my childhood attempting to keep the peace in my family, and instead ended up isolated and afraid.

In the midst of all this disturbance, my mother planted within me the seed of faith in God, and for that I will remain forever grateful. That seed would eventually save my life. At my mother's insistence, I was involved in church activities throughout my youth. Today I see that God remained with me through all the hardships that lay ahead.

I began early to develop some unhealthy habits with food. Often, instead of playing outdoors with my friends I would remain inside watching television and nibbling on junk food. I preferred to bake and cook for my family rather than participate in social functions with my peers. I gradually developed the obsession with food that would dominate my life for the next thirty years.

I also loved team sports like volleyball and basketball and, when I was fourteen, heard my coach warn the team that being overweight would always prevent us from competing well. Although I was of normal weight at the time, I heard his admonition as an order to go on my first diet.

For the next seven years I engaged in "yo-yo" dieting. Lose a few pounds, gain them back, over and over again. I hated feeling hungry and could never sustain my diet for more than a few weeks. When I was twenty-one I learned about bulimia and immediately thought of it as the solution to my problem. I could have my cake and eat it too!

The first year was difficult. I was initially unsuccessful in purging and had to deal with the anxiety of gaining weight from my binges. As time went by, purging became easier and easier, and for the next twenty years I was hooked. There were few days that I did not binge and purge at least once, and sometimes I did it four or five times. Always in secret. Always with great disgust for myself and with increasing shame, for I simply could not stop. Bulimia became my method for dealing with every emotion and yet, as I used it, I felt more and more worthless. Summoning all my willpower to quit, I still could not succeed for more than a few days. What a roller-coaster!

I became an expert liar, concealing my behavior from co-workers, friends, and even from my husband. For that I hated myself even more. On the outside I wore a mask of success, pursuing a career as a dietitian that filled up my days. In my early thirties I became pregnant, to my great delight, but even that did not solve the problem of my powerlessness over bulimia.

Over the years I sought professional help many times. Doctors, psychiatrists, psychologists, hypnosis, an inpatient eating disorder program at a well-known hospital—everything failed to alter my behavior. I finally came to believe that I was a hopeless case, that bulimia had become so much a part of my identity that no one and nothing could remove it from me. Life without bingeing and purging was unimaginable, unthinkable.

When I turned forty, something crumbled in me. I felt at last that I couldn't go on living my life like this any longer. On the inside I was dying, even though I still looked good on the outside. My husband had been aware of my bulimia for some time, and he was getting extremely tired of it. Tired of my deception, tired of the promises I never kept, tired of my primary commitment to bulimia instead of to him and to our son. I heard about Anorexics and Bulimics Anonymous and attended a meeting. But when I heard about the time and effort that recovery would require from me, I rebelled. Surely there was an easier way!

It took another two years for me to admit complete defeat. By then I had begun having a few drinks almost every day as an alternative means of escape from the pain of my life. With great sadness my husband gave up on me and left, taking our son with him, leaving me to face the unvarnished truth about what my life had become. I realized that I was beaten. I felt completely dead inside. My family was gone. I couldn't go on living the lie anymore. It required too much effort, and I had none left. I was devastated, not even knowing if I had the strength to survive recovery.

I know today that it was grace alone that led me to take the next action, one that was to be the first in a long series of actions called recovery. I visited a doctor who understood my bulimia and its addictive nature. She helped me see that I needed to quit drinking first, since time and again I had proven that alcohol robbed me of any willingness I might have to get sober with food. I began participating in Alcoholics Anonymous to deal with my drinking. It worked, and three months later I received the courage to take the next step.

I learned about a treatment center for eating disorders based on the Twelve Steps, and at that time I was willing to do whatever was necessary for sobriety. I needed to leave my job in order to free up the time and space to participate in treatment, and that was a difficult decision. Work was the very core of whatever self-esteem I had maintained over the years, yet I also realized that I allowed my job to consume me, thereby repeatedly triggering my need to binge and purge.

So I left my job and started in outpatient treatment. My husband and son came back home, but I attended the center to eat two meals every day and receive a lunch-sack containing breakfast for the following day. In this way I got sober. I attended A.B.A. and A.A. meetings daily. I found a sponsor and started working the Twelve Steps. I acquired the tools to begin living one day at a time. Very quickly I began to feel better physically, emotionally, and spiritually than I had in many years. After two months in treatment I was well enough to begin preparing some of my own meals, and after another month I was discharged from the center.

That was more than four years ago, and by the grace of God I have not relapsed in either of my addictions. Some days can still be difficult, but not nearly as difficult as they were when bulimia was my solution to everything. I know today that whatever feelings I may be going through will eventually pass and that I don't have to escape from them. It is no longer an option to escape from them, and for that I am grateful.

Through my recovery, my family has been restored to a degree of health I would never have dreamed possible. My husband is still in awe of the changes in me and of the intimacy that is now possible between us. Because I am sober, I have been available to support my son in his adolescent trials, including a chronic illness that struck him two years ago. We can now talk about anything in our home without fear that I will run away again.

As I look back over my recovery from the vantage point of today, I see the greatest change is that I no longer expect other people, places, or things to meet my emotional needs. I am responsible for those needs, for becoming conscious of them in the present moment, and for filling them through doing the will of God to the best of my ability. I still have many defects of character that may be with me until the day I die, but I am aware of them today and, with my Higher Power alive in me, I do the best I can, one day at a time.

In sobriety my childhood seed of faith in a Higher Power has taken root, sprouted, and blossomed as I have nourished it through the tools of recovery. It has also greatly evolved. Today I know that my God is one who has always been with me and has always loved me unconditionally. My entire healing journey starts with me forgiving myself, being responsible for my life, and being the best I can be on a daily basis. Today I can choose the path of wholeness, and for that I thank my Higher Power. It is grace from that Power that has saved me!

D.J.'s Story: Why So Hard, God?

6

DEFEATED AND broken, sick and despairing, with nowhere to go but down. At that point I hoped only that my life would end. I could stand no more pain and suffering. Although I did not really want to die, I could see no other way out of the insanity that had become my life.

That was my condition when I arrived at my first meeting of Anorexics and Bulimics Anonymous. There, I would hear others speak the words that described my life. There, I would finally be able to tell the story of my anorexia and be heard by those who understood. There, I would begin to grieve the loss of thirty-seven years of my life, more than three-quarters of my entire time on this planet.

I lived my life "hard," from the beginning. I remember being five years old and already feeling different, feeling sad, feeling that I needed to take care of everyone and please them all. I empathized so deeply with others that I felt their pain within myself. Frequent stomach aches and nosebleeds plagued my life. I remember the terror of coping with the torment heaped upon me by my older brother, of arriving home from school to an empty house, of knowing that my parents were out working in the fields to keep our poor farm afloat, of cleaning myself up when I was sick because they could not be there.

When I was seven, I was sexually abused by a cousin. How happy I was at the beginning of that day when he and my brother allowed me to tag along behind them. Someone was paying attention to me, was talking to me! What a contrast to the end of the day, when all I could feel was shame and horror and overwhelming fear that my parents would discover my dreadful secret, would blame me for what had happened. This experience, in addition to the torture inflicted upon me by my brother, haunted my dreams for many years. Night after night I would awaken to a pillow drenched with lonely tears. My sole defense was to make myself invisible.

We moved from the farm into a small town when I was ten. There fresh hardships awaited me as I struggled to cope with a new school, a new curriculum. I was having increasing difficulty concentrating, and a teacher who constantly berated and ridiculed me for my poor performance aggravated my problems.

The theme of my life became to attend to the needs of others while ignoring my own. My father operated a combination barber shop, beauty salon, and billiard hall, and drove a school bus to supplement our income. My role by the age of eleven was to rush home from school to operate the billiard room until my father arrived, then dash upstairs to cook dinner for the family if my mother was at work, and finally round out the evening by taking over from my dad to give him some time off after eight o'clock. I felt good when my father praised me for my overdeveloped sense of responsibility. How wonderful finally to be getting some attention from him! I loved being labeled a "good girl" and being compared favorably to my two brothers.

That same year my hatred of school increased as a result of a male teacher who pinched me and brushed up against my already mature body at every available opportunity. I stood up to him, however, and consequently was banished frequently to the hallway. My means of escape from these trials was to go out drinking over the lunch hour with my more rebellious classmates, and after school to eat ten buns smothered with peanut butter, using the food as a drug to soothe my troubled soul.

When I was fifteen I quit school and moved to a faraway city to study hairdressing, something I had loved for many years. My father was able to give me money for books and uniforms, but I worked nights and weekends to pay for rent and food. Although I was often tired and lonely, I felt a great sense of accomplishment as my skills increased and my instructors praised me. In my spare time I filled up on whatever cheap food my meager budget allowed, and gained a lot of weight.

A year later, I returned to my hometown and opened up a beauty salon. Working seven days a week I quickly paid for my equipment. I failed to notice how much pressure I was putting on myself. Meanwhile I acquired a boyfriend, and was mortified one day when he and my dad commented that I was getting a little "round." My boyfriend said, apparently in jest, that he would shoot me if I got fat. Immediately I decided to lose some weight. In this venture I was aided by the increasing difficulty I was having with my stomach, which developed pain and bloating every time I ate. Still, losing weight was a long and slow process to which I devoted more and more energy as time went by.

I married at eighteen and continued to diet, making excuses to justify my refusal of food. I was baffled by my depression and loneliness in the midst of what should have been intimacy with my husband. My solution was to work harder and eat less, while catering to my spouse's every need. I carefully concealed all my emotions, all my fears, and dealt with my exhaustion by pushing myself harder. By the age of twenty-one I was teaching hairdressing, working seventy hours a week, and was often simply too tired to eat.

A year later my stomach and pelvic symptoms escalated. I consulted a doctor and learned that I was pregnant, to my amazement and delight. For the first four months I lay in bed vomiting, and subsequently my fear of getting fat drove me to a diet club, where I learned to count calories and measure my food. I consulted a dietitian, and even she prescribed a diet too low in nutrients to adequately nourish me and my unborn child.

The first year of my elder daughter's life was a nightmare. She was colicky and intolerant of every type of milk I gave her, and she remained so small that I feared for her life. I spent my nights walking the floor with her and my days escaping my anxiety through a new eating ritual: chewing large amounts of food and spitting it out. I did not know then that this behavior would become my principal tool for coping with life for the next twenty-five years.

During my second pregnancy I reverted to a rigid diet, weighing and measuring every bit of food I put in my mouth. By now the fear of getting fat dominated my mind at all times, and still I confided in no one about my thinking or my behavior.

When my second daughter was four months old, my physical health entered a downhill slide as every system in my body seemed to fall apart. I developed kidney stones, needed surgery to remove them, then promptly became hyperthyroid and required another operation, followed by a hysterectomy to relieve pelvic pain. Then my skin began reacting to textiles. I feared I would go mad. I could control nothing and I sank into despair.

Yet on the outside I struggled to maintain the appearance of a normal life. For my family I cooked and baked delectable meals that I never allowed myself to enjoy. My house was always spotless and the laundry always done. Between those household chores, a full-time outside job, and aerobics classes on my days off, I had little time to sleep, especially after I started night school to prepare myself to begin a nursing career.

But that was not to be. In my late thirties I was seriously injured at work and my poor body, which I had ignored and abused for a quarter of a century, finally got my attention. I developed headaches, back pain, chest pain, weakness in my arms and legs, and trouble breathing. I became bedridden, completely helpless, and was diagnosed with fibromyalgia and an inflamed chest wall. Still, my major fear was of gaining weight because of my inactivity. The more physical symptoms I developed, the greater became my need to control my weight. I wiggled my toes and vibrated my legs in an attempt to get my body moving again. I eventually succeeded and was able to walk with a cane.

I consulted dozens of doctors, pain experts, naturopaths, herbalists, environmental specialists, allergists. I told none of them about my eating disorder, even though by now I was certain that I had one, and no one asked. One expert recommended removal of the amalgam fillings from my teeth, followed by chelation. I went into debt to have those treatments, and only ended up with abscesses and undetected bone infection. For the next eighteen months I needed morphine, and in the end lost most of my teeth. Then came osteoporosis, stomach problems, more pelvic pain, and a debilitating bladder disorder.

Physically ravaged and in constant pain, I became desperate to find a drug that would ease my condition. Sometimes I banged my head on the floor, hoping to escape from my pain through unconsciousness. At other times I begged my husband to shoot me.

Emotionally I was a wreck. I was filled with anger at my body, at the doctors, at life, at God. I was short-tempered with my family, yet my feelings were otherwise dead. I couldn't bear to have anyone touch me or hold me. My skin was itchy, strong odors made me vomit, I couldn't sleep without drugs. I consulted yet another practitioner, who told me that foods were making me sick and prescribed a highly restrictive diet. I was unhappy with this because he was taking away from me the one thing that was a source of comfort. The more out of control my body was, the more in control I needed to feel over my food and my weight.

My despair reached its peak and I began to contemplate suicide, planning a method and a day to carry it out. Fortunately, my daughter interrupted me in the nick of time, and instead of making another attempt I resolved to visit a counselor. This man was the first professional to confront me with the diagnosis of an eating disorder. I offered no argument; in fact, I was relieved to finally say the words out loud. I was forty-seven years old.

My counselor accompanied me to my first meeting of Anorexics and Bulimics Anonymous. I listened to stories similar to my own. Then I heard about a Higher Power and my heart sank. I knew there was a God, but not for me. However, I shared my story honestly and was told to keep coming back. Since I had no better idea about what to do, I continued attending meetings and slowly developed a few friends in the group. I started to feel a small flicker of hope.

I next consulted a doctor who understood the addictive nature of my problem, and I applied for admission to a treatment program where I could get sober in my eating. When my request was denied, I was devastated. I went home and wept, feeling all alone in the world. That was my rock-bottom, although I didn't recognize it at the time. I thought again of suicide, but rejected that idea. I simply couldn't leave that legacy to my daughters.

My sobriety began without fanfare and slowly proceeded forward in tiny increments of surrender. I started adding small amounts of food to my diet, and I refrained from chewing and spitting out food, one meal at a time, one day at a time. I stopped weighing myself, although at first I continued weighing and measuring my food.

On my first day of surrender I tried phoning other A.B.A. members for support, but not one person was home. Nor could I reach anyone by telephone the next day. But somehow my action of picking up the phone gave me the courage to eat a little bit more that day.

Meanwhile I asked my doctor for advice on what I needed to eat to regain the weight I had lost and to nurture my body. With her guidance and my own knowledge of the Canada Food Guide, I prepared a daily plan of three meals and two snacks. I then consulted a dietitian, who sanctioned this plan. I instinctively knew it was time to let go of my food scale, so I asked my husband to hide it. Then I came face-to-face with the depth of my insanity, for I spent three hours tearing the house apart searching for that scale. I never did find it, but I heard an inner voice say, "You are crazy!" I sat down and ate the food without weighing it.

The next few months were difficult, but not as burdensome as the years had been prior to A.B.A., for now I was spurred on by a deep sense of moving forward, of getting well. I ate according to my sober meal plan. I put all four food groups on my plate. If I wasn't hungry, I ate anyway. I ate no low-fat or reduced-calorie foods. I checked in with the doctor regularly to monitor my progress and receive encouragement. My weight steadily increased and my clothes became tight, so I got rid of them and bought new ones. I read Twelve-Step literature, attended meetings, obtained a sponsor. I cried. I pouted. I cursed. But I continued to take the actions of recovery, day after day.

Thirty-seven years of sickness is not healed in a week or a year. Sometimes I felt more crazy than ever, because I no longer had a means to numb my feelings or calm me. My best friend—chewing up food and spitting it out—was no longer available to me. Nor were alcohol and drugs. I had to find a substitute, a Higher Power, and that took time. I began by doing what was suggested to me: asking for help in the morning and giving thanks at night. As I stayed sober, I realized there must be some Power hearing and answering my prayers. I came to believe that God was present and was restoring my sanity.

Today, with almost four years of sobriety, I am convinced that God was with me all along, throughout my life, and was directing me through my instincts—when I listened to them. The key was to start paying attention to my own needs and to put them first. I needed to learn to take care of myself, and that has been the toughest learning of all. I now take responsibility for my health, and I have learned to examine critically all professional advice I receive.

The benefits of recovery are many, beginning with the simple joy of being able to eat. I can go to a restaurant for a meal with a friend. I no longer have to lie, to find an excuse for not eating. I don't have to stand in front of a mirror and cry because I see a huge body. I am not driven to excessive exercise and ceaseless activity. I don't have to think about food and my body all the time.

I still have problems today, but by being sober I believe that God will give me what I need to deal with them. I still have regrets, especially for all that I missed in my children's lives, yet I have hope that one day this pain will be gone and I will be grateful for everything. In the meantime I am thankful for the many gifts I have already received.

Lara's Story: Another Lifetime

7

MY NAME is Lara, and I am a recovering anorexic and bulimic. As far into my past as I can remember, I never had a normal relationship with food. I was overweight as a child and always felt as if I didn't quite belong or fit in. I recall being deeply depressed by my early teens, painfully shy and insecure and convinced there was something terribly wrong with me.

I began experimenting with alcohol in my early teens and loved how I felt when I drank: confident, at ease with myself and others, and more outgoing. However, drinking provided no lasting solution, and at the age of fifteen I decided that I needed to lose weight before starting high school. I went on my first diet that summer and lost some weight. People noticed and began complimenting me. I liked the attention, wanted more, and thought that losing more weight was what I needed to do to get it. That would make me more attractive and confident, less awkward and uncomfortable.

From that point on, I lived in an endless cycle of dieting, then becoming so hungry that I lost control and binged on food, then once again starving myself to compensate for that. I thought that if I had enough willpower, I would stick to my diet. Since I could not, I felt even more inadequate and depressed.

I switched schools for eleventh grade, hoping to reinvent myself and leave my troubles behind. It didn't work, because I took myself with me. I met some new acquaintances and began hanging out with them, drinking and trying out a variety of drugs. I didn't like any of them, since hallucinating and feeling paranoid all the time was not my definition of feeling good.

I changed schools again for my last year of high school, not having learned that, wherever I went, my problems followed. Here I felt completely and utterly alone. Sometimes I hid in the bathroom and wept before class, and I wandered the streets over lunch hour in order to avoid sitting alone in the cafeteria. When around other people I was tormented by the feeling that I was trying to be something or someone that I was not. The few "friends" that I did make over that year were people whom I did not like, and our only common interest was drinking.

I thought these school years were supposed to be the happiest ones of my life, so I wondered even more what was wrong with me. I lost all hope of ever having a normal life and began to fantasize daily about suicide. I longed for an escape from my inner pain and misery. As the months went by, dieting ceased to be about weight loss and became instead a means of disappearing. By this time I had also discovered that if I made myself vomit after overeating, then I could eat whatever I wanted without gaining weight. I no longer cared about what happened to me, nor about my isolation and alienation from others.

Around that time I was introduced to heroin. Since all I wanted was escape from my pain, I decided to try it. It worked. Like a warm blanket, it comforted me and let me believe that everything was okay. I thought I had found God and the answer to all my problems. Heroin worked faster on my mind than dieting and also suppressed my appetite and induced vomiting. At last I had something to live for. I began mixing heroin with cocaine, and this concoction—known as "speedballs"—quickly became my drug of choice.

My life became centered around my addictions. When I could not obtain drugs, I binged and purged. And since I could not afford to buy drugs every day, bingeing and purging quickly became a daily event, further isolating me from family and friends in order to keep it all a secret. Addiction consumed me. I spent increasing amounts of money to support my growing habits. I lied to obtain money from my parents and friends. I lied to conceal my behavior. The more lies I told, the more shame and remorse I felt. But I could not stop.

Because severe depression had predated my drug use, my suicidal thoughts brought me to a bottom rather quickly, and I found myself in a meeting of Narcotics Anonymous. I felt immediately that I had come home, that I had found the acceptance and belonging for which I had been searching all my life. Although I relapsed many times, I eventually got clean and stayed there. Through this process, I acquired the beginnings of a belief in a Higher Power.

However, I was still practicing my eating disorder and knew I needed help. I heard about Anorexics and Bulimics Anonymous and started attending meetings. I felt some sense of hope during the meetings, but as soon as I got home my need to binge and purge would overpower all my good intentions. I attended meetings now and then for four years without relief from my bulimia. I had no idea about what sobriety looked like or how to get sober. I was deeply ashamed of my bulimia, of my inability to live even one day without bingeing and purging.

Through the course of these years I tried a variety of routes in order to help myself. I consulted a hypnotist, a herbologist, naturopathic doctors, and psychiatrists. I tried numerous psychiatric drugs and therapies. I tried applying the Twelve Steps to my eating disorder. Nothing worked.

After a failed suicide attempt I was admitted to a specialized eating disorder unit in hospital. I stayed there for three months, underwent electroshock treatment, and gained back the weight I had lost. Following my discharge I went home and promptly resumed bingeing and purging, lost all the weight I had gained, and felt just as sick and miserable as before. Only now I believed I was a complete failure. I lost hope of ever recovering from my eating disorder.

By this time I was bingeing and purging eight or ten times a day. It was all I did. I was unemployable, lived on social welfare, and could barely function. I left my apartment only to attend N.A. meetings or to obtain more food. I accepted that this was my fate—that I would die alone in my apartment, bent over my toilet, vomiting.

I believe now that it was my Higher Power who gave me the grace to make one last-ditch attempt at recovery. I decided to consult a doctor who was a recovered anorexic. She informed me about the existence of a residential recovery center for women with eating disorders. It was based on the Twelve Steps of Anorexics and Bulimics Anonymous. I knew that I could never get better alone at home, that I needed to be somewhere safe, twenty-four hours a day. Although I did not want to let go of my apartment, which symbolized my independence, I knew this was my last hope.

Living at that treatment center was one of the hardest things I have ever done in my life. My eating disorder had become so deeply ingrained in my nature that I found it excruciatingly difficult to surrender and achieve consistent sobriety. Several times I left the house to binge and purge, sometimes lying about where I was going and what I was planning to do. However, deep within I wanted to recover, so I always went back and was honest about what I had done. I was ashamed and humiliated by my own behavior, yet felt powerless to stop. The staff and other women in the house welcomed me back every time. Their understanding and patience appeared to be infinite and, because they never gave up on me, I started to believe that I could actually recover.

After multiple relapses, one of which required a brief hospital admission to correct my dehydration and potassium abnormality, I finally grew tired of fighting. I remember the day that I said to myself, "I will do whatever I need to do to stay sober and find some peace of mind. If I have to weigh three hundred pounds in order to be happy, I will do it." That was my surrender. I was immediately filled with an incredible sense of freedom and relief.

Despite that moment, in early sobriety while I was returning to a healthy weight I was horribly uncomfortable in my body. I was angry, resentful, judgmental, filled with self-pity and indescribable fear. I had no idea who I was without my eating disorder. I believed that it was the only thing that made me special or unique, so to let it go was terrifying. I had to blindly trust what others were telling me, that recovery would get easier and I would be okay.

After eight months of treatment I moved into my own apartment and almost immediately found a job as office manager of a small textile shop. I stayed sober for six months, but after I was laid off from my job I binged and purged, having not yet acquired the tools to deal with life's challenges in a more healthy manner. I became depressed again and for many months was unable to stay continuously sober for more than a week or two. I finally hit another bottom and was faced with another surrender. Out of that relapse I learned that if I wanted to maintain sobriety in my eating, recovery had to take priority over employment. I resolved to stay sober no matter what happened in my life, and through the grace of God I have been sober ever since.

That was more than three years ago. I am now twenty-seven years old, eight years free from drugs and alcohol, and have come a long way from where I once was. Recovery has been a lengthy and slow process for me, but the rewards are worth all the time and energy I have invested in getting well. I can eat today without obsessing about calories or experiencing the need to purge afterward. Food is no longer the enemy. I have energy to do the things I want to do. I have friends who genuinely care about me and who have walked with me through it all. I have been employed steadily at the same job for almost three years, in a field I enjoy. I now have a relationship with a Higher Power, and I am strengthening that relationship through working the Twelve Steps. I am slowly becoming the person who I believe God intended me to be.

Life still happens and isn't always perfect or easy, but I have been given some tools to deal with whatever comes along. It seems strange to me now that I lived the way I did for so many years. It seems like another lifetime, like a bad dream from which I have now awakened. I have become so accustomed to being sober in my eating that it seems absurd that I once did the insane things I did.

This Program has been the only thing that ever worked for me. If it were not for Anorexics and Bulimics Anonymous, the recovery center that took me in nearly five years ago, the love of my sponsor, and the support I received from others recovering from eating disorders, I probably would not be alive today. I no longer believe that eating disorders are something one should "learn to live with" or need to deal with alone. There is hope. Full recovery, one day at a time, is possible. I am living proof.

Rachael's Story: I Am Enough

8

I WAS anorexic long before I restricted my first dessert or skipped my first meal. I believe that I had an anorexic mindset from a very young age.

I grew up in a middle-class family with parents who separated when I was eight years old. My considerably older siblings, a brother and a sister, moved out soon after my father did, leaving me and my mother alone. My mother did the best she could to build up my self-confidence, praising me for my honor grades at school and for the medals I won in Highland dancing, telling me that I was an exceptional student and a "good kid." However, all her love and encouragement was insufficient to dispel my deep-seated insecurity. I doubted other people and did not trust that they truly cared for me. I thought they were lying when they declared their affection, and I shrugged off their hugs; I was completely unable to receive their love.

As I grew older, I dealt with my uncertain sense of self in a number of ways, one of which was through alcohol. As a university student pursuing a four-year nursing degree, I went with my friends to the campus bar every Friday afternoon, and I stayed there drinking well into the night. I became a different person under the influence of alcohol. I became "more." More alive, more popular, more fun, more attractive. I felt wonderful, until I awoke the next morning and reflected on what I had done the night before, or until my friends told me what I had done. Then I would cringe as my sense of worthlessness welled up, stronger than it had been before. Clearly, alcohol was not the answer. I needed to find something else to make me feel good about myself.

That "something else" showed up in the summer before my third university year. I found a job in a small town and lived there with my best friend for three months. For the first time in my life I was in charge, coming and going as I pleased and doing whatever I decided to do. I felt freedom. That freedom, however, was to be short-lived, for I was about to become a slave to anorexia.

Over the course of that summer I inadvertently lost a few pounds, and when I returned to classes in September a number of people noticed and complimented me on my appearance. Many wanted to know how I had achieved that weight loss. I was an instant hero. Suddenly, without benefit of alcohol, I had become "more." More people were noticing me, talking to me. I equated that with being more alive, more popular, more fun, more attractive. I had stumbled upon something that numbed my painful feelings of inadequacy. Only this time there was no dreadful next morning in which to awaken and hate the things I had done—at least, not in the beginning.

That changed quickly, for I soon started to lie. I felt driven to do so in order to maintain my weight loss. I had to say that I wasn't hungry, that I didn't need as much food as before, that I didn't like fried foods. I had to lie to avoid eating. I had to lie about what I had or had not eaten.

I also quickly became addicted to my scale. Prior to that September I almost never weighed myself, but now I simply had to see if other people were correct in their perception of my weight loss. They were. Now I too could see the result of my actions, and I was immediately hooked. I learned that I could control the number on that scale by what I did or didn't eat. My daily weight determined everything. It controlled my mood, my plans for the day, my thinking, my interactions with people. If I lost weight, I felt good. If I gained or stayed the same, I frantically searched for any means of regaining control. The number on the scale dictated whether I could eat, what I could eat, and how much I could eat. I gave away all my power to that scale.

And I rapidly discovered the effect of exercise on weight loss. I had started exercising because it was fun. Soon, it was no longer fun. I could no longer go rollerblading because I wanted to do so. I went because I *had* to go. I felt as if I had no choice in the matter. I began planning my routes to find the greatest wind resistance and the steepest hills. The windier and colder the day, the better it suited my goal. If I were in pain, that meant I was burning more calories and would lose weight faster.

I lost a great deal of weight within a few short months, and positive feedback continued to flow in for some time. Everyone said I looked great, at first. Then a few close friends began telling me that I had lost too much weight and was not looking well anymore. Paradoxically, I loved hearing that. I reasoned that anyone could tell me I looked good, but only someone who truly cared for me would tell me I looked awful. My old insecurity was receding.

But not for long. As I ignored the people expressing concern about my weight and continued to shed more pounds, their comments ceased. Or, at least, I could no longer hear them. I began to crave gifts, tangible evidence of people's acceptance of me, something I could hold onto as proof of their caring. What irony existed in this! The more I craved affection, the further I distanced myself from others by my relentless pursuit of thinness. In my obsessive drive for control over my body, I drove a wedge between me and others. I excluded myself from the possibility of authentic love.

My house of cards began to collapse only one year after I began building it. One day I felt frustrated by a plateau in my weight loss, by the failure of my usual techniques to impact on that number on the scale. I fasted all day, then went for a particularly grueling bicycle ride. In my anorexic trance, I narrowly avoided a collision with a pedestrian by braking hard. My feather-weight body flew over the handlebars onto the pavement, and I separated my shoulder. Only the presence of my helmet prevented a serious brain injury. I found myself in hospital being X-rayed and placed in a sling, yet I felt no physical or emotional pain. I was anesthetized by my anorexia. My principal reaction came the next morning when I discovered that my weight was unchanged.

But something else had changed. My injury caused a tiny chink in the armor of my disease. Two days later, as I sat at home with my mother, six words tumbled unbidden out of my mouth. "I am tired of being hungry." I don't recall being aware of my hunger before that day, but I had constantly thought about food, every waking moment of every day, for the past year. I even dreamed about food. I thought about what I wanted to eat, whether I could allow myself to eat it, and what I would have to do to burn it off if I did eat it. If I occasionally relented and ingested a cookie or doughnut, I felt intense guilt and such shame that I hid while I ate, lest someone discover my action. Loud voices in my own mind cursed me for my weakness. Although I didn't know it, those voices were breaking me down, and I crumbled that morning in the living room. I admitted to my mother how much pain I was in.

She had known for many months that I was anorexic, and she had been quietly gathering information, waiting for me to admit my problem. Now she asked if I was ready to hear what she had learned, and I agreed to do so. I finally knew that I was sick and needed help.

My mother gave me the phone number of a doctor who specializes in eating disorders, and I called and made an appointment.

For the next few days I tried to eat normally, but I could not. I was terrified of gaining weight. I could not eat anything other than salads and low-fat foods, but I did manage to consume more of them than before. However, when I stepped on the scale and discovered a small weight gain, I panicked and returned to more severely restrictive practices. But the difference now was that I possessed knowledge I could no longer evade. I could not blunt my awareness that I indeed was suffering from an eating disorder. I began attending Anorexics and Bulimics Anonymous a few days later.

I remember the amazement I felt at my first meeting. Here were people, total strangers to me, who were telling *my* story, expressing *my* feelings, sharing *my* deepest secrets. I saw at last that my behavior had been symptomatic of a disease, that I had not devised new and unique ways to practice it, that it had all been done before. I felt such relief that I was no different from anyone else in the room.

I continued attending those meetings, and I now believe that anyone who does so will eventually get sober, although it may take a while. I needed more than eight months before I finally found true sobriety.

At first I thought I could get sober using my mother's support. She agreed to prepare my meals and serve them, following the directions of a knowledgeable dietitian, and we tried that for many months. However, despite valiant effort from both of us, I simply could not surrender to my Higher Power when my mother's hands were the ones preparing the food. We were too close, our relationship too burdened. I was too sick, my disease too powerful. It overcame both of us, and my weight continued to drop. I was dying from anorexia, yet I could not see its effect on my body. When I looked in the mirror at my grey skin and skeletal frame shrouded in oversized clothing, all I observed was fat.

At the time, I was completing the senior practicum of my nursing studies. Every day when I left home to go to the hospital, my mother anticipated a phone call to inform her that I had collapsed. I knew by this time that I was going to die, but I was so numb I did not even care. I felt chained to this disease. I saw no way out other than through death.

My bottom finally came as I approached the time of my graduation as a nurse. I had completed my degree and was looking at job postings when my doctor, who had personal experience with anorexia, told me not to bother applying for work. She told me that no one would hire me, because I appeared so ill. A prospective employer would know that I was suffering from terminal cancer, AIDS, or anorexia nervosa. I felt great pain when I heard her words and, more than that, I felt angry that I had worked for four years to achieve this degree and now anorexia was standing between me and my chosen career. Then I went deeper into my feelings and realized that not only did I not *look* well enough to be hired, I truly was not emotionally and spiritually well enough to work. I admitted I was too sick to be a good nurse. I was too obsessed about food to concentrate. I existed in a constant state of hypoglycemia. I couldn't be me because I was trapped in anorexia. I could no longer do the things I loved to do because they interfered with my disease! That was my bottom. I knew at that moment that I truly wanted to get well more than I wanted to stay thin.

I still could not see a pathway out of my disease, a route to sobriety. That's when my Higher Power intervened in a major way, working through my sponsor, A.B.A., my doctor, and a community of loving strangers.

On Easter Monday I went to a meeting of Anorexics and Bulimics Anonymous. The group was celebrating my sponsor's sobriety birthday that evening. I was asked to share, and in a nonchalant way I spoke about how I was dying from anorexia. I was completely numb. The next few speakers were all sober and spoke about the joy and freedom in which they lived from day to day. I wanted what they had. I wanted to be free of the inner voices that enslaved me. Then the newcomers were invited to share, and each of them revealed the pain and despair in which they were living. I saw myself in them.

Something broke inside me and I started to cry. I curled up in a corner of the couch and wept and wept. My sponsor sat beside me and held me. After the meeting closed, she offered me a piece of her birthday cake. I refused it. She looked at me and said, "Rachael, I will sit with you for four hours if that's how long you need to eat this cake."

By the grace of God, I accepted her offer. I ate the cake, my first sober snack. After I finished it, my sponsor invited me to come home with her and allow her to prepare dinner for me. I accepted that too. Then I slept at her house, and she provided my meals and snacks for the following day. I felt enclosed in love.

On Wednesday I and my doctor met with a community of nuns to ask for their help. My doctor informed them about eating disorders and the nature of sobriety, and I shared briefly about myself and my life and my deep desire to live free of my disease. Their response was overwhelming.

No one bothered to ask if I was affiliated with their religion. It seems that issue was irrelevant to everyone present. Every person in the room demonstrated great compassion and offered to support me. That same day I moved into their home and they began serving food to me, three meals and three snacks every day, as directed by the dietitian.

For the next four months all I did was pray, eat, attend Twelve-Step meetings, cry and process my feelings, reach out by phone to others in recovery, meditate, write in my journal, read Twelve-Step literature, work with my sponsor, visit my doctor, and learn to live again. At first I hated and dreaded the food I was served, seethed with anger when I looked at my plate, and sometimes wept for hours before or after I ate. My sponsor and my doctor encouraged me to pay attention to what I was feeling and to take care of myself respectfully, one meal at a time. Sometimes I needed to ask someone to sit with me so that I could eat; at other times I needed to ask them to leave.

Getting sober was the most difficult undertaking of my life, and also the most rewarding. As my weight increased, I felt my physical strength return and my thinking become clearer. And gradually, as I surrendered to my Higher Power's will around my food and my weight, my obsession began to fade. I started to trust my body and to enjoy what I was eating. I began to feel gratitude for the gift of being able to nourish my body again. Like a child, I learned how to eat. I learned how to love and care for myself. I learned that I am never alone, that my Higher Power is always with me. I learned that I am a miracle and that miracles are ongoing all around me.

Four months sober, I was well enough to select all my own food and to leave the convent. Two months after that, I moved to my own apartment and started working for the first time as a registered nurse. Today I am in my second year of sobriety and my life is full. I work in the field of obstetrics, doing what I love the most: serving women who are birthing their babies. As I help bring new life into the world, I often reflect on the new life created within me nearly two years ago when I surrendered to my Higher Power and got sober. Unburdened of my anorexic obsession, I am able to be fully present to and for the mothers I work with, their families, and their precious newborns. I don't think it gets any better than that.

I am alive today and I am me. I feel happiness, sadness, anger. I don't have to run away from any of my feelings. I honor myself and love myself. I don't need a number on a scale or anything else to make me feel more. I am enough.

Rita's Story: I Tried to Do It Alone

9

I WAS the most "put-together" person I knew, and if I met someone who looked better than I did I soon found something wrong with them. They were arrogant or snobbish or something else equally unattractive.

When I moved out of home and went to the "big city," I knew I would set the world on fire. I would not be like my mother and my siblings, dull and ordinary. I would show them how to live life. I had always possessed a secret intuition that I was put on this earth for a reason, for some special purpose yet to be revealed.

Living at last on my own, I plunged into life to find that purpose. I worked hard and partied hard. But I felt vaguely that something was wrong. Perhaps it was my body, so I started dieting and exercising. I did that, too, with the same intensity I applied to everything else. I read a host of exercise and diet books, counted calories, tried every fad diet I discovered. I felt great and looked great, yet I always thought true happiness was just out of reach in that last two or three pounds I had yet to lose.

Still uneasy and discontent, I plunged into self-help books, accumulating a complete library of them. Surely the next one would provide the answer to my questions and set my life straight. Whenever I encountered a problem or felt depressed I would read another book, consult a naturopathic doctor for that quick remedy, see a hypnotherapist, or pursue some other imaginative course to magically fix me. Even as I felt so mysteriously incomplete, I continued to judge others and concluded that I was superior, that their problems were far worse than mine.

My world changed abruptly when at the age of thirty-two I gave birth prematurely to my first child. She weighed less than two pounds at delivery, and seven days later I learned she had sustained a severe brain hemorrhage that would result in cerebral palsy. As I absorbed this shocking news, I wondered what I had done to deserve this tragedy. Sure, I was having sex and drinking every weekend by the age of thirteen. Sure, I started using drugs at fourteen. Sure, I had an abortion when I was sixteen, and another one six years later. But I *had* to do these things to make people like me. So this was what I was being punished for, wanting people to like me. I had broken the chain, I had dared to be different from my parents, and this was what God was giving me for all my hard work. Thanks, God, and screw you too!

Many people tried to help me deal with my grief, but I pushed them away and isolated myself. I didn't need anyone, and I didn't trust anyone. I would figure this out for myself, using the wisdom I had gleaned from my books and from my life experiences. I was certain that I knew everything there was to know. I had wonderful moments caring for my baby in hospital, moments when I felt electricity passing between us, moments when I felt a surge of something giving her the power to be more than the medical staff thought she could be. I believed that was my doing, not God's.

When I returned to work after my maternity leave, I waited and waited for my life to become normal again. Three years later I gave birth, less prematurely, to my second child. My mother moved into a house half a block away from ours, my spouse started a new job that took him out of the city for four days out of seven, and I was still waiting for life to get back to normal.

Two pregnancies had left their mark in the form of thirty extra pounds on my petite frame and, upon my second return to work, I felt frantic about that, but had so little energy I could not stick to a diet or exercise program. Besides, I deserved to eat whatever I wanted as compensation for all the pain God had sent into my life. I hated my body; hated my job; hated my co-workers who failed to recognize my truly remarkable abilities; hated my mother for her kindness in caring for my children while I worked; hated my husband for abandoning me; hated the doctor at the neighborhood clinic who refused to give me diet pills. Meanwhile I wanted desperately to be the best parent in the world and proceeded to read every book published on that subject.

I started to recognize the depth of my misery and finally consulted my family doctor about my lack of ambition and my fatigue, but especially about my weight. She had the audacity to suggest antidepressant medication, and I was deeply insulted. Did she think I was crazy? She also discovered a vitamin B12 deficiency and recommended weekly injections at her office. On those visits she slowly and gently teased out of me the information I needed to admit about what I was feeling and what my life was like. Halfway through the injections, she introduced me to the subject of eating disorders and suggested that I attend a meeting of Anorexics and Bulimics Anonymous. I was horrified! How could a fat creature like me be anorexic? But she had induced me to share so many deeply hidden feelings that I was willing to try anything to get the old me back, the fun-loving, happy, slim person I had been before.

I decided to go to the stupid meeting, reasoning that if I saw some thin people I might become so disgusted with my body I would be triggered to go home and lose weight. But from the moment I sat down at that first meeting and started to listen to the chairperson, something shifted inside me. I felt safe. Each person who shared said something about what I was feeling, thinking, and longing for. I sensed that these people might actually understand how I felt. I was shocked by my experience and even tried to deny it. Maybe I was just particularly vulnerable right then and would soon snap out of it. I went to another meeting, and the same thing happened. Yet these people were such a varied lot. Sick, depressed, confused, angry, joyful, grateful, young, old, thin, fat. How could I identify with them? I was different from all of them.

I had been attending A.B.A. meetings for about six months when my perceptions shifted. I realized that, although I had been looking at my reflection in the mirror for thirty-six years, I didn't know who I was. Once I turned away from the mirror, I could not accurately describe myself as I could describe the features of a good friend. And, to be more honest, I didn't really *want* to look that closely at myself, because there was nothing worth remembering in that reflection. I started to glimpse some hard truths about myself, and I felt crushed by them. I was in fact a manipulative, controlling, codependent, angry woman; I had all the despicable qualities that I had seen in my mother. I wanted to die, run and hide from myself, kill my mother for making me like this, hurt my father for abandoning me in childhood.

Today I realize that I had a Higher Power working with me and in me through that difficult period. That Power kept me going to meetings, week after week. I saw that I desperately needed the Twelve-Step

Program if I wanted my life to change. I decided to work those Steps and figured I would have them perfectly completed in about a year.

But first I faced a terrible problem: What was sobriety, and how was I going to get it? What was a sober meal? Was this going to be just another diet plan? I rebelled at that thought; but I needed answers and, true to my old patterns, set out all alone to find them. I obtained an outline of meal ideas and bought a book in which to compulsively record my intake. That allowed me to critique myself. I could decide each day whether I had done it right or done it wrong. I never did get it right. My perfectionism would never permit me to see that I had done my best and that was enough. I continued to falter and try again, meanwhile watching my one-year deadline rushing toward me.

For six months I bounced back and forth on my see-saw called anorexic-overeater. If I ate any "junk food," if I consumed a couple eggs, if I put some butter on my bread, the anorexic side of my mind would tell me I wasn't sober. But if I felt angry about denying myself something, if I craved a particular food, if I was disturbed by my feelings and wanted to bury them in sugar, then the compulsive eater in me said I wasn't sober. I felt like a dog chasing its tail. I was hopelessly confused, and my life was no better than before I arrived at A.B.A.

Finally, I surrendered. I admitted that I needed help, that I couldn't find sobriety on my own. I found a sponsor who asked me to check in with her daily for specific directions around my food. A good dietitian provided me with guidelines for sober eating. My husband took over much of the food preparation and service. Even my children helped me, by modeling healthy eating behaviors.

As my mind started to clear, what I heard at meetings changed. I heard people struggling with one issue or another. I heard about how difficult it often was to remain in an attitude of surrender to God. I heard about celebrating the small milestones and being grateful for them. I heard about learning important lessons through making mistakes and through relapse. I began to realize that I was going through the same process as everyone else. I finally started to believe I was okay.

What keeps me coming back to Twelve-Step meetings is contentment. I have found some now, and I want more. I can no longer bear to live in insanity, with a committee of dissenting voices inside my own mind. The first time I felt some inner peace, I panicked and wondered what was going on with me. I shared what I was feeling at a meeting, and another member laughed and said, "Welcome to serenity!" Today I live with an inner calm that is strong enough to weather whatever is going on around me. I am present in the moment and I finally feel truly alive. I have new energy, I am learning to feel my feelings, and when I walk away from a mirror I remember what my face looks like.

I am grateful to have learned a new way of life. In my second year of sobriety, I have stopped demanding of myself that I complete the Program and graduate, because I love continuing to learn about honesty and acceptance of life as it is. I have found a Higher Power deep within me that loves me, no matter what I do. I want to continue participating in Twelve-Step meetings because they are my guide to living life sober.

Recovery is an open-ended process, and I don't have to do it alone. I eagerly look forward to today's journey even if it brings dark times; those times hold such great learning that I now welcome them with open arms. I know my Higher Power is with me, and together we can do what I cannot do alone. My prayer today is, "God, lead me where you need me; and if I be afraid, let me know that you are always there." For this I am grateful.

Cindy's Story: Both Sides of the Coin

10

MY NAME is Cindy, and I am in recovery from compulsive overeating and anorexia. My story and my experiences are uniquely mine, yet I know today about the common threads that bind me to my sisters in recovery. I hope that what follows may allow someone reading this account to identify with me and thereby learn that recovery is possible.

My father is a recovering alcoholic and my mother grew up in an abusive alcoholic home. Both of them had been previously married and had other children before they met, married, and produced me. I remember my early childhood as happy and fun-filled. I always knew my family loved and cared for me. Never was I ridiculed or put down at home. Never did I receive anything but positive input and encouragement, despite the hard times we all went through.

When I was ten, our circumstances traumatically changed when my parents separated without warning. One day we were a normal family; the next day my mother picked me up from school, took me home to pack, and we left. I didn't understand, and I felt angry and scared. But I pushed my feelings away by turning to food as my sole comforter.

I went on my first diet a few months later. My sister was getting married and I was to be a bridesmaid. When the dresses ordered the month before arrived, I was embarrassed and ashamed to discover that mine no longer fit. Since there was no money or time to obtain another dress, I had to lose the weight I had gained. My mother prepared my meals, and I did my part with exercise by walking and roller-skating. I succeeded in losing the extra pounds and managed to fit into my dress when the wedding day arrived. I don't recall feeling thrilled by my success. I do recall that food was still my champion.

Within a year my mother and I moved to another town, and once again I felt angry and confused and very much alone. Continually comparing myself to everyone I saw or met, I do not recall being content or at peace with my path in life. I had no tools to deal with my pain and insecurity. Instead I tried to numb myself through eating. Reading, music, and daydreaming in my room provided alternative escapes, and many nights I cried myself to sleep to the strains of Olivia Newton John coming from my record player.

I went on my next diet at the age of twelve. My overeating had resulted in considerable weight gain, and I was self-conscious and depressed about being heavier than most of my peers. I was not pretty or thin, I had terrible teeth and strong opinions, and none of the boys or popular kids noticed me. The few who did made unkind remarks about my weight. I was thoroughly miserable. I judged myself as either inferior or superior to others. Never could I connect with them as an equal. At that time my mother suggested that I join a popular weight-loss franchise. Several family friends had used it successfully, so I joined. I adhered rigidly to the eating plan and began losing weight rapidly. Oh, what a high! I felt on top of the world. Food no longer had me in its grip. I lost thirty pounds and switched to the "maintenance" plan. I received heaps of praise from friends and family, and I was certain that being thin meant I had become a better person.

I continued to rigidly control my food intake, eating the same way every day, and I spent most of my time between meals thinking about when and what I could eat next. When I was fifteen, my final growth spurt added weight along with height to my body, and I became obsessed with losing "just" five pounds. I talked about it all the time. But even going back to the diet club now failed to get me to that perfect number on the scale. I felt frustrated and began secretly eating foods I had labeled as "bad." I felt powerless to stop myself from eating those foods after a few days of stringent dieting.

When I was seventeen, I grew tired of feeling hungry and abandoned my diet, deciding that I could accept my body if I could only get physically fit. I reasoned that I could eat anything if I exercised enough. The two would balance each other out and the equation would be solved. Thus began my love affair with exercise. It provided another means to feel high, to feel in control. I spent hours every day on my exercise machine. It was my new friend, taking me to new heights. And, when I couldn't manage to use it, I would fantasize about it. That was often the nature of my disease: fantasies about starving and exercising and achieving that perfect body were constantly in my mind.

During the following year, I finally realized how powerless I had become over my eating behaviors. The vicious cycle of eating, feeling guilty about it, then eating more, was taking over my life. I often binged, threw away food that I was determined not to eat, then ate it right out of the garbage container. I battered my body with exercise whenever I tore myself away from the kitchen. By this time I had heard about bulimia and it seemed glamorous to me. All the bulimics I saw on television were very thin, and I couldn't think of anything better than being free from a bloated stomach, so I tried to purge by inducing vomiting. But, despite several desperate attempts, I could not get the food to come up. What a failure I was!

I became increasingly depressed, started drinking heavily at parties, and put myself in dangerous situations with people I hardly knew. I no longer cared if I lived or died. I had no idea that I was sick, believing instead that I was a loser of the worst kind.

Shortly after that period, I found myself in a Twelve-Step meeting for compulsive overeaters. The relief I felt was immense. I have no memory of what was said that first night or of what I shared, but I remember crying uncontrollably. I knew that I belonged, and I recognized that recovery would be a lifelong commitment. I was not yet ready to make that commitment, however, and for the next four years I obtained only band-aid relief by periodically attending meetings and accessing the Fellowship. I was not yet desperate enough to get sober and fully embrace the Program and its Twelve Steps. However, that Fellowship still saved my life. The information that I had a disease, that I was not alone in my insanity with food, that there was always a place for me to go and find understanding, was a gift from a Higher Power in whom I gradually came to believe.

That gift kept me alive until I was finally in enough pain that I became willing to surrender to other members' suggestions regarding my food. I had always heard that I needed to eat three proper meals every day and to avoid refined sugar and other foods that triggered me to binge. Although that plan seemed simple, I had yet to achieve it. I finally admitted that I couldn't do it on my own, and I dropped to my knees and asked a Higher Power for help. I attended meetings regularly, believing that God would grace me with sobriety, and God did just that, one day at a time.

The first few months were extraordinarily difficult. I often felt anxious and irritable when I was hungry, yet by the grace of God I stayed sober. After several months I discovered that sobriety had resulted in an unexpected bonus: I had lost some weight. That had not been my intention. When I surrendered, all I wanted was freedom from the pain of compulsive overeating. All I wanted was to actually live my life instead of watching it pass me by. I had been willing to accept my body exactly as it was. Truly a miracle.

As I entered my second year of sobriety, I began to struggle again. I had not yet asked anyone to sponsor me and I had not moved past Step Three in the Program. Around that time a good friend asked me to accompany her to her first meeting of Anorexics and Bulimics Anonymous. I wanted to support her, and I was certain that any Fellowship based on the Twelve Steps would benefit me also, so I began attending meetings.

To my surprise and discomfort, I noticed as the weeks went by that I was strongly identifying with the anorexics as they shared in meetings. It was clear to me that I had used restrictive eating practices in my early teens. I also started to take a good hard look at my current eating behaviors, and I had no choice but to admit that my motivation for avoiding sugar and between-meal snacks had subtly changed. In the dark corners of my mind, I deeply wanted to maintain my weight loss and perhaps to lose a little more. Slowly and insidiously over the course of my sobriety in the other Fellowship, I had lapsed out of surrender and into self-will, and I was now running riot in it. I had become highly restrictive of my fat intake and had even contemplated eliminating wheat and white flour. I had so enjoyed all the praise and recognition I received for my weight loss and self-control; never had I entertained the possibility that I had crossed the line from surrender into anorexic restriction of my food intake. I had simply believed that I was healthier than others who had less control than I had. Besides, I reasoned, this was a gift from God; how could it be wrong? Furthermore, I had always believed the stereotype of the classic anorexic: less than a hundred pounds, skipping meals, subsisting on lettuce, requiring hospitalization, and so on. I definitely did not fit the picture. And yet I too was trapped by my own rigid guidelines around eating; the freedom that I had felt at the beginning of my sobriety had vanished.

I went to see a doctor who treats patients with eating disorders, and she confirmed my dreaded suspicions. I was indeed practicing anorexic restriction in my eating patterns. My life was being controlled by what I could and could not eat, by the number of hours that had to elapse between meals, and by a host of other rules. I no longer trusted my body and had begun to think of it as the enemy, accusing it of disloyalty and dishonesty if I felt hungry at unusual times. Everything I put in my mouth had to be justified.

At that point my recovery shifted in a new direction. I opened myself up to the possibility that the drug of my eating disorder was not food itself, nor my restrictive eating practices, nor my rituals with food. All these things were mere symptoms of my real drug: the feeling of *control*. The illusion of controlling (or of not controlling) my eating was a continuous and all-consuming distraction from myself, my life, and my deep self-loathing. This illusion also filtered into every other area of my life. Attempting to control my food, my weight, and my body shape was only the tip of the iceberg. I really wanted to feel in control of my life.

I saw that I have a spiritual disease that slowly eats away at my soul. At the tender age of ten I had begun to shut down my feelings and my inner life-process, creating a void within myself. Now at twenty-three there was not enough food, exercise, or restriction in the whole world to fill that void. I began to accept at a much deeper level that I was not, and had never been, a "bad" person. I was a very sick person. And I saw that my disease had helped me survive a period of my life that I had no other means to deal with.

I wish I could say that coming to this knowledge allowed me to get sober immediately and live happily ever after. But I cannot. My progress from awareness, through acceptance, then into action, has always been slow. I have experienced no overnight miracles. Over the next eighteen months I went through a seemingly interminable series of relapses. Staying sober for weeks or months, only to relapse again. Always I tried to do it on my own, sometimes allowing other people to suggest what I should prepare and eat.

Finally, I reached a place of such despair and depression that I could no longer feed myself. At that point I became willing to surrender all my food to my Higher Power through the aid of another human being. That human being was my husband, and I will be forever grateful for his willingness to be my Higher Power's hands in that dark time. I was also given grace to be honest and reveal blatantly sick behaviors that I had never previously acknowledged. Things like hiding to eat whenever I consumed foods I labeled as "bad."

However, once again I was unable to stay sober for more than a month. My slips after that became more subtle. Not skipping meals or outright bingeing, but rather "little vestiges of control" to which I clung: low-fat dressings and mayonnaise, diet yogurt and skim milk. And always returning to sneaky eating when I was alone in the house: two candies here, a piece of licorice there. I had by now regained all the weight I had lost in the other Fellowship. I sensed that I was getting more and more ill and felt increasingly depressed. Still I sank lower. It was Christmas-time, and I binged a few times over the holidays as I wallowed in self-pity.

Throughout this period I continued attending A.B.A. meetings. Sometimes all I could do was occupy a chair, and yet I was always encouraged to "keep coming back." Many times I heard people say that everyone who continued attending meetings eventually got well, and I clung to that hope and always shared as honestly as I could about my current state.

In the New Year, I began to experience a number of small shifts that led to a bigger shift. I got on my knees and surrendered my food directly to God, asking to have removed from me my insane ideas about eating. This prayer was not answered overnight, and it has been answered, one meal at a time. Today I have been gifted with many months of consecutive sobriety. My Higher Power is changing my thinking in those areas over which I am powerless, as long as I continue doing my recovery work and following God's will for me.

My work today consists of praying every morning and throughout the day, attending and chairing meetings, reading the literature, journaling, and, most importantly, reaching out to others in recovery. Their fellowship and their acceptance and love of me are true gifts. My disease would have me believe that it's better to do things alone and figure out everything for myself, that other people are far too busy to be troubled by my little needs. I know today that these ideas are lies. I have discovered that the more contact I have with my sisters in recovery, the better I feel. The more calls I make, the more I receive.

Today I believe the future is bright. I don't know what God has planned for me, and I know it will be great. I feel no loneliness when I open myself to God's love for me, because it exists within me. I am no longer compelled to use insane eating practices to get through my day. Nor do I need to escape from my feelings by using other addictive behaviors to numb them. My feelings are simply my feelings, and I will not die from embracing them and honoring them with my whole body. I will die if I do not. I am learning to trust my body today, to know that it never lies to me, and now that I am sober I can live in my body as the wondrous gift from God that it is. My body holds a wealth of wisdom and an amazing capacity to process information for me if I but listen. Sober, I can do that. I *am* my body; it completes me as a whole person.

The Twelve-Step Program is my guide to living life fully. It comprises a set of spiritual principles that, although simple, are not easy to follow. I now believe that anything is possible in a world directed by my Higher Power. When I run on self-will I imprison myself in a small box of limited opportunities. It is my Higher Power that relieves me of my insane eating practices and supports me to live in the present moment. I am no longer a spectator in my life. I am in it, right here and right now.

I owe a great deal to Anorexics and Bulimics Anonymous, and I know that the best way to keep what has so generously been given me is to pass it on. Keep coming back. It really works!

Joelle's Story: Running For Freedom

11

WHY DID I become anorexic? I demanded an answer to that question. How could I, such a strong-willed, talented, and kind daughter of a well-known family possibly succumb to such a thing? Looking back, I see that my pathway clearly signaled that I was headed for trouble at a very young age.

I grew up, the youngest of three girls, on my family's farm. As I was long-awaited, my family showered me with affection, and I knew I was loved. However, guilt—one of the most corrosive factors in my life—began at an early age. Somehow I discovered that my mother's chronic pain and fatigue, conditions that sometimes made it impossible for her even to hold me, started only *after* I was born. As soon as I learned that, I resolved to dedicate my life to doing everything within my power to make up for her pain. Sleepovers and birthday parties became a thing of the past. I was convinced that, without me there to clean the house, run errands, cut pills, and deliver them to her with water, Mommy might be unable to walk the next day. Never did I speak one word of my guilt-laden knowledge, except as I said my nightly prayers, asking God to "make Mommy better." My prayers were never answered, and I could only watch, with ever-increasing guilt and self-loathing, as her condition worsened.

Until I started kindergarten, the loving environment of my family sheltered me from outside influences. However, my life dramatically changed the moment I set foot on a school bus bound for town. From that time forward through the next ten years, my experience in our small rural community school shredded my self-confidence. Constant teasing from both older and younger kids would have heightened the normal insecurities of anyone my age. But I was a sensitive child, and my tormentors fed on my obvious emotional breakdown resulting from their taunting lies. Lies that I began to believe. Nothing could stop them or me.

Despite this torture, I was an honor student, active in extracurricular activities, and my passion lay in sports. I tried to hide my insecurity, to prove I truly was good at or for something, through a string of achievements. And other sources of support, like summer camps, helped me survive. After attending a summer volleyball camp, my confidence ran high. Unable to bear further torment from my beastly peers back home, I decided something had to be done. I would never let them hurt me again. As I entered tenth grade, I was certain that things would be different.

My exhilarating debut to drinking seemed at first like the answer to all my problems. Now I momentarily fit in, although doing so required that I lie to the few people I trusted: my family. I continued drinking, however, desperate to find acceptance from my peers. The frequency of these evenings filled with drinking and deception increased, until one day I decided I no longer liked the sensation of alcohol controlling me. I was stronger than that.

All I ever wanted was to be a strong and healthy woman. I had never been overweight. I enjoyed food and cooking, ate when I was hungry, and stopped when I was full. Now, at this pivotal time in my life, I decided that to be the woman I desired to be—and to prove myself once and for all to my peers—I would lose fifteen pounds and train to run a marathon. That would be my ticket to success! So, off I went....

Snacks, second helpings, and fats were easy to eliminate in my "wellness" program. My parents joined the bandwagon, and soon the only food I ate was what I bought and cooked for myself. A popular TV personality on a weight-loss rampage bolstered my commitment to my plan; if she could do it, so could I. Anything sanctioned by national television had to be healthy and reasonable.

When I started with the base of my addictive predisposition and added one physically taxing activity daily to an already active lifestyle, I concocted a recipe for disaster. Running elicited an emotional high and a deep sense of release within me. It was *mine*. And it was the answer I had always needed. The weight fell off my body as my necessary dose of exercise augmented the effect of my food restrictions. Soon I was never alone as the cunning voice of anorexia whispered, then roared, in my mind twenty-four hours a day. "Food, exercise, bodies, fat grams, sit-ups, calories, food, exercise...." A never-ending obsession took over my mind and soon extinguished what life-flame I had left after ten years of living hell.

Not only was my body soon depleted, but within six months I was drained of all spirit, personality, and desire to live. School was an unwanted distraction, and friends an inconvenience to my insane schedule. Up at six in the morning to run, avoid breakfast, weigh in, run to school, vibrate throughout classes or skip them entirely to run, avoid dinner, run again and, if sleep didn't overtake me, run all night long.

My family, after breaking through their denial, began interfering. But with my obsession raging in my mind, convincing me that I was strong and healthy, I could not heed their warning until my body was ready to shut down. Their pleas enraged me. Any alteration in my subsistence on fruit and vegetables, alongside fifteen to thirty miles of daily running, would surely kill me. I believed running was all I had to live for; giving it up would push me to suicide.

My family, desperate for help, decided that only in a city four hours from home might I get the aid I needed. Only six months earlier I had been their vibrant daughter. Now I was reduced to nothingness. At five foot eight and eighty-five pounds, still certain that I was an obese slob, I arrived in the provincial capital. But resources proved nonexistent until a social worker who knew my sister informed us of a book written by a local physician. For the first time, reading the experiences of another anorexic broke through my hardened shell. Never before had I seen my thoughts, actions, and pain on paper. For a moment I was willing, and a crevice within me opened. My body soon collapsed. A subsequent six-month stay on a psychiatric ward sustained me physically but failed to heal my ravaged mind and soul.

Then, I believe my family's prayers were truly answered. As I left the hospital, I still felt trapped, driven by a power I had never been able to control. One day, my sister dropped me off at a tiny house and instructed me to go down the stairs. That was the day my life began to change. When the door opened, Anorexics and Bulimics Anonymous wrapped itself around me, providing through its members the unconditional love and acceptance I had always been seeking. Although I had no idea how meeting weekly with other anorexics and bulimics would help me, I kept coming back. I had nowhere else to turn.

For the next six months, my inner spirit and the disease that gripped me waged a battle for my life. Often I didn't know which one would win, yet I kept attending meetings even though this thing called "sobriety" continued to elude me. Despite my great resolve to recover, I could not pass a flight of stairs without running them repeatedly, nor drink a glass of milk without pouring its last ounce down the kitchen sink when no one was watching. Nevertheless, beyond my consciousness, I was gradually becoming open, willing, and desperate enough to end this war.

When my rock-bottom presented itself one horror-filled night, I was certain that only suicide could end the battle within me. I had two options: to surrender and live, or to die. Miraculously, I chose life. I got down on my knees, defeated, and asked my Creator for help—even if it meant weighing three hundred pounds. I would do whatever it took to get well. I could never have imagined how quickly would appear the human help I needed to facilitate my healing.

From that point on, I was gifted with surrender. I was able to allow God to work through those around me to provide me with food to eat, shoulders to cry on, people to call upon, healing work to do, meetings to attend, and even places to live. I moved in with my sponsor and she prepared and served all my meals, under the direction of a dietitian. An understanding physician gave me daily support and monitored my physical condition as my weight increased. My teachers and school counselor encouraged me to take a semester away from my studies to devote myself full-time to my healing process. Recovering people in A.B.A. and other Twelve-Step Fellowships welcomed me at daily meetings, listened to my pain, hugged and encouraged me.

Learning how to live again has been a difficult and often grueling process. Feeling my feelings, expressing myself, feeding my body and spirit, overcoming old patterns of thinking and behavior, and creating a new life—all require time and patience and commitment. However, my Higher Power is gentle and always provides me with further willingness to take action. One action leads to the next, one Step to the next, and my healing process has been miraculous. The changes that have taken place in me could not have been brought about by human power. Indeed, when I opened the door, God gladly restored my sanity. Anorexics and Bulimics Anonymous was my guide, support, and haven, and it remains that today.

Looking back from my seventh year of sobriety, I can scarcely believe what I used to be like. I lead a life filled with freedom. Freedom from my obsession, from ill health, from loneliness, and from spiritual sickness. I eat with pleasure today, to nourish my body. I exercise for health, not to make myself sick. Life is beautiful, and I can occupy my space in this world. I feel more secure than ever before, and I love myself. All these changes have been orchestrated by my Higher Power.

If the Twelve Steps of Anorexics and Bulimics Anonymous can work for a hopeless case like mine, then they can work for you too. I hope you will give yourself a chance.

Denise's Story: Journeying With My Higher Power 12

MY NAME is Denise and I am in recovery from bulimia. My path to recovery from my eating addiction started six years ago after I attended my first A.B.A. meeting. Nearly two years earlier, I got my first inkling that I might be bulimic after meeting a woman from a different organization who knew about the subject. I had always dieted and vomited when I was younger and, although I no longer needed to stick my finger down my throat to throw up, I continued purging. This was addiction. Something I kept doing even though I wanted to quit. Now, with eighteen months of continuous sobriety behind me, I have the life that my Higher Power intended me to have.

I am the eldest of four girls. We grew up in a family in which addiction affected everyone. Both my grandmother and mother had issues with body weight, dieted, and disliked people who gained weight. My grandmother, who abused codeine, weighed ninety pounds when she died. My mother, a closet drinker, was also thin and briefly attended Alcoholics Anonymous before committing suicide. One of my sisters is now in early recovery from drug use and attends Twelve-Step meetings. The men in my family drank, and that was simply the norm. I grew up in the age of rock 'n' roll, loving it, satisfying men to find what I thought was love, and living in the drug culture without knowing there was another life to choose.

At sixteen I heard about a diet that kept carbohydrates out of the body and required testing the urine for ketones. I had a diabetic friend who tested his urine, so I grabbed onto the diet and went with it. Soon dieting and exercise became the answer to my problems. I dropped in weight and felt worthy to choose new friends in my high school, thinner women. I hooked up with a man who had recently emigrated from England, and who had also grown up surrounded by drug addiction. What began as a friendship became an eight-year common-law relationship. He encouraged me to diet, and I needed his support to continue doing so. However, he became physically violent, and I wore a lot of bruises and emotional scars during my years with him. By that point my drug addiction had gained full control of me. After we split up, I moved on to heavier drugs and even more restrictive eating practices, and he moved on to a codependent who didn't dip into his stash of pot and beer.

Now settled in my own apartment, safely away from my ex-partner, I thought life would be different. But I didn't like living alone and felt sad much of the time, so I allowed other drug addicts to invade my space. I always hid my purging, and usually my bingeing as well, and my huge ego made it impossible for me to ask for help. I spent my days sewing patchwork quilts. No one could have told me that bulimia and drug addiction were threatening my life. At twenty-eight I fell in love with a man who engaged in crime to support his drug habit, and I made him my everything. Until recently I continued to seek his approval, believing that I was nothing without him. Ultimately I need to turn this relationship over to a Higher Power in order to find freedom.

Within a few short years I could go no lower in my use of chemicals, and at thirty-one I found myself in a meeting of Narcotics Anonymous. By the grace of my Higher Power and the love I encountered in that Fellowship, I kept showing up there and have stayed clean from substance abuse for more than thirteen years.

Bulimia, however, has been a different story. At seven years clean I was still bingeing and purging every day and my weight fluctuated wildly. My experience with the Twelve Steps allowed me to see that I needed to let go of my bulimia. I heard about Anorexics and Bulimics Anonymous and attended meetings sporadically over the following four years. I felt accepted, and at times I caught a glimpse of the possibility of sober eating and a manageable life. Other members encouraged me to let go. But I was not yet prepared to admit defeat. Occasionally I would get close to committing myself to the A.B.A. path, but I would invariably develop a reservation of one sort or another.

Throughout that period my grief over my mother's death led me on a spiritual quest. I was sponsored to start a program of education to become an addictions counselor. Six months into training, my bulimia had progressed to the point that I was throwing up into a bucket while bathing. I woke up and realized I needed help. I made a call and was referred to a physician who works with anorexics and bulimics. She would eventually prove to be instrumental in my getting sober. I also clung to the belief that dealing with my childhood abuse would fix everything. I took counseling and group therapy, but I was not ready to reveal all my shameful secrets there. It took a long time for me to see that I needed to get sober in my eating *first*, thereby allowing other areas of my being to heal.

In the twelfth year of my recovery from drugs and alcohol, bulimia caught up with me. Unable to bear the pain of it any longer, I surrendered. I began attending A.B.A. regularly, acquired a sponsor, and discussed with the physician who understood my disease just how I might get sober. I was too sick to plan meals for myself, and I lived alone with no one readily available to prepare my food. So I allowed a Higher Power to feed me through liquid meal replacements for the first year. This was not easy. I needed to pray, attend meetings, work with my sponsor, and get a lot of support to continue surrendering. I could only do it one day at a time, setting aside all thoughts about the future.

From the beginning of my sobriety, I was generally able to eat one daily meal of solid food at the direction of a dietitian and my sponsor. After my first A.B.A. birthday, I gradually returned to solid food for the remaining meals, still relying upon the guidance of those two people. I continue to need that level of support today.

It is now more than eighteen months since I last binged and purged, and life has changed a great deal. As long as I keep showing up, my Higher Power works everything out. I need to detach from addicted people in my life, including my family and ex-boyfriend, and to find my new family in Twelve-Step recovery. Last week I did service work by speaking about my bulimia at a local rehabilitation center for chemically dependent adults, and I got to see how far I have come. I have been an outreach worker in the inner city, am working on a university degree, study Native issues, paint and draw. I find my Higher Power through many routes, including Blackfoot traditional culture and sweats. The simplicity of my life helps me remain grateful for all that I have. My needs are always provided for, and I have many friends in recovery. My N.A. sponsor is dying of liver cancer, and this week I was able to tell him how I feel about that. I can accept my feelings today, and I no longer *want* to take control of my life or of my body weight and shape. My Higher Power can do a much better job of that than I, and I await further instructions for the future.

I still wonder why I could not surrender my eating practices at the same time as I surrendered drugs and alcohol, but I guess that was just not to be my story. Most of the time, I am simply grateful to have found sobriety from bulimia, and for the Twelve Steps that are restoring me to sanity. My recovery has made me a stronger person and sent me on a spiritual journey that I would never have believed possible. If anyone reading this is wondering if Anorexics and Bulimics Anonymous can work for you too, I say, "Yes!" I am worth it, and so are you.

Donna's Story: When I Asked For Help... 13

MY DISTURBED relationship with food and obsession with my weight began early in life. In my childhood home, food was used to show love, offer comfort, and provide a sense of closeness. Additionally, most of my female role models were fixated on their weight and body shape. My mother in particular was always on one diet or another, and her mood was controlled by the number on her scale.

As a teenager I was acutely aware of how I looked in comparison to my peers. Being thin and trim was not only my goal; it became my way of life. It seemed simple to restrict what I ate and exercise regularly. The thinner I became, the smaller my dress size, the more powerful and in control I felt. My self-esteem was determined by how many days I could last without eating or how many sit-ups I could perform. Coffee and cigarettes were my appetite suppressors. I prided myself on never eating sweets and never eating after seven p.m. The mirror kept telling me that I needed to lose only five or ten more pounds before I would reach the perfect size.

In the midst of my rituals with eating and exercise, I began adding drugs and alcohol to the list of things I attempted to control. As my focus on these things increased, my life started to unravel. My children, husband, parents, friends, and job all took second place to my addictions. My fears of being found out led me to isolate myself from others, and my sense of self slowly disintegrated. I felt joyless, hopeless, and completely defeated, yet clung to the belief that losing five more pounds or making my stomach flatter would change it all.

Although I did not believe in a God, I started to pray for my life to end. Paradoxically, that was to bring about the beginning of hope. That summer my drinking, drugging, and starving reached their apex. By then I could last a week without eating and needed to do sit-ups and jump rope six or seven times a day. My husband had decided he didn't want to live with me anymore, and I was unable to care for my two young daughters. Most of my friends and family did not want to be around me. The business I owned was in financial disarray. After an evening of partying and overdosing on drugs and booze I came to a crossroad. A small voice in my mind said I could continue in the direction I was headed and be dead shortly, or I could ask for another way. I had no idea what "another way" would look like, but I got down on my knees and asked for help. I thought I was speaking to the air, for I had no notion of God or Spirit or Creator, but I knew that I was completely lost. At that moment, I could see no alternative other than to pray.

At my workplace a few days earlier, someone had tacked up a poster announcing a meeting of Narcotics Anonymous. I frantically dialed the contact number on the poster, but I could reach no one. I kept phoning over the course of four or five hours before getting an answer, yet that evening someone was on my doorstep to take me to my first meeting. I began attending N.A. and A.A. regularly, recognizing that I had a problem with drugs and alcohol. At meetings I heard people share about the importance of proper nutrition to the recovery process, and especially for lessening withdrawal symptoms. I had no clue about how to eat, even though I had always fed my family well. I consulted my family doctor; he too talked about my weight, good nutrition, and the need for vitamin supplements.

I was admitted to a treatment center for my chemical addictions, and there I learned about nutrition and healthy exercise. Using that avenue, as well as my knowledge of the Canada Food Guide, I started to find sobriety in my eating. I felt elated that I had finally let go of the obsession that had controlled my life for fifteen years. I came to understand that, along with drugs and alcohol, my eating and exercise behaviors were things over which I had no control, and that I needed to ask God and others for help. My doctor became an important support for me as he monitored my weight and general health on a weekly basis. He encouraged me to eat several small meals and lots of nutritious snacks. I surrendered to his advice. Almost immediately I lost the desire to exercise compulsively; today I know that was a gift from my Higher Power.

Once I started talking about anorexia, the people closest to me opened up and shared what they had observed over the course of my disease. I began to pray and meditate on a daily basis, asking each morning for God to help me throughout the day. In the beginning, I sometimes needed to break the day into hours, or even minutes, in order to get through it. New doors opened and I met fellow Twelve-Step members who carried me at times when I lost my way. I became very active in Alcoholics Anonymous. I obtained a sponsor; read the Big Book again and again; did the Steps to the best of my ability; and attended five or six meetings every week, even though that required traveling significant distances from the small town where I lived. I chaired meetings, made coffee, and assumed a variety of service roles in the group. Eventually I reached the point in my recovery when I was able to sponsor others and pass on some of the gifts I had received.

Some years later, I moved to a new city and heard about Anorexics and Bulimics Anonymous. I immediately began attending meetings, recognizing that I both needed support and needed to offer what I could to others who were suffering. The A.B.A. Fellowship assumed an important place in my recovery journey as it helped me become more grateful for the awesome sobriety with which I had been blessed.

Many changes have occurred since that fateful day fifteen years ago when I asked for help. I have divorced my partner, and my children are now adults. My mother, my greatest support, has died. I have moved around a great deal, returned to school, and started a new career. My financial situation has improved. Some of those close to me have relapsed or died because of their disease. I still have days when I experience powerful and frightening echoes of those old feelings of worthlessness and despair, but I know today that all feelings pass. I am fully confident that as long as I am sober and keep asking God for help, there will always be hope.

Glossary

All terms specific to Anorexics and Bulimics Anonymous or to other recovery groups are enclosed in quotation marks.

ADDICTION: Any substance or behavior over which a person is powerless, that takes control of the individual, inducing obsession and compulsion and leading over time to destructive consequences. Involves the phenomena of tolerance and withdrawal symptoms.[1]

ALLERGY: An abnormal reaction, particularly one mediated by the body's immune system, to a substance that is harmless in similar amounts to a majority of people.

ANOREXIA (NERVOSA): Mental illness characterized by an intense fear of becoming obese, a relentless drive to achieve thinness, reluctance to maintain a normal weight for one's height and body build, a distorted perception of one's true body size and shape, and cessation of menses for at least three consecutive cycles. Sometimes accompanied by periodic bingeing or purging or both.[2]

AMPHETAMINE: A particular addictive drug that stimulates the brain, causing increased alertness and appetite suppression, as well as other organs such as the heart. Also known colloquially as "speed."

BEHAVIOR MODIFICATION: The use of a system of cues, rewards, or punishments to alter the actions of a subject.

BINGE: The uncontrolled eating of an unusually large amount of food within a relatively short period of time, often followed by intense guilt and shame.

BIPOLAR DISORDER: Mental illness characterized by unusually wide fluctuations in mood, ranging from extreme, often suicidal, depression to exaggerated elation, both of which are disproportionate to external reality.

BORDERLINE TRAITS: Aspects of a personality disorder marked by low self-esteem, fear of abandonment, widely fluctuating mood, desperate attempts to control others, impulsive and self-harming behavior, fits of anger, feelings of being victimized, and unstable relationships.[3]

BULIMIA (NERVOSA): Mental illness characterized by periodic binge-eating followed by attempts to realistically or symbolically rid the body of the food that has just been ingested, using self-induced vomiting, laxatives or enemas, diuretics, exercise, or fasting.[4]

CELIAC DISEASE: Intestinal disorder preventing the body from digesting and absorbing gluten, a protein component in certain grains such as wheat and rye.

CHELATION: Procedure for removing a heavy metal such as lead or mercury from the bloodstream by means of a chemical compound known as a chelate.

CHEMICAL DEPENDENCY: Mental illness involving abuse of addictive drugs when characterized by the development of tolerance and withdrawal symptoms, resulting in preoccupation with the substance and drug-seeking behavior to ensure its steady supply.

CHOLESTEROL: Natural molecule, occurring in animal tissues, that is manufactured in the liver, circulates in the bloodstream, and in high concentrations is one factor leading to "hardening of the arteries."

"CLEAN": Term used by drug addicts to denote the state when they have refrained from using drugs.

COCAINE: Highly addictive drug that stimulates the brain, causing intense but brief sensations of pleasure and euphoria, as well as other physical effects such as increased blood pressure and appetite suppression.

CO-DEPENDENCE: Particular form of addiction used by those living in connection with an addict, characterized by extreme and obsessive focus on the addict and attempts to control the addict's behavior, thereby allowing neglect of one's own feelings, needs, and life issues.

COMPULSION: Intense and undeniable need, like thirst, that is experienced in the body and that drives a person to consume a particular substance or perform a particular action.

"COMPULSIVE EATING DISORDER": Mental illness characterized by the daily or periodic ingestion of an amount or type of food that exceeds the body's needs.

"COMPULSIVE EXERCISE": Mental illness characterized by an intense need to drive one's body through routines of physical activity in order to control one's weight or body shape or fitness level, while often ignoring such cues as fatigue, pain, and physical illness.

CONTROL: To manage and direct a person or thing, to take command over.

"CRACK": Slang term for rock cocaine, a particular formulation of the drug that can be smoked rather than snorted or injected.

DEHYDRATION: State of the body when it is depleted of water; commonly occurs through repeated vomiting or diarrhea.

DELUSION: A false idea with no basis in reality.

DIETITIAN: A person with a recognized degree in nutrition and food science from an accredited university.

DISSOCIATIVE DISORDER: Mental illness characterized by repeated episodes of loss of memory, out-of-body experiences, loss of touch with one's surroundings, or loss of one's sense of self.[5]

DSM-IV™: Abbreviation for the *Diagnostic and Statistical Manual of Mental Disorders, Fourth Edition*; a textbook compiled and published in 1994 by the American Psychiatric Association, containing detailed lists of standardized diagnostic criteria and widely used by psychiatrists and other medical doctors throughout the world in order to achieve precision of diagnosis and comparability of data, results, and conclusions in scientific studies.

DIURETIC: Substance or medication that forces the kidneys to increase their production of urine for a period of time, thereby removing water and salt from the body.

"DRUG": Substance or activity that serves to alter one's feelings or inner state of being.

ELECTROCONVULSIVE THERAPY: Treatment used for certain mental illnesses, such as severe depression, whereby an electric current is passed through the brain to induce an epileptic fit.

ELECTROSHOCK THERAPY: Synonymous with "electroconvulsive therapy."

ENEMA: Insertion of fluid into the rectum in order to stimulate a bowel movement.

EMOTIONAL: Pertaining to the feelings of an individual, such as happiness, sadness, anger, and fear.

ESOPHAGUS: Tubular organ that leads from the mouth to the stomach.

FASTING: The intentional act of refraining from eating for an unusually prolonged period of time.

FEEDING TUBE: A plastic device, inserted into the stomach through the mouth or nasal passages, for the purpose of administering liquid nutrients to someone who is unable or unwilling to swallow.

GASTROSTOMY: Artificial passageway, fashioned directly through the overlying skin, leading into the stomach.

HEROIN: Highly addictive narcotic drug that relieves pain, sedates the mind, and often induces pleasurable sensations.

HIGHER POWER: A source of strength or might that is greater than (as in *more than*) oneself. Used synonymously with such terms as "God," "Creator," "Great Mystery," and "Great Reality."

ILLUSION: False perception or impression with no basis in reality.

IMMUNE: Pertaining to the body's mechanism for resistance to disease through the production of antibodies and other factors that recognize and destroy invading micro-organisms.

LAXATIVE: Substance or medication that forces the bowels to empty, often resulting in diarrhea.

MALNUTRITION: Physical state that results from prolonged underfeeding or inappropriate feeding.

"MEAL-SUPPORT": The practical assistance required for the sobering-up process of the individual anorexic or bulimic, involving planning, preparation, and serving of meals and snacks to her by another person.

"MEAL-SUPPORT HELPER": A person who plans, prepares, and serves food to one who is incapable of doing it for herself due to fear or distorted perceptions of her body's requirements.

MENTAL: Pertaining to the mind or to any of its functions, including intellect, reason, memory, intuition, imagination, planning, and will.

MIND: The non-physical aspect of a living being; often used synonymously with "spirit."[6]

MOOD DISORDER: Mental illness characterized by long-lasting irrational alteration in one's feeling state, whether depressed or abnormally elated or both.

OBESITY: The condition of weighing a great deal more than is normal and healthy for one's height and skeletal structure.

OBSESSION: Persistent, intrusive, and inescapable thought or idea that takes over the mind, driving out every other thought or idea.

OBSESSIVE-COMPULSIVE TRAITS: Aspects of a personality disorder marked by extreme perfectionism, rigidity of thought and action, a need to be organized or tidy, scrupulous attention to detail, overworking and overachieving, miserliness, inability to compromise or let go, and drastic attempts to control.[7]

OVEREATING: Consumption of an amount of food that is greater than the body's requirements for optimum health.

PARENTERAL NUTRITION: Feeding measures that bypass the stomach and intestines, e.g. intravenous feeding.

PATHOLOGY: Abnormality of body, mind, or other entity, e.g. "family pathology" or "societal pathology."

PEDIATRICS: Branch of medicine that specializes in children and adolescents.

PERSONALITY DISORDER: An entrenched, lifelong manner of thinking, feeling, acting, and interacting with others that damages one's capacity to be happy and to function successfully in one's life.[8]

PHYSICAL: Pertaining to the body.

"PHYSICAL ALLERGY": Phenomenon wherein the body craves more of a particular substance or behavior once one begins to take it in or perform it, respectively.

POTASSIUM: Essential element for the healthy functioning of the body, especially of the heart and muscles; becomes depleted through repeated vomiting and diarrhea.

POSTTRAUMATIC STRESS DISORDER: Mental illness that follows, either immediately or some time later, a life experience in which serious harm occurred to oneself or others and in which one was terrified or helpless. Characterized by insomnia; short temper; trouble concentrating; hyper-alertness; and repeated reliving of the harmful event through flashbacks, disturbing memories, nightmares, and overreaction to events that trigger the frightening memory.[9]

PSYCHIATRY: Branch of medicine that specializes in diseases of the mind.

PSYCHOLOGY: Branch of science that studies the normal and abnormal mental functioning of individuals and groups.

PSYCHOTIC: Pertaining to one who is suffering from psychosis: a class of mental illness marked by complete loss of touch with reality, delusions, and often hallucinations.

PSYCHOSPIRITUAL: Pertaining to the mind and spirit.

PSYCHOTHERAPY: Treatment of disorders of the mind or emotions using verbal techniques, as opposed to behavioral or physical methods such as medication.

PURGE: Any means used to rid the body of ingested food, including self-induced vomiting, use of laxatives or diuretics, enemas, exercise, or fasting.

RESTRICTIVE ANOREXIC: An anorexic who does not binge or purge, but rather controls her weight by eliminating certain foods from her diet or by decreasing portion sizes.

"SOBER": The condition of surrendering all control of one's eating behavior, exercise behavior, and body weight and shape to a Higher Power.

SOBRIETY: The state of one who is sober.

SPIRIT: The life-force of a creature, the element that distinguishes a dead body from a living one; often used synonymously with "mind."[10]

SPIRITUAL: Pertaining to the spirit.

"SPONSOR": Recovering, sober person who facilitates the sobering-up process of another person and guides her through the Twelve-Step Program.

THERAPY: Treatment of one who is ill. Often used colloquially as a shortened form of "psychotherapy."

THYROID: Gland located in the neck that produces thyroxine, a hormone with widespread effects that include regulation of metabolic rate.

TOLERANCE: Phenomenon seen in addiction, whereby the mind-altering substance or behavior loses its effectiveness upon repeated use, necessitating an increase in dosage to achieve its former effect.

WILL: Mental faculties governing intention, motivation, and the making of decisions.

WITHDRAWAL: Phenomenon seen in addiction, whereby distressing, painful, and sometimes life-threatening physical symptoms result from the sudden removal of the addictive substance or behavior from the individual.

Notes

Preface

1. The term "Big Book" is a colloquial one for *Alcoholics Anonymous: The Story of How Many Thousands of Men and Women Have Recovered From Alcoholism,* 4th ed. (New York: Alcoholics Anonymous World Services, Inc., 2001). The first edition of the Big Book was published in 1939, and the content of pp. xiii-175 has not been altered in subsequent editions.

Chapter 1

1. S. Lunn, "Individual Psychotherapeutic Treatment of Anorexia Nervosa," *Acta Psychiatr Scand Suppl.* 361 (1990) 82:23-28.
2. See Anne Wilson Schaef, *Living in Process* (New York: Random House, Ballantine Publishing Group, Ballantine Wellspring, 1998), 203.
3. American Psychiatric Association, *Diagnostic and Statistical Manual of Mental Disorders,* Fourth Edition (Washington, DC: American Psychiatric Association, 1994).

Chapter 3

1. We distinguish between these types of eating behavior in the same way the Big Book delineates three different types of drinkers (pp. 20-22).
2. The Big Book identifies enjoyment of the effect of alcohol as a key element in what distinguishes an alcoholic from a normal drinker (p. xvi).
3. Progression of the disease of alcoholism is described in many places in the Big Book (pp. 1-16, 21-22, 37-38, 151-52).
4. The Big Book refers to the difficulty alcoholics experience in admitting their disease to themselves (pp. 30-31) and the attempts they make to control their drinking (pp. 31-33).
5. The Big Book is eloquent on the subject of loss of control (pp. 30-32).
6. The concept of the two-fold nature of the disease of alcoholism is introduced in the Big Book in "The Doctor's Opinion." The physical allergy (p. xvi) and the mental obsession (pp. xvi-xvii) are emphasized later in the text (pp. 22-24) and then illustrated in three anecdotes (pp. 32-33, 35-37, 39-43).
7. The Big Book relates that Carl Jung believed chronic alcoholism to be a near-hopeless mental illness that could only be relieved by a transformative spiritual experience (pp. 26-27). In other places it repeats the statement that the chronic alcoholic is a hopeless case when left to his own devices (pp. 24, 43).
8. The Big Book describes vividly how the alcoholic's mind will always eventually lead him to the first drink (pp. 32-43).

Chapter 4

1. American Psychiatric Association, *Desk Reference to the Diagnostic Criteria From DSM-IV*™ (Washington, DC: American Psychiatric Association, 1994), 254.
2. Term used by Overeaters Anonymous, a long-established Twelve-Step Fellowship for people who are powerless over food.
3. Examples are Overeaters Anonymous (O.A.) and Food Addicts Anonymous (F.A.A.).

Chapter 5

1. Anne Wilson Schaef, Ph.D., puts names to these aspects of insanity in *When Society Becomes an Addict* (New York: HarperCollins, HarperSan Francisco, 1987), 37-93. We believe that what we regard as the bottom of the iceberg, comprising all these insane characteristics operating together, is similar to what Schaef terms "The Addictive System" in the aforementioned text, and the "Addictive Process" in a later work *Beyond Therapy, Beyond Science* (New York: HarperCollins, HarperSan Francisco, 1992), 128-29, 131-32, 264-82.
2. Identified in the Big Book as the principal underlying problem of the alcoholic (pp. 61-64). Discussed by Schaef in *When Society*, 37-41, and also by Matthew Fox in *The Coming of the Cosmic Christ* (New York: HarperCollins, HarperSan Francisco, 1988), 76-77.
3. Worthlessness and grandiosity are identified as dualistic opposites by Schaef in *When Society*, 116-18, 121-22.
4. Schaef describes the illusion of control in *When Society*, 41-50, as well as in her later work, *Living in Process,* 135-37.
5. Schaef explores the issue of the addict's dishonesty in *When Society*, 50-59, as does Brennan Manning in *The Gentle Revolutionaries* (Denville, NJ: Dimension Books, Inc., 1976), 7-18. M. Scott Peck has written an entire book about dishonesty, *People of the Lie* (New York: Simon & Schuster, Touchstone, 1983).
6. Dishonesty with self often takes the form of denial. See *When Society*, 66-67.
7. The Big Book states that this phenomenon occurs in the alcoholic (p. xvi).
8. Discussed by Schaef in *When Society*, 68-70.
9. Inherent in judgmentalism is the fact of competition: In sizing up ourselves in relation to another, we must be judged either superior or inferior. Matthew Fox explores competition and its destructiveness to the human psyche in *A Spirituality Named Compassion* (Minneapolis: Winston Press, 1979. Reprint, with new preface, New York: HarperCollins, HarperSan Francisco, 1990), 69-74.
10. The illusion of separateness, its detrimental effect on human beings, and our need to become aware of our interconnectedness with all that is, is explored by Fox in both *A Spirituality Named Compassion*, 2-33, and in *Cosmic Christ*, 49-52. Schaef discusses the subject extensively in both *Beyond Therapy, Beyond Science*, 219, 279-80, 290-307, and in *Living in Process*, 78-84, 106-10, 162-67, 203-12, 215-26.

11. See Schaef, *When Society*, 78-80.

12. Dualistic thinking is explored in depth by Schaef in *When Society*, 112-130, and in *Beyond Therapy, Beyond Science*, 207-9, 277-79; and by Fox in *A Spirituality Named Compassion*, 79-87.

13. See Schaef, *When Society*, 86-88.

14. Ibid, 122.

15. The Big Book identifies fear as a major destructive element in the alcoholic's way of thinking (pp. 67-68).

16. The subject of self-hatred is important enough to merit at least one entire book of its own. Such a work has been written by Brennan Manning, *A Stranger to Self-Hatred* (Denville, NJ: Dimension Books, Inc., 1982). Fox touches upon the subject in *Cosmic Christ*, 53.

Chapter 6

1. The Big Book vividly describes the progression of the disease as the alcoholic reaches a bottom (pp. 151-152).

2. In a similar vein, Schaef refers to the limitations of cognitive understanding in the healing process of the addict's mind. See *Beyond Therapy, Beyond Science,* 142-43, 146, 148, 240-42, 251-57, 287, 310.

3. This definition of a bottom is derived from a statement in the Big Book regarding willingness (p. 58).

4. The Big Book refers often to the power that passes between them when one alcoholic reaches out to another (pp. 9-12, 18-19, 42-43, 89, 91-93, 180).

5. The concept that the drug to which we become addicted suppresses our feelings is expressed by many writers. Schaef discusses it in *When Society*, 18-24.

Chapter 7

1. This paradox is discussed by Manning in *The Gentle Revolutionaries,* 106-9.

2. The Big Book discusses how maintaining sobriety becomes effortless, in the section of the text dealing with Step Ten (pp. 84-85). It also makes the paradoxical observation that this phenomenon is dependent upon the effort the alcoholic puts into ongoing spiritual recovery (p. 85).

3. Schaef discusses this in *Living in Process*, 203-5, and in *Beyond Therapy, Beyond Science*, 33, 280, 304.

Chapter 8

1. Alcoholics Anonymous, *Twelve Steps and Twelve Traditions* (New York: Alcoholics Anonymous World Services, Inc., 1952).

2. Alcoholics Anonymous, *Daily Reflections* (New York: Alcoholics Anonymous World Services, Inc., 1990), 19.

3. M. Scott Peck explores the concept of rugged individualism and its destructiveness in *The Different Drum* (New York: Simon & Schuster, Touchstone, 1987), 53-58.

4. The Big Book discusses the alcoholic's loss of choice in graphic detail (pp. 21-25).

5. We have found only five occurrences of the words "choice" or "choose" in the Big Book, at least in the first 164 pages, which explores the Program of recovery in great detail (pp. 12, 24, 28, 34, 53).

6. The Big Book states this repeatedly (pp. 36-37, 39, 41, 44-45).

7. This concept is encapsulated succinctly in *Daily Reflections*, 16, and explored in depth by Harold S. Kushner, *When Bad Things Happen to Good People* (New York: The Hearst Corporation, Avon Books, 1981), 79-80.

8. Tom Weston, S.J., from Oakland, CA, discusses the importance of opening ourselves up to some new ideas about God, in an audiotape made at the *Mothers' Day Retreat 1998* (Upper Room Communications), S48.

9. The concept that God is distinctly *unlike* us originates in the Bible. "For my thoughts are not your thoughts and your ways are not my ways, declares Yahweh." (Isaiah 55:8)

10. This idea is stated clearly in the Big Book (pp. 12, 46-47).

11. This simple concept was stated by a long-time A.A. member at a women's retreat held near Helena, Montana, 23 July 1994.

12. *Twelve Steps and Twelve Traditions* discusses this concept with regard to the alcoholic (pp. 35-36).

13. We believe this is one reason why Alcoholics Anonymous has been so successful. The principle is stated clearly in the Big Book and accounts for two occurrences of "choice" (pp. 12, 28).

Chapter 9

1. Virtually all spiritual guides throughout history have emphasized self-inventory and squarely facing the truth about oneself as fundamental to spiritual growth. Jesus, for one, said, "You will come to know the truth, and the truth will set you free" (John 8:32). In our day, Scott Peck discusses this concept in *The Road Less Traveled* (New York: Simon & Schuster, Touchstone, 1978), 51-53, and in *People of the Lie*, 71-72. Schaef explores it in *Living in Process*, 138-146; Manning in *The Gentle Revolutionaries,* 7-18, 43; Fox in *Cosmic Christ*, 53, to name only a few.

2. We are indebted to A.A. speaker Bob B. from St. Paul, MN, for naming these five stages of change in relation to Step Six, in an audiotape recorded at the *25th Annual Banff A.A. Roundup* (Upper Room Communications), S43. He in turn derived these stages from the classic work of Elisabeth Kübler-Ross, *On Death and Dying* (New York: Macmillan, 1969), 38-137.

3. The concept of the immanent, indwelling God is an ancient one in many spiritual traditions. The Bible states, "Do you not realize that you are a temple of God with the Spirit of God living in you?" (1 Cor 3:16). Peck discusses this in *The Road Less Traveled*, 280-84; Manning in *The Gentle Revolutionaries*, 57-61; and the same theme is found throughout the writings of Matthew Fox. Examples are *Original Blessing* (Santa Fe: Bear & Company, Inc., 1983), 35-41, and *Cosmic Christ*, 49-51, 64. Schaef formulates a similar concept of a "Living Process" residing deep within each one of us, in *Beyond Therapy, Beyond Science*, 132, 275, 323, and in *Living in Process*, 81-83.
4. See Manning, *The Gentle Revolutionaries*, 70.
5. Ibid, 70-74.
6. The theme that only divine unconditional love has the power to dispel self-hatred is explored by Manning throughout *A Stranger to Self-Hatred.* See in particular pp. 25-45. He discusses it again in *The Gentle Revolutionaries*, 64-76.
7. Weston discusses this concept at length in *Mothers' Day Retreat 1998*, S48.
8. Ibid, S48.

Chapter 10

1. Manning discusses the relationship between true self-love and love of others in *The Gentle Revolutionaries*, 70-78.
2. This concept is emphasized by Bob B., *25th Annual Banff A.A. Roundup.*
3. Schaef emphasizes this idea in *Beyond Therapy, Beyond Science*, 8.
4. This concept of liberating others through making amends to them was heard in an A.A. meeting in Edmonton, Sept 2002.
5. Schaef discusses the insanity of attempting to achieve stasis in *Living in Process*, 21-25, 55-56, 74-76.
6. We are indebted to Don Coyhis, Mohican Elder, for this profound yet simple truth. His words are quoted by Schaef in *Living in Process,* 104.
7. Bob B. discusses this phenomenon also, *25th Annual Banff A.A. Roundup.*

Chapter 11

1. Schaef's work is brimming with the subject of spiritual wholeness and how it connects us with all of creation. See in particular *Living in Process*, 57-73, 213-26, 333-57. Fox also emphasizes this theme; it is the underlying thesis for *A Spirituality Named Compassion.*
2. Manning explores this desire for connection with God in *The Gentle Revolutionaries*, 118-31. In less passionate terms, the great Danish philosopher Sören Kierkegaard has written extensively on the importance of seeking to live in relationship with God, according to Peter Vardy, *Kierkegaard* (Liguori, Missouri: Ligouri Publications, Triumph, 1996), 73-82. Schaef discusses it in *Living in Process*, 251-55.

3. Manning discusses this topic in *A Stranger to Self-Hatred*, 26-32, and in *The Gentle Revolutionaries*, 60-61.
4. Weston articulates this clearly in *Mothers' Day Retreat 1998,* S48.
5. See Peck, *The Different Drum*, 248.
6. Manning discusses the lower levels of consciousness that can enslave us in *The Gentle Revolutionaries*, 20-61.
7. We are grateful to George Goodstriker, Blackfoot Elder and medicine man, for this learning (Private Conversation, 8 Feb 99).
8. Weston discusses this idea in *Mothers' Day Retreat 1998*, S48, as does Peck in *The Road Less Traveled*, 311.
9. Kierkegaard is eloquent on the God-relationship as the primary one in a human's life, according to Vardy, *Kierkegaard*, 73-88. Schaef's work is replete with this theme, especially *Living in Process*, 57-73, 251-55.
10. See Note 3 in Chapter 9 above.
11. The Big Book discusses the radical personality change occurring as a result of connecting with a Higher Power through the Twelve Steps (pp. xvii, 27, 567-68).
12. See *Kierkegaard*, 83-88, and Manning in *The Gentle Revolutionaries*, 98-102, 109-12. Weston emphasizes this point in *Mothers' Day Retreat 1998*, S47.
13. The Big Book, xiii, 14-15, 89, 180-81, 185.

Chapter 12

1. Schaef discusses this in *When Society*, 146-47.

Chapter 13

1. Vardy attributes this profound and important truth to Kierkegaard's great spiritual classic, *Purity of Heart is to will one thing*, trans David Swenson. See *Kierkegaard*, 74.
2. For an insightful discussion of meditation, see Fox, *Original Blessing*, 132-39.
3. See Schaef, *Living in Process*, 314.
4. Ibid, 96-98.
5. Schaef discusses this issue in several places. She views it as an aspect of co-dependence. See *When Society*, 29-33, and *Living in Process*, 205, 237-40.
6. Heard in a recovery meeting in Boulder, Montana, July 2002.
7. Heard in an A.A. meeting in Edmonton, May 1997.
8. For a rich discussion of this theme, see Fox, *Original Blessing*, 9-29, 35-36.
9. Novelist Andrew Greeley uses this designation for God in *Rite of Spring* (New York: Warner Books, 1987), 198.

10. See Schaef, *Living in Process*, 185-87.

11. See Schaef, *Beyond Therapy, Beyond Science*, 248, and *Living in Process*, 237-38.

12. Peck notes that young adolescents are only beginning to develop the capacity to identify their feelings, *People of the Lie*, 9. Perhaps one reason that we anorexics and bulimics in early recovery have such difficulty knowing what we are feeling is because our emotional development halted when we started our addictive behaviors (early adolescence for most of us). Schaef observes that in order to feel our feelings we must be capable of noticing what is going on within our bodies, something that as active anorexics and bulimics we could rarely do. See *Beyond Therapy, Beyond Science*, 146-52, and *Living in Process*, 92-95.

13. Hawaiian *Kapuna* (Elder) Alex Pua uttered a statement to this effect, according to Schaef, *Living in Process*, 138.

14. Schaef describes this work as an essential aspect of healing from addiction, and she sees it done most effectively with the support of a community. For a full discussion, see *Beyond Therapy, Beyond Science*, 130-87, and *Living in Process*, 183-97.

15. See Fox, *Original Blessing*, 188-200.

16. The Big Book emphasizes working with others in order to stay sober (pp. xiii, 14-15, 89-103, 180-81, 185).

17. This touches on the subject of co-dependence, an area of great importance to all of us in A.B.A. See Schaef in *When Society*, 29-33, and in *Beyond Therapy, Beyond Science*, 191-97.

18. See Note 3 in Chapter 11 above.

Chapter 14.

1. See Schaef, *Living in Process*, 203-5.

2. See Peck, *The Different Drum*, 58.

3. Psychiatrist Hilde Bruch observed this long ago in *The Golden Cage: the Enigma of Anorexia Nervosa* (Cambridge, Mass: Harvard University Press, 1978), xi.

4. The line between pathological individualism and authentic individuality is discussed by Peck, *The Different Drum*, 53-58; by Fox, *Cosmic Christ*, 64-65; and by Schaef, *Living in Process*, 213-15, 227-50.

5. See Note 16 in Chapter 13 above.

6. The Big Book refers to this in relation to Step Nine (p. 77). For a lengthy discussion, see Schaef, *Living in Process*, 112-22.

7. Weston discusses this in *Mothers' Day Retreat 1998*, S45.

8. Transparency as the ultimate spiritual goal is discussed by Manning, *The Gentle Revolutionaries*, 19-23.

Chapter 15

1. The concept of alcoholism as a family disease underlies the philosophy of the Al-Anon Family Groups. For a full discussion, see *How Al-Anon Works for Families & Friends of Alcoholics* (Virginia Beach, VA: Al-Anon Family Group Headquarters, Inc., 1995), 27-34.

2. The Al-Anon Family Groups are a fellowship of relatives and friends of alcoholics only. Although Ab-Anon has adopted many of the concepts originated by Al-Anon, we wish to emphasize that Al-Anon exists for the sole purpose of helping families and friends of alcoholics. It has no affiliation with any other organization, nor does it endorse the use of the Twelve-Step Program for any purpose other than recovery from the disease of alcoholism and from its effects on families. Reference to the literature of the Al-Anon Family Groups in the context of Chapter 15 does not imply otherwise.

3. For a discussion regarding the dawning of awareness of the disease of alcoholism, see *How Al-Anon Works*, 21-26.

4. Weston emphasizes that family members are rarely instrumental in carrying the message to the alcoholic and recommends praying for "the stranger" who will show up in a loved one's life to be the vehicle for God's healing power. See *Mothers' Day Retreat 1998*, S44.

5. The importance of ending the isolation of the alcoholic's family is discussed in *How Al-Anon Works*, 35-41.

6. These ideas, pertaining to the disease of alcoholism, originate in Al-Anon. See *Courage to Change: One Day at a Time in Al-Anon II* (New York: Al-Anon Family Group Headquarters, Inc., 1992), 74, 214.

7. The concept of powerlessness over a loved one's drinking is fundamental to the Al-Anon Program and is discussed throughout its literature. See *Courage to Change*, 8, 14, 32, 240.

8. This is a familiar Al-Anon slogan addressed to one who is in relationship with an alcoholic. See *Courage to Change*, 8, 252.

9. Detachment from the alcoholic is a central Al-Anon principle. See *Courage to Change*, 124, 187, and *How Al-Anon Works*, 84-86.

10. The importance of allowing alcoholics to experience the consequences of their actions is discussed in *Courage to Change*, 124, 168, 203.

11. This principle is embodied in another Al-Anon slogan. See *How Al-Anon Works*, 75.

12. Finding serenity through allowing a Higher Power to direct one's life is discussed in *Courage to Change*, 248, 318.

13. Al-Anon addresses this point to families and friends of alcoholics in *Courage to Change*, 2.

14. The concept of living one day at a time is emphasized for anyone in relationship with an alcoholic. See *Courage to Change*, 10, 15, 138.

15. The importance of self-care for families of alcoholics is discussed in *How Al-Anon Works*, 88-94.

Glossary

1. Bears some resemblance to the definition found in Schaef, *When Society*, 18.
2. Derived from definition found in DSM-IV™. For full citation see Note 1 in Chapter 4 above (pp. 251-52).
3. Loosely derived from definition found in DSM-IV™. For full citation see Note 1 in Chapter 4 above (pp. 280-81).
4. Ibid, 252-53.
5. Ibid, 229-32.
6. Peck believes that it is not possible in practical terms to distinguish between the mind and the spirit. See *The Road Less Traveled*, 11.
7. Loosely derived from definition found in DSM-IV™. For full citation see Note 1 in Chapter 4 above (p. 285).
8. Ibid, 275-76.
9. Ibid, 209-11.
10. See Note 6 above.

Suggested Readings

As we ponder how to close this text, we are deeply moved by how abundantly the Creator has blessed us with a wide array of spiritual guides and mentors. As we journey along the Twelve-Step recovery path, their influences have been critical ones in shaping our minds into a new way of thinking and knowing ourselves and the world about us. They have truly been channels of grace for us, and it seems fitting to let their names and the titles of some of their works be the last word in this volume. And yet even as we compose these sentences, we are sadly aware of how incomplete this section of our text will be, for the influences of these beloved guides have become so thoroughly integrated into our own experience of recovery that it is impossible to name them all. Indeed, we will do well to name even a small fraction of them. Many of them are referenced in the Notes immediately preceding this section, and all are listed in the bibliography that follows. However, we wish to give them further credit in a more expansive form here.

We need first of all to pay tribute once more to Alcoholics Anonymous and its pivotal influence on us and on this text. The textbooks *Alcoholics Anonymous* and *Twelve Steps and Twelve Traditions* have been essential sources of learning for us in the youthful Fellowship of A.B.A. Notwithstanding our resolve to avoid merely repeating what is already written in those two sources, we found it well-nigh impossible to compile our text without incorporating countless A.A. principles. We have credited as many of these as possible in the foregoing Notes. Without Alcoholics Anonymous many of us would be dead today. How can anyone adequately express their gratitude for that?

We are indebted also to other A.A. General Service Conference-approved literature for many learnings discussed in our text. In particular, as indicated in the notes on Step One, the *Daily Reflections* for January 8 and January 11 contributed richly to our understanding of powerlessness and of the vitally important issue of "choice."

The unwitting contribution of individual members of Alcoholics Anonymous to the creation of this book is impossible to gauge, for as our authors have participated in A.A. meetings they have soaked up the wisdom of literally thousands of women and men. In keeping with the tradition of public anonymity, they, like us, will remain unnamed. And yet we want them to know how deeply they have touched our hearts and minds and changed the course of our lives.

We appreciate A.A. circuit speaker Bob B. from St. Paul, Minnesota for his brilliant analysis of the process of Step Six. His words mirrored our own experience and assisted us by putting language to our inner process of this Step.

We are grateful for the literature of the Al-Anon Family Groups, which greatly helped our loved ones in the Ab-Anon Fellowship as they struggled to cope with our disease. Many of the Al-Anon principles have brought comfort and peace of mind to our families who, bound to us by their loving concern for our welfare, endured the torture of anorexia and bulimia along with us. We thank Al-Anon for inadvertently providing such solace to those we love. Rich storehouses of wisdom are *How Al-Anon Works for Families & Friends of Alcoholics* and *Courage to Change*.

Other men and women who have been our spiritual guides come from a diverse array of backgrounds. Writer, educator, and Cherokee Elder Anne Wilson Schaef, through her groundbreaking work, *When Society Becomes an Addict*, contributed lavishly to our understanding of the bottom of the iceberg of our disease. A later text, *Beyond Therapy, Beyond Science*, also names many concepts for us, not only about the abnormalities in our addictive mode of thinking, but also about the need to trust our feelings in sobriety if we wish to heal at a deep level of our being. Her further work, *Living in Process*, explores this whole subject in exquisite detail and helped shift many of us to a broader and deeper level of our healing process. Her influence has assisted an inestimable number of A.B.A. members to become more responsible members of society. Finally, her compilation of the words of other Native Elders and healers in *Native Wisdom for White Minds* continues to inspire a number of us today.

Many other native Elders have been catalytic to our growth. George Goodstriker, a Blackfoot Elder and medicine man, once said to some of us, "You need to learn to pray for *yourselves*. The Creator wants you to ask for what you need!" That statement altered our understanding of Step Eleven, and our subsequent experience with asking has confirmed the wisdom of what George told us that day. Don Coyhis, a Mohican writer, contributed to our grasp of Step Ten through his insights about mistakes and how we humans were created to learn through them. Hawaiian *Kapuna* Alex Pua taught us to put more trust in our feelings.

Psychiatrist M. Scott Peck, a deeply spiritual man, authored a number of books that have influenced the spiritual growth of many of our members. *The Road Less Traveled* is a popular work that started some of us on a spiritual quest, igniting a desire to be free from our addiction. His provocative book, *People of the Lie*, a sweeping exploration of dishonesty and self-centeredness, helped us to see the scope of these character defects. In a later work, *The Different Drum*, Peck names several concepts important to us, including the idea that the goal of our development as humans is to become who we already are; that "rugged individualism" is a destructive fallacy; and that authentic relationship with a Higher Power involves sometimes getting angry at that Power.

Franciscan priest Brennan Manning, through his evocative work, *A Stranger to Self-Hatred*, catalyzed our critically important awareness of self-hatred as the bedrock of our insanity as addicts. We have also been gifted by his further insight that only the power of unconditional love can heal us of this deadly flaw in our thinking. An earlier text, *The Gentle Revolutionaries,* guided us to further learnings about the illusion of power that is the drug for us anorexics and bulimics, and to a deeper grasp of the importance of honesty and transparency in recovery.

Tom Weston, a Jesuit priest and retreat leader from Oakland, elucidated for many of us the concepts that God is *not* one like us but is decidedly mysterious, compassionate beyond comprehension, and far bigger than we can imagine; that character defects become character assets in the hands of such a Higher Power; that imperfection is to be celebrated; that Step Eleven is about seeking *conscious* contact with this Power, not *emotional* contact. His influence has been profound in helping us to break through the prejudices in our thinking that blocked us from spiritual growth.

While still a Dominican priest, Matthew Fox wrote a number of books that have guided many of us spiritually, including *Original Blessing*, which helped us to see how the Creator actually intends us to be and gave us a vision of the sanity to which we can be restored through our recovery process. *A Spirituality Named Compassion* contains a stunning exploration of the vital concept of dualism and the damage it creates in our minds. *The Coming of the Cosmic Christ* further elucidates the compassion of the Creator and has helped many of us in sobriety to see the magnificent interconnectedness that exists among all created beings.

Nineteenth-century Danish philosopher Sören Kierkegaard touched many of us with his insights about prayer and about the nature of humankind's relationship with God. We are grateful to Peter Vardy for introducing us to this great man's thinking in *Kierkegaard*.

Rabbi Harold Kushner, through his arresting work, *When Bad Things Happen to Good People*, directed some of us by his exploration of the subject of choice and helped shed light on a Higher Power who never abandons us and is skilled at improvisation. His wisdom guided many of us as we grappled with Step Two.

Frederick Franck, a remarkable man who is artist and writer and disciple of Zen Buddhism, wrote a challenging book entitled *To Be Human Against All Odds*. His work allowed a number of us to glimpse the magnificence of our calling as human beings, a destiny that we can fulfill solely through pursuing sobriety at any cost. Only through sobriety can we become authentically human: loving, compassionate, and insightful beings, truly restored to sanity.

To all these men and women who have been such blessings in our lives and in our life as a Fellowship, we express our gratitude. And to those many others whom we have neglected to mention, whether from blithe unawareness or mere forgetfulness, we express our apology. The Creator has worked through all of you, and we thank you.

Select Bibliography

Al-Anon Family Groups. *Courage to Change: One Day at a Time in Al-Anon II*. New York: Al-Anon Family Group Headquarters, Inc., 1992.

———. *How Al-Anon Works for Families & Friends of Alcoholics*. Virginia Beach, VA: Al-Anon Family Group Headquarters, Inc., 1995.

Alcoholics Anonymous. *Alcoholics Anonymous*. 4th Ed. New York: Alcoholics Anonymous World Services, Inc., 2001.

———. *Daily Reflections*. New York: Alcoholics Anonymous World Services, Inc., 1990.

———. *Twelve Steps and Twelve Traditions*. New York: Alcoholics Anonymous World Services, Inc., 1952.

Bob B. Speaker at *25th Annual Banff A.A. Roundup*. Upper Room Communications, S43. Audiocassette.

Fox, Matthew. *The Coming of the Cosmic Christ*. New York: HarperCollins, HarperSan Francisco, 1988.

———. *Original Blessing*. Santa Fe: Bear & Company, Inc., 1983.

———. *A Spirituality Named Compassion*. Minneapolis: Winston Press, 1979. Reprint, with new preface, New York: HarperCollins, HarperSan Francisco, 1990.

Franck, Frederick. *To Be Human Against All Odds*. Berkeley: Jain Publishing Co., Asian Humanities Press, 1991.

Kübler-Ross, Elisabeth. *On Death and Dying*. New York: Macmillan, 1969.

Kushner, Harold. *When Bad Things Happen to Good People*. New York: The Hearst Corporation, Avon Books, 1981.

Manning, Brennan. *The Gentle Revolutionaries*. Denville, NJ: Dimension Books, Inc., 1976.

———. *A Stranger to Self-Hatred*. Denville, NJ: Dimension Books, Inc., 1982.

Peck, M. Scott. *The Different Drum*. New York: Simon & Schuster, Touchstone, 1987.

———. *People of the Lie*. New York: Simon & Schuster, Touchstone, 1983.

———. *The Road Less Traveled*. New York: Simon & Schuster, Touchstone, 1978.

Schaef, Anne Wilson. *Beyond Therapy, Beyond Science*. New York: HarperCollins, HarperSan Francisco, 1992.

———. *Living in Process*. New York: Random House, Ballantine Publishing Group, Ballantine Wellspring, 1998.

———. *Native Wisdom for White Minds*. New York: Random House, Ballantine Books, One World, 1995.

———. *When Society Becomes an Addict*. New York: HarperCollins, HarperSan Francisco, 1987.

Weston, Tom. Facilitator of *Mothers' Day Retreat 1998*. Upper Room Communications, S44-48. Audiocassettes.

Vardy, Peter. *Kierkegaard*. Liguori, Missouri: Ligouri Publications, Triumph, 1996.

Index